28/–

I G Macdonald

July 1964

COMPLEX MULTIPLICATION OF ABELIAN VARIETIES AND ITS APPLICATIONS TO NUMBER THEORY

PUBLICATIONS OF THE MATHEMATICAL SOCIETY OF JAPAN

1. The Construction and Study of Certain Important Algebras. By Claude Chevalley.
2. Lie Groups and Differential Geometry. By Katsumi Nomizu.
3. Lectures on Ergodic Theory. By Paul R. Halmos.
4. Introduction to the Problem of Minimal Models in the Theory of Algebraic Surfaces. By Oscar Zariski.
5. Zur Reduktionstheorie Quadratischer Formen. Von Carl Ludwig Siegel.
6. Complex Multiplication of Abelian Varieties and its Applications to Number Theory. By Goro Shimura and Yutaka Taniyama.
7. Équations Différentielles Ordinaires du Premier Ordre dans le Champ Complexe. Par Masuo Hukuhara, Tosihusa Kimura et Mme Tizuko Matuda.

COMPLEX MULTIPLICATION OF ABELIAN VARIETIES

AND ITS APPLICATIONS TO NUMBER THEORY

BY

GORO SHIMURA

AND

The late YUTAKA TANIYAMA

THE MATHEMATICAL SOCIETY OF JAPAN

1961

Printed in Japan
by Kenkyusha Printing Co., Ltd., Tokyo

PREFACE

The history of complex multiplication began with the works of Gauss and Abel on elliptic functions. It would be right, however, to call Kronecker the initiator of number-theoretic investigation of the subject. The main theorem of Kronecker's theory asserts that the abelian extensions of every imaginary quadratic field are generated by the special values of certain elliptic or elliptic modular functions; as Kronecker left the work unfinished, the accomplishment needed the efforts of the later authors, Weber and Takagi. A similar and simpler result, which is also due to Kronecker, holds for the field of rational numbers: the abelian extensions of the field of rational numbers are generated by the roots of unity, the special values of the exponential function. Hilbert conceived an idea to generalize these results, namely, to construct abelian extensions over any given algebraic number field by means of special values of analytic functions; he took this up as the 12th problem in his Paris Vortrag and emphasized its importance in number theory; it should be also mentioned that Kronecker had already thought of the problem. The first essential progress in this direction was made by Hecke, by following the idea of Hilbert. He succeeded to construct unramified abelian extensions of certain biquadratic fields by means of singular values of Hilbert modular functions of two variables. This was the last work, as well as the first, till recent years, which attacked the problem successfully. On the other hand, a new development took place in the theory of complex multiplication of elliptic functions. First H. Hasse perceived the connection between complex multiplication and the Riemann hypothesis for congruence-zeta-functions, which was later proved by A. Weil in a fully general form. This observation led M. Deuring to establish a purely algebraic treatment of complex multiplication of elliptic curves. He could, moreover, along the same line of ideas, determine the zeta-functions of elliptic curves with complex multiplication. The definition of zeta-function of an algebraic curve defined over an algebraic number field is originally due to Hasse; and Weil is the first contributor to this subject.

Now the advancement in algebraic geometry of late years, especially in the abstract theory of abelian varieties, due to Weil, enabled us to approach the problem in a fairly general form, as was shown in three papers, published in the Proceedings of the International Symposium on algebraic number theory, Tokyo-Nikko, 1955, of Weil and the authors of the present monograph. It is the purpose of the monograph to provide a full exposition of the results announced in these memoirs.

Our chief object is the arithmetic of an abelian variety A of dimension n, whose endomorphism-ring is isomorphic to an order in an algebraic number field K of degree $2n$ over the field of rational numbers. The first task is to show that the field of moduli of A, whose definition must and can be given by virtue of the notion of polarization, and the fields generated by the coordinates of the points on A of finite order, are class-fields over a certain algebraic number field K^*, corresponding to the ideal-groups determined by the arithmetical structure of A (Main Theorems 1, 2, 3 of Chap. IV). The number field K can not be taken arbitrarily; it must be a totally imaginary quadratic extension of a totally real number field. K^* is the algebraic number field determined by K and the representation of K in the linear space of invariant differential forms on A. If $n = 1$, we have $K = K^*$, while if $n > 1$, both the cases $K = K^*$ and $K \neq K^*$ may occur. The abelian extensions of K^* thus obtained from A do not provide all the abelian extensions of K^* unless $n = 1$; at any rate, the classical results of Kronecker and Hecke are included in our main theorems as particular cases. It is noticeable that the prime ideal-decomposition of the $N(\mathfrak{p})$-th power endomorphism $\pi_{\mathfrak{p}}$ of $A(\mathfrak{p})$ is fundamental in our whole theory, where $A(\mathfrak{p})$ denotes the reduction of the variety A modulo a prime ideal $\mathfrak{p}$ of a field of definition k for A. The above result is in close connection with the investigation of the zeta-function of the abelian variety A. In fact, a more precise analysis of $\pi_{\mathfrak{p}}$ shows that the correspondence $\mathfrak{p} \rightarrow \pi_{\mathfrak{p}}$ determines a Grössen-character of the field k. We are then led to the expression of the zeta-function of A by the product of several Hecke L-series attached to Grössen-characters (Main

Theorem 4 of Chap. IV); this is a generalization of the results of Weil and Deuring mentioned above.

We now give a summary of the contents. Chap. I is an exposition of more or less known results on abelian varieties, which are mostly given without proofs; the only exception is § 2, where we have given a detailed (but elementary) treatment of invariant differential forms on abelian varieties. § 3 deals with the analytic representation of abelian varieties, their homomorphisms and divisors by means of complex tori. In § 4, first the notion of polarized varieties is introduced and then the definitions of field of moduli and Kummer variety are given. Chap. II is devoted to the algebraic part of the theory of complex multiplication. §§ 5, 6 contain a necessary and sufficient condition that an algebraic number field K of degree $2n$ be realized as the endomorphism-algebra of an abelian variety of dimension n. § 7 is the study of mutually isogenous abelian varieties in connection with the ideals of the endomorphism-rings; § 8 concerns the phenomena which are essential only in the case of dimension $n > 1$ and related to the definition of the number field K^*. Chap. III contains the theory of reduction of algebraic varieties modulo a prime divisor of the basic field. We shall prove in § 13 the fundamental theorem concerning the prime ideal-decomposition of $N(\mathfrak{p})$-th power homomorphism. Our final aims are achieved in Chap. IV. The first step (§ 14) is the investigation of the relations between abelian varieties, of the same type of complex multiplication, whose polarization are also of the "same type". Then, in § 15, we prove the first main theorem; an unramified class-field is obtained by the field of moduli. A similar argument together with the analysis of the points of finite order gives us also class-fields, whose characterization is the object of § 16. These results are obtained assuming the endomorphism-ring to be the principal order of the number field. In § 17, the case of non-principal order is completely investigated. The last § 18 is devoted to the determination of the zeta-function of an abelian variety of the type described above.

The large part of the contents was prepared in collaboration of both authors during 1955–56 and published in 1957 in Japanese as the first six chapters of the book with the title "Kindai-teki Seisu-ron".

The English version was then planned; but, owing to the sudden death of the second named author in the autumn of 1958, the work had to be completed by the person left behind. The present volume is not a mere translation, however; we have written afresh from beginning to end, revising at many points, and adding new results such as § 17 and several proofs of propositions which were previously omitted.

The present monograph owes much to the idea of Weil [54], though we have not necessarily indicated explicit references in the text. I take this opportunity to acknowledge my cordial gratitude to Professor André Weil for his constant advice, suggestions and encouragement. I wish to acknowledge also my thanks to Mr. Taira Honda who read the manuscript and contributed many useful suggestions.

University of Tokyo,
February, 1960

GORO SHIMURA

The author wishes to express his deep appreciation to Mr. C. Sudler Jr. who gave a financial support for the publication of this volume.
December, 1960.

TABLE OF CONTENTS

CHAPTER I. PRELIMINARIES ON ABELIAN VARIETIES

CHAPTER II. ABELIAN VARIETIES WITH COMPLEX MULTIPLICATION

CHAPTER III. REDUCTION OF CONSTANT FIELDS

CHAPTER IV. CONSTRUCTION OF CLASS-FIELDS

NOTATIONS

We denote by $\boldsymbol{Z}$, $\boldsymbol{Q}$, $\boldsymbol{R}$ and $\boldsymbol{C}$, respectively, the ring of rational integers, the fields of rational numbers, real numbers and complex numbers. l being a rational prime, $\boldsymbol{Z}_l$ and $\boldsymbol{Q}_l$ denote the ring of l-adic integers and the field of l-adic numbers, respectively. $\boldsymbol{R}^n$ and $\boldsymbol{C}^n$ denote the vector spaces composed of all matrices with n rows and 1 column, with real coefficients and complex coefficients, respectively. If x is a matrix with complex coefficients or a function with values in $\boldsymbol{C}$, etc., we denote by $\mathrm{Re}\, x$, $\mathrm{Im}\, x$ and $\bar{x}$ the real part, the imaginary part and the complex conjugate of x. The transpose of a matrix M is denoted by ${}^tM$. We denote the unit matrix of degree m by 1_m. Terminologies and basic notations concerning algebraic geometry will be the same as those of Weil's trilogy [44], [45], [46], with a few exceptions. In particular, k' being a finite algebraic extension of a field k, we denote by $[k' : k]_i$ and $[k' : k]_s$ the inseparable and the separable factors of the degree of k' over k. If σ is an isomorphism of a field k_1 into a field k_2, we denote by z^σ, for every $z \in k_1$, the image of z by σ; furthermore, Y being any algebro-geometric object defined with respect to k_1, Y^σ will denote the transform of Y by the isomorphism σ. If k is a field and x is a point of an affine (resp. a projective) space, we denote by $k(x)$ the field generated over k by the coordinates (resp. the quotients of the coodinates) of the point x. We use also the notation $k(x)$ for the points on an abstract variety (cf. [44]).

CHAPTER I. PRELIMINARIES ON ABELIAN VARIETIES.

1. HOMOMORPHISMS AND DIVISORS.

The purpose of this § is to recall briefly some of the basic concepts on abelian varieties defined over arbitrary ground fields. For the general theory of abelian varieties, we refer to Weil [46] and Lang [26].

1. 1. Let A and B be two abelian varieties. By a *homomorphism* of A into B, or an *endomorphism* when $A = B$, we shall always understand a rational mapping λ of A into B, satisfying $\lambda(x+y) = \lambda(x)+\lambda(y)$; if λ is birational, we call it an *isomorphism*, or an *automorphism* when $A = B$; the image of a point x on A by λ will be denoted by $\lambda(x)$ or λx. We denote by $\mathscr{H}(A, B)$ the set of all homomorphisms of A into B and put $\mathscr{A}(A) = \mathscr{H}(A, A)$; $\mathscr{H}(A, B)$ is a finitely generated free $\boldsymbol{Z}$-module. We put $\mathscr{H}_0(A, B) = \mathscr{H}(A, B)\otimes\boldsymbol{Q}$ and $\mathscr{A}_0(A) = \mathscr{A}(A)\otimes\boldsymbol{Q}$. If $\lambda \in \mathscr{H}_0(A, B)$ and $\mu \in \mathscr{H}_0(B, C)$, we can define the product $\mu\lambda$ in a natural manner as an element of $\mathscr{H}_0(A, C)$. $\mathscr{A}_0(A)$ is then considered as an algebra over $\boldsymbol{Q}$ and $\mathscr{A}(A)$ is an order in the algebra $\mathscr{A}_0(A)$; the identity element of $\mathscr{A}_0(A)$ will be denoted by 1_A. We shall denote by $\mathfrak{g}(\lambda)$ the kernel of a homomorphism λ, and put $\mathfrak{g}(m, A) = \mathfrak{g}(m1_A)$ for every rational integer m. A and B are called *isogenous* if they are of the same dimension and there exists a homomorphism λ of the one onto the other; such a λ is called an *isogeny*. A and B being of the same dimension, let λ be a homomorphism of A into B; let k be a common field of definition for A, B and λ, and x a generic point of A over k. We put, if λ is an isogeny,

$$\nu(\lambda) = [k(x) : k(\lambda x)],$$

$$\nu_s(\lambda) = [k(x) : k(\lambda x)]_s, \qquad \nu_i(\lambda) = [k(x) : k(\lambda x)]_i,$$

and otherwise $\nu(\lambda) = \nu_s(\lambda) = \nu_i(\lambda) = 0$; these numbers do not depend on the choice of k and x. For every isogeny λ of A onto B, we can find an element λ' of $\mathscr{H}_0(B, A)$ such that $\lambda'\lambda = 1_A$, $\lambda\lambda' = 1_B$; λ' is uniquely determined by these relations; we denote λ' by λ^{-1}.

1. 2. *l*-adic representations of homomorphisms. Let A be an abelian variety of dimension n. Let l be a rational prime; put

$$\mathfrak{g}_l(A) = \bigcup_{\alpha=1}^{\infty} \mathfrak{g}(l^\alpha, A).$$

If l is different from the characteristic of fields of definition for A, then $\mathfrak{g}_l(A)$ is isomorphic to the direct sum $\mathfrak{M}$ of $2n$ copies of the additive group $\boldsymbol{Q}_l/\boldsymbol{Z}_l$. We call any one of the isomorphisms of $\mathfrak{g}_l(A)$ onto $\mathfrak{M}$ an *l-adic coordinate-system* of $\mathfrak{g}_l(A)$; we shall consider every element of $\mathfrak{M}$ as a matrix with $2n$ rows and one column, with coefficients in $\boldsymbol{Q}_l/\boldsymbol{Z}_l$. Let B be another abelian variety of dimension m and λ a homomorphism of A into B. Choose l-adic coordinate-systems $\mathfrak{v}$ of $\mathfrak{g}_l(A)$ and $\mathfrak{w}$ of $\mathfrak{g}_l(B)$. Then there exists a matrix M with $2m$ rows and $2n$ columns, with coefficients in $\boldsymbol{Z}_l$, such that, for every $t \in \mathfrak{g}_l(A)$, we have $\mathfrak{w}(\lambda t) = M\mathfrak{v}(t)$. If we fix $\mathfrak{v}$ and $\mathfrak{w}$, the mapping $\lambda \rightarrow M$ is uniquely extended to a representation of $\mathscr{H}_0(A, B)$ by matrices with coefficients in $\boldsymbol{Q}_l$, which we call the *l-adic representation* of $\mathscr{H}_0(A, B)$ with respect to $\mathfrak{v}$ and $\mathfrak{w}$. Let ξ be an element of $\mathscr{A}_0(A)$. M_l being an l-adic representation of $\mathscr{A}_0(A)$, let

$$P(X) = X^{2n} + a_1 X^{2n-1} + \cdots + a_{2n}$$

be the characteristic polynomial of $M_l(\xi)$. Then, the a_i are rational numbers; and we have

$$P(\xi) = \xi^{2n} + a_1 \xi^{2n-1} + \cdots + a_{2n} 1_A = 0.$$

$P(X)$ is determined only by ξ and independent of the choice of l and l-adic coordinate-system. We call $P(X)$ *the characteristic polynomial of* ξ and the roots of $P(X)$ *the characteristic roots of* ξ. Furthermore, if $\xi \in \mathscr{A}(A)$, the a_i are rational integers and

(1) $$\nu(\xi) = \det M_l(\xi).$$

We shall put, for every $\xi \in \mathscr{A}_0(A)$,

(2) $$\mathrm{tr}(\xi) = \mathrm{tr}\ M_l(\xi).$$

1. 3. Picard variety. Let A be an abelian variety; let $\mathscr{G}_a(A)$ and $\mathscr{G}_l(A)$ denote respectively the set of divisors on A algebraically equivalent to 0 and the set of divisors on A linearly equivalent to 0. Then there exists an abelian variety A^* canonically isomorphic to $\mathcal{G}_a(A)/\mathcal{G}_l(A)$, which is called a *Picard variety* of A. Every divisor Y contained in $\mathcal{G}_a(A)$ defines a point of A^*, which we denote by $\mathrm{Cl}(Y)$. Let B be an abelian variety and B^* a Picard variety of B. For every homomorphism λ of A into B, we obtain a homomorphism λ^* of B^* into A^* such that

$$\lambda^*(\mathrm{Cl}(Y)) = \mathrm{Cl}(\lambda^{-1}(Y)) \tag{3}$$

whenever $\lambda^{-1}(Y)$ is defined. The mapping $\lambda \rightarrow \lambda^*$ is uniquely extended to an isomorphism of $\mathcal{H}_0(A, B)$ onto $\mathcal{H}_0(B^*, A^*)$; we denote by ${}^t\alpha$ the image of α by this isomorphism and call it the *transpose* of α. If $\alpha \in \mathcal{H}_0(A, B)$ and $\beta \in \mathcal{H}_0(B, C)$, we have ${}^t(\beta\alpha) = {}^t\alpha{}^t\beta$. Let X be a divisor on A; we shall denote by X_u the transform of X by the translation $x \rightarrow x+u$ on A. Now define the mapping φ_X of A into A^* by the relation

$$\varphi_X(u) = \mathrm{Cl}(X_u - X) \tag{4}$$

for $u \in A$. Then φ_X is a homomorphism of A into A^*. The divisor X is said to be *non-degenerate* if φ_X is an isogeny. For any two divisors X, Y on A, we have $\varphi_X = \varphi_Y$ if and only if X and Y are algebraically equivalent (Barsotti [3], Serre [31]). Assuming X to be non-degenerate, put for every $\xi \in \mathcal{A}_0(A)$,

$$\xi' = \varphi_X^{-1}\ {}^t\xi\varphi_X. \tag{5}$$

Then, it can be proved that $\xi \rightarrow \xi'$ is an involution of $\mathcal{A}_0(A)$ and we have, for every $\xi \neq 0$,

$$\mathrm{tr}(\xi\xi') > 0. \tag{6}$$

We call this involution *the involution of $\mathcal{A}_0(A)$ determined by X*. Let λ be a homomorphism of A into B and Y a divisor on B; assume that $\lambda^{-1}(Y)$ is defined. Then, putting $X = \lambda^{-1}(Y)$, we have

$$\varphi_X = {}^t\lambda\varphi_Y\lambda. \tag{7}$$

1. 4. *l*-adic representations of divisors. Let a be an integer and Y a divisor on A such that aY is linearly equivalent to 0. Then there exist two functions Φ and Ψ on A such that $(\Phi) = aY$, $\Phi(ax)$

$= \Psi(x)^a$, where (Φ) denotes the divisor of Φ. For every point u on A such that $au = 0$, put

$$e_a(u, Y) = \Psi(x+u)\Psi(x)^{-1};$$

then $e_a(u, Y)$ is an a-th root of unity. Now let X be a divisor on A; and let u, v be two points on A such that $au = av = 0$. Since $a(X_v - X)$ is linearly equivalent to 0, we can consider $e_a(u, X_v - X)$. Put

$$e_{X,a}(u, v) = e_a(u, X_v - X).$$

Let k be a field of definition for A; and let l be a rational prime other than the characteristic of k. Let U_l denote the set of roots of unity, contained in the algebraic closure of k, whose orders are powers of l; then U_l is isomorphic to $\boldsymbol{Q}_l/\boldsymbol{Z}_l$. Take an isomorphism of U_l onto $\boldsymbol{Q}_l/\boldsymbol{Z}_l$ and denote it by lg; choose an l-adic coordinate-system $\mathfrak{y}$ of $\mathfrak{g}_l(A)$. Then there exists a matrix $E_l(X)$ with coefficients in $\boldsymbol{Z}_l$ satisfying

$$\lg e_{X, l^\nu}(s, t) \equiv l^\nu \cdot {}^t\mathfrak{y}(s) E_l(X) \mathfrak{y}(t) \qquad \mathrm{mod}\ \boldsymbol{Z}_l$$

for every point s, t on A such that $l^\nu s = l^\nu t = 0$. We call $E_l(X)$ the *l-adic representation* of X with respect to $\mathfrak{y}$. We have $E_l(X) = 0$ if and only if X is algebraically equivalent to 0.

1. 5. q-th power homomorphisms. Let A be an abelian variety defined over a field k and σ an isomorphism of k onto a field k^σ. Then we obtain in a natural way an abelian variety A^σ, defined over k^σ, taking the transform 0^σ of the origin 0 of A as the origin of A^σ. If B is an abelian variety and λ is a homomorphism of A into B, both defined over k, we denote by λ^σ the homomorphism of A^σ into B^σ, whose graph is the transform by σ of the graph of λ. Now suppose that the characteristic p of the universal domain is not 0; let $q = p^f$ $(f > 0)$ be a power of p. We shal denote by X^q the transform of any algebro-geometric object X by the automorphism $z \to z^q$ of the universal domain. We can define a homomorphism π of A onto A^q by

$$\pi x = x^q$$

for $x \in A$. We call π the *q-th power homomorphism* of A. If A is defined over a finite field with q elements, A^q coincides with A, and hence π is an endomorphism of A; we call then π the *q-th power endomorphism* of A. All the characteristic roots of the q-th power endomorphism have absolute value $q^{1/2}$; this is the so-called "Riemann hypothesis for congruence zeta-functions" proved by A. Weil. Let λ be a homomorphism of A into B; let π_A and π_B denote respectively the q-th power homomorphisms of A and B. We have then

$$\lambda^q \pi_A = \pi_B \lambda.$$

In particular, if A is defined over a finite field k with q elements, we have

$$\alpha\pi_A = \pi_A \alpha$$

for every endomorphism α of A, defined over k.

2. DIFFERENTIAL FORMS.

2. 1. Definitions. In this §, the varieties are all assumed to be defined over fields contained in a universal domain Ω which we fix once for all. Let V be a variety and k a field of definition for V. We shall denote by $k(V)$ the field of rational functions on V defined over k and by $\Omega(V)$ the field of all rational functions on V. If x is a generic point of V over k, the mapping $k(V) \ni f \rightarrow f(x)$ gives an isomorphism of $k(V)$ onto $k(x)$. We denote by $\mathscr{D}(V)$ and $\mathscr{D}(V;\, k)$ respectively the set of all derivations of $\Omega(V)$ over Ω and the set of all derivations of $k(V)$ over k. If V is of dimension n, $\mathscr{D}(V;\, k)$ is a linear space of dimension n over $k(V)$ and $\mathscr{D}(V)$ is a linear space obtained from $\mathscr{D}(V;\, k)$ by the scalar extension $\Omega(V)$ over $k(V)$. We shall denote by $\mathfrak{D}(V)$ the dual space of $\mathscr{D}(V)$ and by $\eta \cdot D$ the scalar product of $\eta \in \mathfrak{D}(V)$ and $D \in \mathscr{D}(V)$; then $(\eta,\, D) \rightarrow \eta \cdot D$ is a bilinear mapping of $\mathfrak{D}(V) \times \mathscr{D}(V)$ into $\Omega(V)$. Now, by a *differential form* of degree m on V, we shall understand a homogeneous element of degree m in the Grassmann algebra defined over $\mathfrak{D}(V)$. If f is a function on V, the mapping $\mathscr{D}(V) \ni D \rightarrow Df$ gives a linear mapping of $\mathscr{D}(V)$ into $\Omega(V)$, and hence defines an element of $\mathfrak{D}(V)$, a differential form of degree one on V; we denote it by df; then we have $df \cdot D = Df$. We see that $\mathfrak{D}(V)$ is generated over $\Omega(V)$ by the forms df for $f \in \Omega(V)$. If

V is of dimension n, then there exists a set of n functions $\{g_1,\cdots,g_n\}$ in $k(V)$ such that $k(V)$ is separably algebraic over $k(g_1,\cdots,g_n)$. If $\{g_1,\cdots,g_n\}$ is taken as this, $dg_1,\cdots,dg_n$ form a basis of $\mathfrak{D}(V)$ over $\Omega(V)$. By our definition, every differential form ω on V has an expression

$$\omega = \sum_{(i)} f_{(i)} dg_{i_1}\cdots dg_{i_r},$$

where the $f_{(i)}$ are elements of $\Omega(V)$. We shall say that a differential form ω on V is *defined over* k if ω is written in the form

$$\omega = \sum_{(i)} \varphi_{(i)} d\psi_{i_1}\cdots d\psi_{i_r},$$

with the $\varphi_{(i)}$ and the ψ_i in $k(V)$. $\{g_1,\cdots,g_n\}$ being as above, a differential form

$$\sum_{i_1<\cdots<i_r} f_{(i_1\cdots i_r)} dg_{i_1}\cdots dg_{i_r}$$

is defined over k if and only if the $f_{(i)}$ are contained in $k(V)$.

Let V' be a simple subvariety of V. We shall say that a differential form ω on V is *finite along* (or *at*) V' if ω is written in the form $\omega = \sum_{(i)} f_{(i)} dg_{i_1}\cdots dg_{i_r}$ where the $f_{(i)}$ and the g_i are functions on V which are all defined and finite along V'. If that is so, denoting by the $f'_{(i)}$ and the g'_i the functions on V' induced by the $f_{(i)}$ and the g_i, we obtain a differential form $\omega' = \sum_{(i)} f'_{(i)} dg'_{i_1}\cdots dg'_{i_r}$ on V' which is determined only by ω and V'; ω' does not depend upon the choice of the $f_{(i)}$ and the g_i. We call ω' the differential form on V' induced by ω.

2. 2. Local parameters. Let K be a field and $u_1,\cdots,u_n$ be n independent variables over K. If K_1 is a separably algebraic extension of $K(u_1,\cdots,u_n)$, there exist n derivations $D_1,\cdots,D_n$ of K_1 over K such that

$$D_i u_i = 1, \qquad D_i u_j = 0 \qquad \text{for } i \neq j.$$

The D_i are uniquely determined by these relations; we shall denote D_i by $\partial/\partial u_i$ for each i.

Now let V be a variety of dimension n, defined over k, and y a simple point on V. We call a set of n functions $\{\tau_1,\cdots,\tau_n\}$ in $k(V)$ a *system of local parameters* for V at y defined over k, if the following conditions are satisfied.

(L1) *$k(V)$ is separably algebraic over $k(\tau_1,\cdots,\tau_n)$.*

(L2) *The τ_i are all defined and finite at y.*

(L3) *For every f in $k(V)$, defined and finite at y, the function $\partial f/\partial\tau_i$ is defined and finite at y for every i.*

Let x be a generic point of V over k; let V_α, y_α, x_α be affine representatives of V, y, x and S the ambient space for V_α; let N be the dimension of S. Then, by Koizumi [23], we know that n functions $\tau_1,\cdots,\tau_n$ in $k(V)$ form a system of local parameters for V at y, defined over k, if and only if the following conditions are satisfied.

(L′1) *The τ_i are all defined and finite at y.*

(L′2) *There exists a set of N polynomials $F_i(X_1,\cdots,X_N,T_1,\cdots,T_n)$ with coefficients in k such that $F_i(x_\alpha,\tau(x))=0$ for $1\leqq i\leqq N$ and* $\det(\partial F_i/\partial X_j(y_\alpha,\tau(y)))\neq 0$.

We shall prove this in § 10. 3 in a more general case. If $\{\tau_1,\cdots,\tau_n\}$ is a system of local parameters at y, then $d\tau_1,\cdots,d\tau_n$ form a basis of $\mathfrak{D}(V)$; and, by (L3), every differential form

$$\omega=\sum_{i_1<\cdots<i_r} f_{(i_1\ldots i_r)}d\tau_{i_1}\cdots d\tau_{i_r}$$

is finite at y if and only if the $f_{(i)}$ are all defined and finite at y.

2. 3. Let V and W be two varieties and T a rational mapping of V into W; we denote by the same notation T the graph of T, and by Y the projection of T on W. For every f in $\Omega(W)$, defined and finite along Y, we shall denote by $f\circ T$ the function on V defined by $f\circ T(x)=f(T(x))$ with respect to a field k of definition for V, W, T and f, where x is a generic point of V over k. Assuming that Y is simple on W, let ω be a differential form on W finite along Y. Then ω is written in the form $\omega=\sum f_{(i)}dg_{i_1}\cdots dg_{i_r}$ where the $f_{(i)}$ and the g_i are elements of $\Omega(W)$ which are all defined and finite along Y. Put

$$\omega'=\sum(f_{(i)}\circ T)d(g_{i_1}\circ T)\cdots d(g_{i_r}\circ T).$$

Then ω' is a differential form on V which is determined only by ω and

T, and does not depend on the choice of the $f_{(i)}$ and the g_i. We shall denote the form ω' by $\omega\circ T$. If V, W, T, ω are all defined over k, then $\omega\circ T$ is also defined over k. If T is defined at a simple point y on V and if $T(y)$ is simple on W, then for every differential form ω which is finite at $T(y)$, $\omega\circ T$ is finite at y.

V, W, T, ω being as above, let U be a variety and S a rational mapping of U into V; suppose that the image X of U by S is simple on V and T is defined along X. Then we obtain a rational mapping $T\circ S$ of U into W, defined by $T\circ S(x) = T(S(x))$. Suppose further that the image Z of U by $T\circ S$ is simple on W and ω is finite along Z. We obtain then a differential form $\omega\circ(T\circ S)$ on U. It can be easily verified that the differential form $(\omega\circ T)\circ S$ is also defined and equal to $\omega\circ(T\circ S)$.

2. 4. Differential forms of the first kind. Let V be a complete non-singular variety. We say that a differential form ω on V is of *the first kind* if ω is everywhere finite on V. Let W be another complete non-singular variety and T a rational mapping of V into W. Then, for every differential form ω of the first kind on W, $\omega\circ T$ is also a differential form of the first kind on V. This is easily proved by means of Proposition 5 of Koizumi [23].

PROPOSITION 1. *Let V_1 and V_2 be two complete non-singular varieties and p_i the projection from $V_1\times V_2$ onto V_i for $i = 1, 2$. Then, for any differential form ω on $V_1\times V_2$ of the first kind and of degree* 1, *there exist differential forms ω_i on V_i $(i = 1, 2)$ of the first kind and of degree* 1 *such that $\omega = \omega_1\circ p_1+\omega_2\circ p_2$.*

This is a restatement of Theorem 3 of [23].

2. 5. Let V be a variety defined over k and σ an isomorphism of k onto a field k^σ. Let f be a function in $k(V)$ and Γ the graph of f. We shall denote by f^σ the function on V^σ whose graph is Γ^σ; then, $f\to f^\sigma$ gives an isomorphism of $k(V)$ onto $k^\sigma(V^\sigma)$. Let ω be a differential form on V defined over k. Then ω has an expression $\omega = \sum_{(i)} f_{(i)}dg_{i_1}\cdots dg_{i_r}$ with the $f_{(i)}$ and the g_i in $k(V)$. It can be easily shown that the differential form $\omega' = \sum_{(i)} f_{(i)}{}^\sigma dg_{i_1}{}^\sigma\cdots dg_{i_r}{}^\sigma$ on V^σ is determined only by ω and σ, and does not depend upon the choice of the $f_{(i)}$ and the g_i. We shall denote the form ω' by ω^σ.

2. 6. Invariant differential forms on group varieties. Let G be a group variety and t a point on G. We shall denote by T_t the left translation $x \to tx$ of G. T_t is obviously a birational correspondence of G onto itself. We call a differential form ω on G a *left invariant* differential form on G if $\omega \circ T_t = \omega$ for every t on G.

PROPOSITION 2. *Let G be a group variety and ω a left invariant differential form on G. Then ω is everywhere finite on G.*

PROOF. Take a field of definition k for G and ω, and a generic point x of G over k. ω is of course finite at x. Then, the relation $\omega = \omega \circ T_{xy}$ shows that ω is finite at any point y^{-1} on G.

LEMMA 1. *Let G be a group variety, ω a differential form on G; let k be a field of definition for G and ω, and t be a generic point of G over k. If the relation $\omega \circ T_t = \omega$ holds, ω is left invariant.*

PROOF. Let s be any generic point of G over k. Then there exists an isomorphism σ of $k(t)$ onto $k(s)$ over k such that $t^\sigma = s$. By the relation $\omega = \omega \circ T_t$, we have $\omega = \omega^\sigma = (\omega \circ T_t)^\sigma = \omega \circ T_s$. Now let x be a point of G. Take a generic point y of G over $k(x)$. Then, since xy and y^{-1} are generic on G over k, we have $\omega \circ T_{xy} = \omega \circ T_{y^{-1}} = \omega$, so that

$$\omega \circ T_x = \omega \circ (T_{xy} \circ T_{y^{-1}}) = (\omega \circ T_{xy}) \circ T_{y^{-1}} = \omega \circ T_{y^{-1}} = \omega.$$

This shows that ω is left invariant.

We shall denote by $\mathfrak{D}_0(G)$ the set of all left invariant differential forms on G of degree one and by $\mathfrak{D}_0(G; k)$ the set of elements of $\mathfrak{D}_0(G)$ which are defined over k.

PROPOSITION 3. *Let G be a group variety of demension n, defined over k. Then $\mathfrak{D}_0(G; k)$ is a linear space of dimension n over k; and we have $\mathfrak{D}_0(G) = \mathfrak{D}_0(G; k) \otimes_k \Omega$ and $\mathfrak{D}(G) = \mathfrak{D}_0(G; k) \otimes_k \Omega(G)$.*

PROOF. It is obvious that $\mathfrak{D}_0(G; k)$ is a linear space over k. Denote by e the identity element of the group G. Let $\{\tau_1, \cdots, \tau_n\}$ be a system of local parameters for G at e, defined over k. Then, every element ω of $\mathfrak{D}(G)$, defined over k, can be expressed in the form $\omega = \sum_i f_i d\tau_i$ with the f_i in $k(G)$. Let x and t be independent and generic on G over k; put $f'_i = f_i \circ T_{t^{-1}}$, $\tau'_i = \tau_i \circ T_{t^{-1}}$. We have then

$$\omega \circ T_{t^{-1}} = \sum_i f'_i d\tau'_i, \qquad f'_i(x) = f_i(t^{-1}x), \qquad \tau'_i(x) = \tau_i(t^{-1}x).$$

Since $\{d\tau_1, \cdots, d\tau_n\}$ is a basis of $\mathfrak{D}(G)$, there exist n^2 functions $g^t{}_{ij}$ $(1 \leqq i \leqq n,\ 1 \leqq j \leqq n)$ in $\Omega(G)$ such that

$$d\tau'_i = \sum_j g^t{}_{ij} d\tau_j \qquad (1 \leqq i \leqq n).$$

The $g^t{}_{ij}$ are contained in $k(t)(G)$, since the τ'_i and τ_i are contained in $k(t)(G)$. Let g_{ij} be the element of $k(G \times G)$ defined by $g_{ij}(t, x) = g^t{}_{ij}(x)$ for each i and j. If y is a point on G where the τ_i are local parameters and if the τ'_i are all defined and finite at y, then the $g^t{}_{ij}$ are all defined and finite at y, so that the g_{ij} are all defined and finite at $t \times y$, and we have $g_{ij}(t, y) = g^t{}_{ij}(y)$. Applying this to the points t and e, we see that the g_{ij} are all defined and finite at $t \times t$ and $t \times e$, and we have

$$g_{ij}(t, t) = g^t{}_{ij}(t), \qquad g_{ij}(t, e) = g^t{}_{ij}(e).$$

Now suppose that ω is left invariant. Then, the relation $\omega = \omega \circ T_t$ implies $\sum_i f_i d\tau_i = \sum_i f'_i d\tau'_i = \sum_{i,j} f'_i g^t{}_{ij} d\tau_j$; hence we have $f_j = \sum_i f'_i g^t{}_{ij}$, namely,

$$(1) \qquad f_j(x) = \sum_i f_i(t^{-1}x) g_{ij}(t, x) \qquad (1 \leqq j \leqq n).$$

Conversely, if n elements $f_1, \cdots, f_n$ of $k(G)$ satisfy this relation, then $\omega = \sum_i f_i d\tau_i$ satisfies the relation $\omega \circ T_t = \omega$, and hence, by Lemma 1, ω is left invariant. Assume that ω is left invariant, namely that the f_j satisfy (1). The f_j are defined and finite at e since ω is finite at e. Hence we can specialize (t, x) to (t, t) in the equation (1). We have then $f_j(t) = \sum_i f_i(e) g_{ij}(t, t)$ for $1 \leqq j \leqq n$. Let h_{ij} be the element of $k(G)$ defined by $h_{ij}(t) = g_{ij}(t, t)$ for each i and j; and put $\omega_i = \sum_j h_{ij} d\tau_j$ for each i. Then we have $\omega = \sum_j f_j d\tau_j = \sum_i f_i(e)\omega_i$. This shows that every element of $\mathfrak{D}_0(G; k)$ is a linear combination of the ω_i with coefficients in k. Hence the dimension of the linear space $\mathfrak{D}_0(G; k)$ over k is not greater than n. We shall now prove that the ω_q $(1 \leqq q \leqq n)$ are all left invariant. To prove this, it is sufficient to show that the equality (1) holds if we substitute h_{qi}, h_{qj} for f_i, f_j, namely,

$$(2) \qquad h_{qj}(x) = \sum_i h_{qi}(t^{-1}x)g_{ij}(t, x) \qquad (1 \leqq q \leqq n,\ 1 \leqq j \leqq n),$$

or, as we have $h_{qi}(x) = g_{qi}(x, x)$,

$$(2') \qquad g_{qj}(x, x) = \sum_i g_{qi}(t^{-1}x, t^{-1}x)g_{ij}(t, x) \qquad (1 \leqq q \leqq n,\ 1 \leqq j \leqq n).$$

Let s be a generic point of G over $k(t, x)$; put

$$\tau''_i = \tau_i \circ T_{s^{-1}}, \qquad \tau'''_i = \tau'_i \circ T_{s^{-1}} = \tau_i \circ T_{(st)^{-1}} \quad (1 \leqq i \leqq n).$$

Then we have

$$d\tau'''_i = (d\tau'_i) \circ T_{s^{-1}} = \sum_j (g^t{}_{ij} \circ T_{s^{-1}}) d(\tau_j \circ T_{s^{-1}}) = \sum_j (g^t{}_{ij} \circ T_{s^{-1}}) d\tau''_j.$$

Define the functions $g^s{}_{ij}$ and $g^{st}{}_{ij}$ on G by

$$g^s{}_{ij}(x) = g_{ij}(s, x), \qquad g^{st}{}_{ij}(x) = g_{ij}(st, x);$$

we have then $d\tau''_i = \sum_j g^s{}_{ij} d\tau_j$, $d\tau'''_i = \sum_j g^{st}{}_{ij} d\tau_j$ for $1 \leqq i \leqq n$. These are obtained from the relation $d\tau'_i = \sum_j g^t{}_{ij} d\tau_j$ by isomorphisms between the fields $k(t)$, $k(s)$ and $k(st)$. It follows that

$$\sum_j g^{st}{}_{ij} d\tau_j = d\tau'''_i = \sum_j (g^t{}_{ij} \circ T_{s^{-1}}) d\tau''_j = \sum_{j,l} (g^t{}_{ij} \circ T_{s^{-1}}) g^s{}_{jl} d\tau_l;$$

this implies $g^{st}{}_{il} = \sum_j (g^t{}_{ij} \circ T_{s^{-1}}) g^s{}_{jl}$ for $1 \leqq i \leqq n$, $1 \leqq l \leqq n$, or

$$(3) \qquad g_{il}(st, x) = \sum_j g_{ij}(t, s^{-1}x) g_{jl}(s, x) \qquad (1 \leqq i \leqq n,\ 1 \leqq l \leqq n).$$

Specializing (s, t, x) to $(t, t^{-1}x, x)$, we obtain (2′); hence the ω_i are left invariant. Our theorem is completely proved if we show that the ω_i are linearly independent over $\Omega(G)$. To see this, it is sufficient to prove $\det(h_{ij}) \neq 0$, since $d\tau_1, \cdots, d\tau_n$ are linearly independent over $\Omega(G)$ and $\omega_i = \sum_j h_{ij} d\tau_j$. As t^{-1} is generic on G over k, the τ_i are local parameters at t^{-1} and consequently the τ'_i are local parameters at e.

Hence, from the relation $d\tau'_i = \sum_j g^t{}_{ij} d\tau_j$ it follows that $\det(g^t{}_{ij}(e)) \neq 0$, namely, $\det(g_{ij}(t, e)) \neq 0$. Specializing (s, t, x) to (s, t, s) in the relation (3), we get

$$g_{il}(st, s) = \sum_j g_{ij}(t, e) g_{jl}(s, s) \qquad (1 \leqq i \leqq n,\ 1 \leqq l \leqq n).$$

Hence we have $\det(g_{ij}(s, s)) \neq 0$; this completes the proof, on account of the relation $h_{ij}(s) = g_{ij}(s, s)$.

Now specialize x to e in the relation (2); we see then that the h_{ij} are defined at e and

$$(4) \qquad \det(h_{ij}(e)) \neq 0.$$

We need this fact later.

2. 7. Invariant differential forms on abelian varieties. As an abelian variety is a commutative group, we call a left invariant differential form on an abelian variety simply an *invariant differential form.*

PROPOSITION 4. *Let A be an abelian variety. Then every differential form of degree* 1 *on A is of the first kind if and only if it is invariant.*

PROOF. By Proposition 2, we have only to prove the "only if" part. Let ω be a differential form on A of degree 1 and of the first kind. Considering A as G in Proposition 3, we use the notations τ_i, ω_i, h_{ij} in the same sense as in that proof. Then, by that proposition, there exist n functions a_i in $\Omega(A)$ such that $\omega = \sum_i a_i \omega_i$. As the ω_i are invariant, we have, for every x on A,

$$\omega \cdot T_x = \sum_i (a_i \circ T_x) \omega_i = \sum_{i,j} (a_i \circ T_x) h_{ij} d\tau_j.$$

Since ω is everywhere finite on A, $\omega \circ T_x$ is also everywhere finite on A; in particular, $\omega \circ T_x$ is finite at e. Therefore, recalling that the τ_j are local parameters at e, we see that the n functions $\sum_i (a_i \circ T_x) h_{ij}$ $(1 \leqq j \leqq n)$ are finite at e, so that, by (4), the $a_i \circ T_x$ are finite at e. As x is an arbitrary point of A, this shows that the a_i are everywhere finite on A. Such functions must be constant, since A is a complete variety.

Hence ω is a linear combination of the ω_i with constant coefficients; so ω is an invariant differential form.

2. 8. Differentials of homomorphisms. Let A and B be two abelian varieties and λ a homomorphism of A into B. If ω is an element of $\mathfrak{D}_0(B)$, then $\omega\circ\lambda$ is defined and contained in $\mathfrak{D}_0(A)$. The mapping $\omega\rightarrow\omega\circ\lambda$ gives an Ω-linear mapping of $\mathfrak{D}_0(B)$ into $\mathfrak{D}_0(A)$. We shall denote this linear mapping by $\delta\lambda$, namely,

$$(\delta\lambda)\omega = \omega\circ\lambda$$

for $\omega\in\mathfrak{D}_0(B)$. If k is a field of definition for A, B and λ, then $\delta\lambda$ gives a k-linear mapping of $\mathfrak{D}_0(B;\ k)$ into $\mathfrak{D}_0(A;\ k)$. For every homomorphism μ of B into an abelian variety C, we have

$$\delta(\mu\lambda) = \delta\lambda\delta\mu.$$

PROPOSITION 5. *Let A and B be two abelian varieties; and let λ and μ be two homomorphisms of A into B. Then we have*

$$\delta(\lambda+\mu) = \delta\lambda+\delta\mu.$$

PROOF. Define homomorphisms α, β, γ, λ_0, μ_0 as follows:

$$A \xrightarrow{\alpha} A\times A \xrightarrow{\beta,\,\lambda_0,\,\mu_0} B\times B \xrightarrow{\gamma} B,$$

$$\alpha(x) = x\times x, \qquad \beta(x\times y) = \lambda(x)\times\mu(y), \qquad \gamma(z\times w) = z+w,$$

$$\lambda_0(x\times y) = \lambda(x)\times 0, \qquad \mu_0(x\times y) = 0\times\mu(y).$$

We have then $\lambda+\mu = \gamma\beta\alpha$, $\gamma\lambda_0\alpha = \lambda$, $\gamma\mu_0\alpha = \mu$, so that $\delta(\lambda+\mu) = \delta\alpha\delta\beta\delta\gamma$, $\delta\lambda = \delta\alpha\delta\lambda_0\delta\gamma$, $\delta\mu = \delta\alpha\delta\mu_0\delta\gamma$. Hence our proposition is proved if we show $\delta\beta = \delta\lambda_0+\delta\mu_0$. Let p_1 and p_2 be respectively the projection from $B\times B$ onto the first and the second factors of $B\times B$. By Proposition 1, for every $\omega\in\mathfrak{D}_0(B\times B)$, there exist two elements ω_1, ω_2 in $\mathfrak{D}_0(B)$ such that $\omega = \omega_1\circ p_1+\omega_2\circ p_2$. It follows that $\delta\beta\omega = \delta\beta(\omega_1\circ p_1)+\delta\beta(\omega_2\circ p_2)$. We see easily

$$p_1\circ\beta = p_1\circ\lambda_0, \qquad p_2\circ 0 = p_2\circ\lambda_0, \qquad p_2\circ\beta = p_2\circ\mu_0, \qquad p_1\circ 0 = p_1\circ\mu_0,$$

so that we have

$$\delta\beta(\omega_1\circ p_1) = \omega_1\circ p_1\circ\beta = \omega_1\circ p_1\circ\lambda_0 = \delta\lambda_0(\omega_1\circ p_1),$$
$$\delta\beta(\omega_2\circ p_2) = \omega_2\circ p_2\circ\beta = \omega_2\circ p_2\circ\mu_0 = \delta\mu_0(\omega_2\circ p_2),$$

$$\delta\lambda_0(\omega_2\circ p_2) = \omega_2\circ p_2\circ\lambda_0 = \omega_2\circ p_2\circ 0 = 0,$$
$$\delta\mu_0(\omega_1\circ p_1) = \omega_1\circ p_1\circ\mu_0 = \omega_1\circ p_1\circ 0 = 0.$$

It follows that $\delta\beta\omega = \delta\lambda_0\omega + \delta\mu_0\omega$; this completes the proof.

LEMMA 2. *Let $k(x)$ be an extension of a field k and s the smallest number of quantities u_i in $k(x)$ such that $k(x)$ is separably algebraic over $k(u)$. Then there exist s and no more than s linearly independent derivations of $k(x)$ over k. Moreover, if the characteristic p of k is not 0, we have $[k(x): k(x^p)] = p^s$ and $[k(x): k(x^q)] \leqq q^s$ for any power $q = p^f$ with $f > 0$.* (cf. [44] p. 14).

PROOF. Let $(u) = (u_1, \cdots, u_s)$ be a set of quantities in $k(x)$ such that $k(x)$ is separably algebraic over $k(u)$. By our definition of s, for every i, $k(x)$ is not separably algebraic over $k(u_1, \cdots, u_{i-1}, u_{i+1}, \cdots, u_s)$. Hence there exists, for each i, a derivation D_i of $k(x)$ such that $D_i u_i = 1$, $D_i u_j = 0$ $(i \neq j)$; the derivations D_i are obviously linearly independent. Let D be a derivation of $k(x)$ over k; put $Du_i = y_i$ and $D' = D - \sum_i y_i D_i$; then D' is a derivation of $k(x)$ over $k(u)$. As $k(x)$ is separably algebraic over $k(u)$, we have $D' = 0$; this proves the first assertion. Now suppose that k is of characteristic $p \neq 0$. As $k(x)$ is purely inseparable over $k(x^q)$ for any power $q = p^f$ with $f > 0$, $k(x)$ is purely inseparable and separable over $k(x^q, u)$; so we have $k(x) = k(x^q, u)$. It follows that we have $[k(x): k(x^q)] \leqq q^s$, since the u_i^q are contained in $k(x^q)$; in particular, we have $[k(x): k(x^p)] \leqq p^s$. Suppose that we have $[k(x): k(x^p)] = p^r < p^s$; then there exist r quantities v_j in $k(x)$ such that $k(x) = k(x^p, v)$. By the first assertion of our lemma, the number of linearly independent derivations of $k(x)$ over $k(x^p)$ is not greater than r. This is a contradiction since every derivation of $k(x)$ over k gives a derivation of $k(x)$ over $k(x^p)$. Hence we must have $[k(x): k(x^p)] = p^s$. This completes the proof.

THEOREM 1. *Let A and B be two abelian varieties and λ a homomorphism of A into B; let k be a field of definition for A, B and λ, and x a generic point of A over k. If the linear mapping $\delta\lambda$ of $\mathfrak{D}_0(B)$ into $\mathfrak{D}_0(A)$ is of rank r, then:*

i) *$k(x)$ is separably generated over $k(\lambda x)$ if and only if* $\dim_k(\lambda x) = r$;

ii) *assuming that A and B have the same dimension n, we have $\nu_i(\lambda) = 1$ if and only if $n = r$;*

iii) *n being as in* ii), *if k is of characteristic $p \neq 0$ and if $k(\lambda x) \supset k(x^q)$ for a power $q = p^e$ $(e > 0)$ of p, then we have $\nu(\lambda) = \nu_i(\lambda) \leqq q^{n-r}$.*

Proof. Let n and m be respectively the dimensions of A and B. Let F denote the subfield $\{f \circ \lambda \mid f \in k(B)\}$ of $k(A)$. Let D be a derivation of $k(A)$ over k. We shall prove that $(\delta\lambda\omega)\cdot D = 0$ for all $\omega \in \mathfrak{D}_0(B)$ if and only if $DF = 0$. Take a basis $\{\omega_1, \cdots, \omega_m\}$ of $\mathfrak{D}_0(B; k)$ over k; then, for every $f \in k(B)$, there exist, by Proposition 3, m functions g_i in $k(B)$ such that $df = \sum_i g_i\omega_i$. If $(\delta\lambda\omega)\cdot D = 0$ for all $\omega \in \mathfrak{D}_0(B)$, we have

$$D(f \circ \lambda) = d(f \circ \lambda)\cdot D = \sum_i (g_i \circ \lambda)(\delta\lambda\omega_i)\cdot D = 0;$$

this shows $DF = 0$. Conversely, suppose that $DF = 0$. Every ω in $\mathfrak{D}_0(B)$ can be expressed in the form $\omega = \sum_i f_i dh_i$ with $f_i \in \Omega(B)$, $h_i \in k(B)$. We have hence

$$(\delta\lambda\omega)\cdot D = \sum_i (f_i \circ \lambda) d(h_i \circ \lambda)\cdot D = \sum_i (f_i \circ \lambda) D(h_i \circ \lambda) = 0.$$

Thus we have proved that $(\delta\lambda\omega)\cdot D = 0$ for all $\omega \in \mathfrak{D}_0(B)$ if and only if $DF = 0$. Now, by our assumption, $\delta\lambda[\mathfrak{D}_0(B)]$ is a linear subspace of $\mathfrak{D}_0(A)$ of dimension r. By Proposition 3, any linearly independent elements of $\mathfrak{D}_0(A)$ over Ω are linearly independent over $\Omega(A)$. Hence there exist exactly $n-r$ linearly independent derivations of $k(A)$ over F. If x is generic on A over k, the mapping $f \to f(x)$ gives an isomorphism of $k(A)$ onto $k(x)$, and F corresponds to $k(\lambda x)$ by this isomorphism; so there exist exactly $n-r$ linearly independent derivations of $k(x)$ over $k(\lambda x)$. By Lemma 2, we can find $n-r$ elements $u_1, \cdots, u_{n-r}$ in $k(x)$ such that $k(x)$ is separably algebraic over $k(\lambda x, u_1, \cdots, u_{n-r})$. If $\dim_k(\lambda x) = r$, the u_i must be independent variables over $k(\lambda x)$, so that $k(x)$ is separably generated over $k(\lambda x)$. Conversely, if $k(x)$ is separably generated over $k(\lambda x)$, then by Proposition 16 of [44] Chap. I, the dimension of $k(x)$ over $k(\lambda x)$ is $n-r$, so that we have $\dim_k(\lambda x) = r$. This proves the assertion i). If $m = n$ and $\nu_i(\lambda) = 1$, $k(x)$ is separably algebraic over $k(\lambda x)$; consequently, by what we have just proved, we have $n = \dim_k(\lambda x) = r$. Conversely, if $\operatorname{rank} \delta\lambda = n$, there is no derivation other than 0 in $k(x)$ over $k(\lambda x)$, so that $k(x)$ is separably algebraic over $k(\lambda x)$, namely, $\nu_i(\lambda) = 1$; this implies ii). Suppose now that k is of characteristic $p \neq 0$ and $k(\lambda x) \supset k(x^q)$ for $q = p^e$ with $e > 0$. Then, by Lemma 2, we have

$$[k(x):\ k(\lambda x)] = [k(x):\ k(\lambda x,\ x^q)] \leqq q^{n-r};$$

this proves iii) of our theorem.

COROLLARY. *Let B be an abelian variety and A an abelian subvariety of B. If α denotes the injection of A into B, we have*

$$\delta\alpha(\mathfrak{D}_0(B)) = \mathfrak{D}_0(A).$$

This is an easy consequence of i) of Theorem 1.

PROPOSITION 6. *Let A, B, λ, k, x be the same as in Theorem 1. Suppose that the characteristic p of k is not 0. Then:*

i) *we have $\delta\lambda = 0$ if and only if $k(\lambda x) \subset k(x^p)$;*

ii) *assume that A and B are of the same dimension; if $\nu_i(\lambda) = 1$, we have $k(x) = k(x^q,\ \lambda x)$ for every power $q = p^e$ with $e > 0$; conversely, if $k(x) = k(x^q,\ \lambda x)$ for some $q = p^e$ with $e > 0$, we have $\nu_i(\lambda) = 1$.*

PROOF. The proof of Theorem 1 implies that $\delta\lambda = 0$ if and only is $DF = 0$ for all derivations D of $k(A)$ over k, the notations being as there. Hence we have $\delta\lambda = 0$ if and only if $F \subset k(A)^p \cdot k$; the latter condition is equivalent to $k(\lambda x) \subset k(x^p)$; this proves i). If $\nu_i(\lambda) = 1$, $k(x)$ is separably algebraic over $k(\lambda x)$; as $k(x)$ is purely inseparable over $k(x^q)$ for every power $q = p^e$ with $e > 0$, we have $k(x) = k(x^q,\ \lambda x)$. Conversely, suppose that $k(x) = k(x^q,\ \lambda x)$ for some power $q = p^e$ with $e > 0$. Then there is no derivation of $k(x)$ over $k(\lambda x)$ other than 0, so that $k(x)$ is separably algebraic over $k(\lambda x)$, namely $\nu_i(\lambda) = 1$.

PROPOSITION 7. *Let A be an abelian variety of dimension n, defined over a field of characteristic $p \neq 0$. Then, $\nu_i(p1_A)$ is a multiple of p^n and the order of $\mathfrak{g}(p,\ A)$ is a divisor of p^n.*

PROOF. By Proposition 5, we have $\delta(p1_A) = \delta(\overbrace{1_A + \cdots + 1_A}^{p}) = p\delta 1_A = 0.$

Hence, by i) of Proposition 6, we have $k(px) \subset k(x^p)$, where k is a field of definition for A and x a generic point of A over k. It follows that $\nu_i(p1_A) = [k(x): k(px)]_i \geqq [k(x): k(x^p)] = p^n$. Since the order of $\mathfrak{g}(p, A)$ is equal to $\nu_s(p1_A)$ and $\nu_s(p1_A)\nu_i(p1_A) = \nu(p1_A) = p^{2n}$, we obtain our proposition.

Let A be an abelian variety of dimension n and k a field of definition for A. Denote by $\mathscr{A}(A; k)$ the set of all elements in $\mathscr{A}(A)$ defined over k and by $\mathscr{A}_0(A; k)$ the subset $\mathscr{A}(A; k) \otimes Q$ of $\mathscr{A}_0(A)$. For every $\lambda \in \mathscr{A}(A; k)$, $\delta\lambda$ gives a linear transformation of $\mathfrak{D}_0(A; k)$. We have seen above that the relations $\delta(\lambda+\mu) = \delta\lambda+\delta\mu$, $\delta(\lambda\mu) = \delta\mu\delta\lambda$ hold, so that the mapping $\lambda \rightarrow \delta\lambda$ gives an anti-representation of $\mathscr{A}(A; k)$. As $\mathfrak{D}_0(A; k)$ is a linear space of dimension n over k, we obtain, with respect to a basis of $\mathfrak{D}_0(A; k)$ over k, an anti-representation of $\mathscr{A}(A; k)$ by matrices of degree n *with coefficients in* k. If k is of characteristic $p \neq 0$, we have $\delta(p1_A) = 0$; so our representation is not one-to-one. If k is of characteristic 0, we get a one-to-one representation. In fact, if $\delta\lambda = 0$, the rank of $\delta\lambda$ is 0, so that by i) of Theorem 1, we have $\dim_k(\lambda x) = 0$; this implies $\lambda = 0$. In case of characteristic 0, we can extend uniquely the representation to a representation of $\mathscr{A}_0(A; k)$. We shall call this anti-representation a *representation of* $\mathscr{A}_0(A; k)$ *by invariant differential forms.*

2. 9. Differential forms on a curve and its Jacobian variety. In the sequel, we denote by $\mathfrak{D}_0(V)$ the set of all differential forms on an algebraic variety V, of degree 1 and of the first kind.

PROPOSITION 8. *Let C be a complete curve without singular point and J a Jacobian variety of C and φ a canonical mapping of C into J. Then, $\omega \rightarrow \omega\circ\varphi$ gives an isomorphism of $\mathfrak{D}_0(J)$ onto $\mathfrak{D}_0(C)$.*

PROOF. Let g be the genus of C; denote by C_g and J_g the product $C\times\cdots\times C$ of g copies of C and the product $J\times\cdots\times J$ of g copies of J, respectively. Let k be a field of definition for C, J, and φ, and $x_1\times\cdots\times x_g$ a generic point of C_g over k; define a rational mapping Ψ of C_g into J by $\Psi(x_1,\cdots, x_g) = \sum_{i=1}^{g} \varphi(x_i)$. Then Ψ is everywhere defined on C_g; and putting $z = \Psi(x_1,\cdots, x_g)$, we see that $k(x_1,\cdots, x_g)$ is separably algebraic over $k(z)$. Let σ and τ denote respectively the rational mappings of J_g into J and of C_g into J_g defined by

$$\sigma(z_1,\cdots,z_g) = z_1+\cdots+z_g, \qquad \tau(x_1,\cdots,x_g) = \varphi(x_1)\times\cdots\times\varphi(x_g).$$

Denote further by p_i the projection of C_g onto the i-th factor and by q_i the projection of J_g onto the i-th factor. We have then $\Psi = \sigma\circ\tau$, $q_i\circ\tau = \varphi\circ p_i$ and $\delta\sigma = \delta q_1+\cdots+\delta q_g$ by virtue of Proposition 5, so that we have, for every $\omega\in\mathfrak{D}_0(J)$,

$$\begin{aligned}\omega\circ\Psi &= \omega\circ\sigma\circ\tau = (\omega\circ q_1+\cdots+\omega\circ q_g)\circ\tau\\ &= \omega\circ q_1\circ\tau+\cdots+\omega\circ q_g\circ\tau = \omega\circ\varphi\circ p_1+\cdots+\omega\circ\varphi\circ p_g.\end{aligned}$$

Hence, if $\omega\circ\varphi = 0$, we have $\omega\circ\Psi = 0$; as the mapping Ψ is separably algebraic, $\omega\circ\Psi = 0$ implies $\omega = 0$. This shows that the mapping $\omega\to\omega\circ\varphi$ of $\mathfrak{D}_0(J)$ into $\mathfrak{D}_0(C)$ is one-to-one. Our proposition is thereby proved, since $\mathfrak{D}_0(J)$ and $\mathfrak{D}_0(C)$ are of the same dimension g.

The notations C, J and φ being as above, let C' be another complete non-singular curve, J' its Jacobian variety and φ' a canonical mapping of C' into J'; and let k be a field of definition for C, J, φ, C', J', φ'. Let X be a positive divisor of $C\times C'$ rational over k. X determines a homomorphism of J into J' as follows (cf. Weil [45, 46]). Take a generic point x of C over k and put

$$X\cdot(x\times C') = \sum_{\nu=1}^{n} x\times y_\nu;$$

then, there exists a homomorphism λ of J into J', defined over k, and a point b on J', rational over k, such that

$$\lambda[\varphi(x)]+b = \sum_{\nu=1}^{n}\varphi'(y_\nu);$$

λ and b do not depend on the choice of k and x.

PROPOSITION 9. *The notations being as above, let C_0 be a complete non-singular curve with a generic point z over the algebraic closure k_1 of k such that $k(z) = k(x, y_1,\cdots,y_n)$; and let p and the q_ν be the rational mappings of C_0 into C and into C' defined by $p(z) = x$, $q_\nu(z) = y_\nu$ with respect to k_1. Then, for every $\omega\in\mathfrak{D}_0(J')$, we have*

$$\omega\circ\lambda\circ\varphi\circ p = \sum_{\nu=1}^{n}\omega\circ\varphi'\circ q_\nu.$$

PROOF. Define the rational mappings α, β, γ as follows:

$$C_0 \xrightarrow{\alpha} C' \times \cdots \times C' \xrightarrow{\beta} J' \times \cdots \times J' \xrightarrow{\gamma} J',$$

where the numbers of the factors in the products are both equal to n, and

$$\alpha(z) = y_1 \times \cdots \times y_n, \qquad \beta(u_1 \times \cdots \times u_n) = \varphi'(u_1) \times \cdots \times \varphi'(u_n),$$

$$\gamma(v_1 \times \cdots \times v_n) = v_1 + \cdots + v_n.$$

Put $\lambda_1 = \lambda + b$; we have then

$$\gamma \circ \beta \circ \alpha(z) = \sum_\nu \varphi'(y_\nu) = \lambda \circ \varphi(x) + b = \lambda_1 \circ \varphi \circ p(z).$$

Let ω be an element of $\mathfrak{D}_0(J')$; as ω is an invariant form, we have $\omega \circ \lambda_1 = \omega \circ \lambda$. Denote by γ_ν the projection of $J' \times \cdots \times J'$ onto the ν-th factor. Then we have $\gamma = \gamma_1 + \cdots + \gamma_n$, so that $\omega \circ \gamma = \omega \circ \gamma_1 + \cdots + \omega \circ \gamma_n$ by Proposition 5. As we have $\gamma_\nu \circ \beta \circ \alpha(z) = \varphi'(y_\nu) = \varphi' \circ q_\nu(z)$, we get $\omega \circ \gamma_\nu \circ \beta \circ \alpha = \omega \circ \varphi' \circ q_\nu$. Hence we have

$$\omega \circ \lambda \circ \varphi \circ p = \omega \circ \lambda_1 \circ \varphi \circ p = \omega \circ \gamma \circ \beta \circ \alpha = \sum_{\nu=1}^{n} \omega \circ \gamma_\nu \circ \beta \circ \alpha = \sum_{\nu=1}^{n} \omega \circ \varphi' \circ q_\nu.$$

3. ANALYTIC THEORY OF ABELIAN VARIETIES.

In this section, we shall recall some of known results from the classical theory of abelian varieties; a modern treatment for this subject can be found in Weil [57].

3. 1. Theta functions and Riemann forms. Let D be a discrete subgroup of $\boldsymbol{C}^n$ of rank $2n$; then $\boldsymbol{C}^n/D$ is a complex torus. An $\boldsymbol{R}$-bilinear form $E(x, y)$ on $\boldsymbol{C}^n$ with values in $\boldsymbol{R}$ is called a *Riemann form* on $\boldsymbol{C}^n/D$ if it satisfies the following conditions.

(R1) *The value $E(x, y)$ is an integer for every $x \in D$, $y \in D$.*

(R2) $E(x, y) = -E(y, x)$.

(R3) *The form $E(x, \sqrt{-1}y)$ is a positive (not necessarily non-degenerate) symmetric form.*

A meromorphic function f on $\boldsymbol{C}^n$ is called a *theta function* on $\boldsymbol{C}^n/D$ if we have

$$f(x+d) = f(x)\exp[l_d(x)+c_d]$$

for every $d \in D$, where $l_d(x)$ is a $\boldsymbol{C}$-linear form on $\boldsymbol{C}^n$ and c_d is a complex number, both depending on d. Then we can show that there exist two $\boldsymbol{R}$-bilinear forms H, H_0 and an $\boldsymbol{R}$-linear form b, with values in $\boldsymbol{C}$, such that

$$(1) \qquad f(x+d) = f(x)\exp\left\{2\pi\sqrt{-1}\left[H(d, x)+\frac{1}{2}H_0(d, d)+b(d)\right]\right\} \quad \text{for } d \in D,$$

$$H_0(u, v) = H_0(v, u),$$

$$H(d_1, d_2) \equiv H_0(d_1, d_2) \mod \boldsymbol{Z} \quad \text{for } d_1, d_2 \in D.$$

Putting

$$E(x, y) = H(x, y)-H(y, x),$$

we call E the *alternating form defined by* f. If f is holomorphic, $E(x, y)$ is a Riemann form on $\boldsymbol{C}^n/D$; we call then E the *Riemann form defined by* f. A theta function f is said to be *normalized* if H is skew-hermitian and b is real valued; if that is so, we have

$$(2) \qquad H(x, y) = \frac{1}{2}\left[E(x, y)-\sqrt{-1}\,E(x, \sqrt{-1}y)\right].$$

Conversely, let $E(x, y)$ be a Riemann form on $\boldsymbol{C}^n/D$. Then there exists a holomorphic theta function f on $\boldsymbol{C}^n/D$ such that E is the Riemann form defined by f.

If f is a theta function on $\boldsymbol{C}^n/D$, then the divisor (f) of f is defined on $\boldsymbol{C}^n/D$, which is an analytic divisor of $\boldsymbol{C}^n/D$. Conversely, if X is an analytic divisor of $\boldsymbol{C}^n/D$, there exists a theta function f on $\boldsymbol{C}^n/D$ such that $(f) = X$. We can prove that the alternating form E defined by f is determined only by X and independent of the choice of f; so we call E the alternating (or Riemann) form defined by X, and denote it by $E(X)$. *A complex torus $\boldsymbol{C}^n/D$ has a structure of abelian variety if and only if there exists a non-degenerate Riemann form on $\boldsymbol{C}^n/D$.*

Let A be an abelian variety defined over $\boldsymbol{C}$. Then we can find a complex torus $\boldsymbol{C}^n/D$ and an analytic isomorphism θ of A onto $\boldsymbol{C}^n/D$. We call the pair $(\boldsymbol{C}^n/D, \theta)$ or simply the isomorphism θ an *analytic coordinate-system* of A. If X is a divisor on A, then $\theta(X)$ is an analytic divisor of $\boldsymbol{C}^n/D$, and conversely; we write $E(X) = E(\theta(X))$ and call it the *alternating* (or *Riemann*) *form defined by* X with respect to θ. We have $E(X) = E(Y)$ if and only if X and Y are algebraically equivalent.

3. 2. Analytic and rational representations of homomorphisms. Let A_1 and A_2 be two abelian varieties defined over $\boldsymbol{C}$; let $(\boldsymbol{C}^n/D_1, \theta_1)$ and $(\boldsymbol{C}^m/D_2, \theta_2)$ be analytic coordinate-systems of A_1 and A_2, respectively. Consider now a homomorphism λ of A_1 into A_2. There exists a linear mapping Λ of $\boldsymbol{C}^n$ into $\boldsymbol{C}^m$ such that

$$\theta_2 \circ \lambda = \Lambda \circ \theta_1;$$

Λ must satisfy $\Lambda(D_1) \subset D_2$. Conversely, every linear mapping of $\boldsymbol{C}^n$ into $\boldsymbol{C}^m$ satisfying this condition corresponds to a homomorphism of A_1 into A_2. With respect to the coordinate-systems (z_i) in $\boldsymbol{C}^n$ and (w_i) in $\boldsymbol{C}^m$, Λ is represented by an $m \times n$ matrix $S = (s_{ij})$ with complex coefficients as follows: regarding the z_j and the w_i as functions on $\boldsymbol{C}^n$ and $\boldsymbol{C}^m$, we have

$$w_i \circ \Lambda = \sum_{j=1}^{n} s_{ij} z_j \quad (1 \leqq i \leqq m).$$

The mapping $\lambda \to \Lambda$ (or $\lambda \to S$) is uniquely extended to a representation of $\mathscr{A}_0(A_1, A_2)$, which we call the *analytic representation of* $\mathscr{A}_0(A_1, A_2)$, with respect to the analytic coordinate-systems θ_1 and θ_2.

Put now

$$\omega_j = dz_j \circ \theta_1, \qquad \eta_i = dw_i \circ \theta_2.$$

Then, we see easily that $\{\omega_1, \cdots, \omega_n\}$ is a basis of $\mathfrak{D}_0(A_1)$ and $\{\eta_1, \cdots, \eta_m\}$ is a basis of $\mathfrak{D}_0(A_2)$; we have obviously,

$$\delta\lambda(\eta_i) = \sum_{j=1}^{n} s_{ij} \omega_j \quad (1 \leqq i \leqq m).$$

This shows that $S = (s_{ij})$ is the transpose of the representation of $\delta\lambda$ with respect to the bases $\{\omega_j\}$ and $\{\eta_i\}$.

Let $\{u_1, \cdots, u_{2n}\}$ and $\{v_1, \cdots, v_{2m}\}$ be respectively bases of D_1 and D_2

over $\boldsymbol{Z}$. Since Λ maps D_1 into D_2, there exists a $2m\times 2n$ matrix $M=(r_{ij})$ with coefficients in $\boldsymbol{Z}$ such that

$$\Lambda(u_j)=\sum_{i=1}^{2m} r_{ij}v_i \quad (1\leqq j\leqq 2n).$$

The correspondence $\lambda\rightarrow M$ is uniquely extended to a representation of $\mathscr{H}_0(A_1, A_2)$, which we call the *rational representation of* $\mathscr{H}_0(A_1, A_2)$ with respect to $\{u_i\}$ and $\{v_i\}$. We can easily verify that the rational representation of $\mathscr{A}_0(A)$ is equivalent to l-adic representations defined in § 1. 2. Let U denote the $n\times 2n$ matrix whose column-vectors are $u_1,\cdots, u_{2n}$ and V the $m\times 2m$ matrix whose column-vectors are $v_1,\cdots, v_{2m}$. We have then

$$SU=VM,$$

so that

$$\begin{pmatrix} S & 0 \\ 0 & \bar{S}\end{pmatrix}\begin{pmatrix} U \\ \bar{U}\end{pmatrix}=\begin{pmatrix} V \\ \bar{V}\end{pmatrix}M,$$

where bars denote complex conjugates. Now suppose that $A_1=A_2$, $n=m$, $D_1=D_2$, $\theta_1=\theta_2$ and $U=V$. Since the matrix $\begin{pmatrix} U \\ \bar{U}\end{pmatrix}$ is invertible, we see that *the rational representation M is equivalent to the direct sum of the analytic representation S and its complex conjugate $\bar{S}$.*

3. 3. Dual abelian varieties. Let $(\boldsymbol{C}^n/D, \theta)$ be an analytic representation of an abelian variety A. We shall now define the dual of $\boldsymbol{C}^n/D$. Let $x=(x_\nu)$ and $y=(y_\nu)$ be two vectors in $\boldsymbol{C}^n$ with the components x_ν and y_ν. Put

$$\langle x, y\rangle=\sum_{\nu=1}^{n}(x_\nu\bar{y}_\nu+\bar{x}_\nu y_\nu). \tag{3}$$

Then, we see that $\langle x, y\rangle$ is a non-degenerate symmetric $\boldsymbol{R}$-bilinear form on $\boldsymbol{C}^n$ with values in $\boldsymbol{R}$; hence, $\boldsymbol{C}^n$ is considered as the dual vector space over $\boldsymbol{R}$ of itself, with respect to this inner product $\langle x, y\rangle$. We have furthermore

$$\langle \sqrt{-1}x, y\rangle=\langle x, -\sqrt{-1}y\rangle. \tag{4}$$

Denote by D^* the set of all vectors $y\in\boldsymbol{C}^n$ such that $\langle x, y\rangle$ is an integer for every $x \in D$; then D^* is a discrete subgroup of $\boldsymbol{C}^n$, so that $\boldsymbol{C}^n/D^*$ is a complex torus of dimension n, which we call the *dual* of $\boldsymbol{C}^n/D$. We can show that $\boldsymbol{C}^n/D^*$ has a structure of abelian variety, and consider $\boldsymbol{C}^n/D^*$ as an analytic representation of a Picard variety A^* of A in the following manner. Let T be the set of all homomorphisms of D into the group of complex numbers of absolute value 1. We see easily that the mapping

$$\boldsymbol{C}^n \ni y \rightarrow \exp\,[2\pi\sqrt{-1}\,\langle y,\ \rangle]$$

gives an isomorphism of $\boldsymbol{C}^n/D^*$ onto T; so we identify T with $\boldsymbol{C}^n/D^*$ by this isomorphism. Let X be a divisor of A. Take a normalized theta function f on $\boldsymbol{C}^n/D$ such that $(f) = \theta(X)$. Suppose that X is algebraically equivalent to 0; we have then $E(X) = 0$. Since f is normalized, we can easily verify that f satisfies the formula

$$f(x+d) = \mu(d)f(x) \quad \text{for } d \in D,$$

where μ is an element of T; it can be seen that μ is determined only by X. Let $\psi(X)$ denote the point on $\boldsymbol{C}^n/D^*$ corresponding to μ. Then we can establish an isomophism θ^* of A^* onto $\boldsymbol{C}^n/D^*$ by the relation

$$\theta^*(\mathrm{Cl}(X)) = \psi(X).$$

This implies, as we have said, that $\boldsymbol{C}^n/D^*$ is considered as an analytic representation of A^*; we call $(\boldsymbol{C}^n/D^*, \theta^*)$ the *dual* of $(\boldsymbol{C}^n/D, \theta)$.

Now we shall consider the mapping φ_Y of A into A^*, defined by (4) of § 1.3. Let Y be a divisor on A and f a normalized theta function on $\boldsymbol{C}^n/D$ such that $(f) = \theta(Y)$. Put $E = E(Y)$; then f satisfies the formula (1) of § 3.1 with the form H given by (2). Put, for every $u \in \boldsymbol{C}^n$,

$$\Phi_u(x) = f(x)^{-1}f(x-u)\exp[2\pi\sqrt{-1}H(u, x)].$$

Let t be a point on A corresponding to u by θ. We observe that

$$(5) \qquad (\Phi_u) = \theta(Y_t - Y),$$

$$(6) \qquad \Phi_u(x+d) = \Phi_u(x)\exp[2\pi\sqrt{-1}E(u, d)] \quad \text{for } d \in D.$$

On the other hand, we obtain an $\boldsymbol{R}$-linear mapping $\mathfrak{E}$ of $\boldsymbol{C}^n$ into itself by the relation

$$\langle \mathfrak{E}(u),\ v \rangle = E(u,\ v).$$

By the properties (R1-3) of Riemann forms and the relation (4), we see that $\mathfrak{E}$ is $\boldsymbol{C}$-linear and maps D into D^*, so that $\mathfrak{E}$ gives a homomorphism of $\boldsymbol{C}^n/D$ into $\boldsymbol{C}^n/D^*$. Then the relations (5) and (6) show that $\mathfrak{E}(u)$ represents the point $\psi(Y_t-Y)$ on $\boldsymbol{C}^n/D^*$; namely, we have

$$\mathfrak{E}(\theta(t)) = \theta^*(\mathrm{Cl}(Y_t-Y)).$$

In other words, $\mathfrak{E}$ is the analytic representation of φ_Y with respect to θ and θ^*.

Let $\{u_1,\cdots,u_{2n}\}$ be a basis of D over $\boldsymbol{Z}$; we can find $2n$ elements u_i^* of $\boldsymbol{C}^n$ such that

$$\langle u_i, u_j^* \rangle = \delta_{ij},$$

where the δ_{ij} denote Kronecker's delta; the u_j^* form a basis of D^* over $\boldsymbol{Z}$. Let $E_0=(e_{ij})$ be the matrix of degree $2n$ which represents the form E with respect to the basis $\{u_i\}$; this means

$$E\Big(\sum_{i=1}^{2n} a_iu_i, \sum_{i=1}^{2n} b_iu_i\Big) = {}^tbE_0a = \sum_{i,j} e_{ij}b_ia_j,$$

where a and b denote respectively the vectors of $\boldsymbol{R}^{2n}$ with the components a_i and b_i. We have then

$$\mathfrak{E}(u_j) = \sum_{i=1}^{2n} e_{ij}u_i^*;$$

this shows that E_0 is the rational representation of φ_Y with respect to the bases $\{u_i\}$ and $\{u_i^*\}$.

Let N be a positive integer and u, v two vectors in $\boldsymbol{C}^n$ such that $Nu \in D$, $Nv \in D$; let s and t be the points on A corresponding to u and v by θ. The functions f and Φ_u being defined for the divisor Y as above, put

$$g(x) = \Phi_u(Nx), \ h(x) = \Phi_u(x)^N.$$

We observe that g and h are considered as functions on $\boldsymbol{C}^n/D$ and satisfy

$$(h) = \theta(N(Y_s-Y)), \ h(Nx) = g(x)^N,$$

$$g(x+v) = g(x)\exp[2\pi\sqrt{-1}E(u, Nv)].$$

Using the notation of § 1.4, we have

(7) $$e_{Y,N}(t, s) = \exp[2\pi\sqrt{-1}NE(u, v)].$$

It follows that, for every rational prime l, E_0 coincides with the l-adic representation of Y, defined in § 1.4, for a suitable choice of l-adic coordinate-system.

Let A_1 be another abelian variety defined over $\boldsymbol{C}$ and $(\boldsymbol{C}^m/D_1, \theta_1)$ an analytic representation of A_1; let A_1^* be a Picard variety of A_1 and $(\boldsymbol{C}^m/D_1^*, \theta_1^*)$ the dual of $(\boldsymbol{C}^m/D_1, \theta_1)$. We shall now consider the transpose ${}^t\lambda$ of a homomorphism λ of A into A_1. Take bases $\{u_i\}$ of D, $\{u_i^*\}$ of D^*, $\{v_i\}$ of D_1, $\{v_i^*\}$ of D_1^*, over $\boldsymbol{Z}$, such that

$$\langle u_i, u_j^* \rangle = \delta_{ij}, \ \langle v_i, v_j^* \rangle = \delta_{ij}.$$

The homomorphism λ has an analytic representation Λ which is a linear mapping of $\boldsymbol{C}^n$ into $\boldsymbol{C}^m$ and a rational representation $M = (c_{ij})$, for which we have

$$\Lambda(u_j) = \sum_i c_{ij}v_i.$$

We can obtain a $\boldsymbol{C}$-linear mapping ${}^t\Lambda$ of $\boldsymbol{C}^m$ into $\boldsymbol{C}^n$ by the relation

$$\langle x, {}^t\Lambda(y) \rangle = \langle \Lambda(x), y \rangle$$

for $x \in \boldsymbol{C}^n$, $y \in \boldsymbol{C}^m$. We shall now show that ${}^t\Lambda$ is the analytic representation of ${}^t\lambda$ with respect to θ^* and θ_1^*, and ${}^tM$ is the rational representation of ${}^t\lambda$ with respect to $\{v_i\}$ and $\{u_i^*\}$. To prove this, take a divisor X on A_1 which is algebraically equivalent to 0 and a normalized theta function f on $\boldsymbol{C}^m/D_1$ such that $(f) = \theta_1(X)$; as is seen above, f satisfies

$$f(y+d_1) = f(y)\exp[2\pi\sqrt{-1}\langle d_1, y^* \rangle] \qquad \text{for} \quad d_1 \in D_1,$$

where y^* is an element of $\boldsymbol{C}^m$ which represents $\mathrm{Cl}(X)$. Put $g = f \circ \Lambda$; we have then,

$$(g) = \theta(\lambda^{-1}(X)),$$

$$g(x+d) = g(x)\exp[2\pi\sqrt{-1}\langle d, {}^t\Lambda(y^*) \rangle] \qquad \text{for} \quad d \in D.$$

These relations show that ${}^t\Lambda(y^*)$ is a point on $\boldsymbol{C}^n$ corresponding to the point ${}^t\lambda(\mathrm{Cl}(X)) = \mathrm{Cl}(\lambda^{-1}(X))$ on A^*. Thus we have proved that ${}^t\Lambda$ is the analytic representation of ${}^t\lambda$ with respect to θ^* and θ_1^*; it follows that ${}^t M$ is the rational representation of ${}^t\lambda$ with respect to $\{v_i^*\}$ and $\{u_i^*\}$.

A, A^*, $(\boldsymbol{C}^n/D, \theta)$ and $(\boldsymbol{C}^n/D^*, \theta^*)$ being as above, let Y be a non-degenerate divisor on A, and $E(x, y)$ the alternating form defined by Y. Let λ be an element of $\mathscr{A}_0(A)$; let $\mathfrak{E}$ and Λ be respectively the analytic representations of φ_Y and λ with respect to θ and θ^*. We have then

$$E(\mathfrak{E}^{-1}\, {}^t\Lambda\, \mathfrak{E}(x), y) = \langle {}^t\Lambda\mathfrak{E}(x), y \rangle = \langle \mathfrak{E}(x), \Lambda(y) \rangle = E(x, \Lambda(y));$$

in other words, $\varphi_Y^{-1}\, {}^t\lambda\varphi_Y$ is the adjoint of λ with respect to the form $E(x, y)$. The involution $\lambda \to \lambda' = \varphi_Y^{-1}\, {}^t\lambda\varphi_Y$ of $\mathscr{A}_0(A)$ is thus described by means of the alternating form.

4. FIELDS OF MODULI AND KUMMER VARIETIES.

4. 1. Polarization of a variety. Let V be a complete variety, non-singular in co-dimension 1, defined over a field k, and X a divisor on V which is rational over k. We denote by $L(X; k)$ the set of functions f on V, defined over k, such that $(f) \succ -X$, where (f) denotes the divisor of the function f. If k' is an extension of k, we have $L(X; k') = L(X; k) \otimes_k k'$, so that the dimension of the vector space $L(X; k)$ over k (which is always finite) is independent of k; we denote this dimension by $l(X)$. Let $\{f_0, \cdots, f_r\}$ be a basis of $L(X; k)$ over k and x a generic point of V over k. Consider $(f_0(x), \cdots, f_r(x))$ as a point of the projective space P^r of dimension r and denote by U the locus of $(f_0(x), \cdots, f_r(x))$ over k. Then we obtain a rational mapping Φ of V onto U defined by

$$\Phi(x) = (f_0(x), \cdots, f_r(x))$$

with respect to k. We say that the divisor X (or the complete linear system defined by X) is *ample* if the mapping Φ is birational and biregular; this definition does not depend upon the choice of k and $\{f_i\}$.

V, X being as above, we denote by $\mathscr{C}(X)$ the set of all divisors X' on V for which there exist two positive integers m, m' such that

mX is algebraically equivalent to $m'X'$. The set $\mathscr{C}(X)$ is called a *polarization* of V if it contains an ample divisor. A variety V is said to be *polarizable* if there exists a polarization of V. We understand by a *polarized variety* a couple $(V, \mathscr{C})$ formed by a variety V and a polarization $\mathscr{C}$ of V; every divisor X in $\mathscr{C}$ is called a *polar divisor* of $(V, \mathscr{C})$. k being a field of definition for V, we say that $(V, \mathscr{C})$ or $\mathscr{C}$ is defined over k if $\mathscr{C}$ contains a divisor which is rational over k. If V has a structure of abelian variety, we call $(V, \mathscr{C})$ with this structure a *polarized abelian variety*; in this case, $(V, \mathscr{C})$ is said to be defined over k only when the structure of abelian variety is also defined over k. Let σ be an isomorphism of k into a field k'; $(V, \mathscr{C})$ being defined over k, we denote by $\mathscr{C}^\sigma$ the polarization $\mathscr{C}(X^\sigma)$ of V^σ, where X is a divisor in $\mathscr{C}$ which is rational over k.

PROPOSITION 10. *If V is defined over k, every polarized variety $(V, \mathscr{C})$ is defined over a finite algebraic extension of k.*

PROOF. Take a divisor X in $\mathscr{C}$. We can find a specialization X' of X over k, which is rational over a finite algebraic extension of k. Then, X' is algebraically equivalent to X, so that X' is contained in $\mathscr{C}$. This proves the proposition.

PROPOSITION 11. *If V is defined over k and polarizable, then V has a polarization defined over k.*

PROOF. By Proposition 10, every polarization contains a divisor X which is rational over a finite algebraic extension k' of k. Put $Y = p^m \sum X^\sigma$, where the sum is taken over all the isomorphisms σ of k' into the algebraic closure of k, and p denotes the characteristic or 1 according as the characteristic is a prime or 0. Then, for a suitable m, Y is rational over k; and we can easily see that Y determines a polarization of V; our proposition is thereby proved.

We shall now confine ourselves to abelian varieties. A theory for a more general case can be found in Matsusaka [28].

4. 2. Fields of moduli of polarized abelian varieties. The following two propositions are due to Weil [56].

PROPOSITION 12. *Every abelian variety is polarizable.*

PROPOSITION 13. *Let X be a divisor on an abelian variety. If there exists an integer $n > 0$ such that nX is ample, X is non-degenerate. Conversely, if X is a positive non-degenerate divisor, there exists an integer $n_0 > 0$ such that nX is ample for $n \geqq n_0$.*

Let $(A, \mathscr{C})$ and $(A', \mathscr{C}')$ be two polarized abelian varieties, of the same dimension. A homomorphism (resp. an isomorphism) λ of A onto A' is called a *homomorphism* (resp. an *isomorphism*) of $(A, \mathscr{C})$ onto $(A', \mathscr{C}')$ if there exists a divisor X' in $\mathscr{C}'$ such that $\lambda^{-1}(X')$ is contained in $\mathscr{C}$; if that is so, for every Y in $\mathscr{C}'$, $\lambda^{-1}(Y)$ is contained in $\mathscr{C}$.

We now give an important theorem which is a base of the definition of field of moduli.

THEOREM 2. *Let A be an abelian variety and $\mathscr{C}$ a polarization of A. Then, there exists a field k_0 with the following property:*

(M) *k and σ being respectively a field of definition for $(A, \mathscr{C})$ containing k_0, and an isomorphism of k into a field, $(A, \mathscr{C})$ is isomorphic to $(A^\sigma, \mathscr{C}^\sigma)$ if and only if σ is the identity on k_0.*

A proof is given in Shimura [36]. For our later use, we need only the case where A is defined over an algebraic number field of finite degree. In this case the field k_0 is easily given by Galois theory. Before showing this, we give an easy consequence of Theorem 2.

PROPOSITION 14. *If the characteristic of the universal domain is 0, the field k_0 with the property (M) of Theorem 2 is uniquely determined by $(A, \mathscr{C})$ and is contained in every field of definition for $(A, \mathscr{C})$.*

PROOF. Let k_0 and k_0' be two fields with the property (M). Take a field of definition for $(A, \mathscr{C})$ containing k_0 and k_0'. Then for every isomorphism σ of k into a field, σ is the identity on k_0 if and only if σ is so on k_0'; this implies $k_0 = k_0'$. Let k_1 be a field of definition for $(A, \mathscr{C})$ and τ an isomorphism of k_0k_1 into a field such that τ is the identity on k_1. Then we have $(A, \mathscr{C}) = (A^\tau, \mathscr{C}^\tau)$, so that by the property (M), τ is the identity on k_0; this proves $k_0 \subset k_1$.

Now let us consider the case where A is defined over an algebraic number field k_1 of finite degree. By Proposition 10, $(A, \mathscr{C})$ is defined over a finite algebraic extension k' of k_1. Take a Galois extension k'' of Q containing k' and call G the Galois group of k'' over Q. Let H be the subgroup of G composed of the elements $\sigma \in G$ such that $(A^\sigma, \mathscr{C}^\sigma)$ is isomorphic to $(A, \mathscr{C})$, and k_0 the subfield of k'' corresponding to H. Then, it is easy to see that k_0 has the property (M).

We call the field k_0 with the property (M), which is uniquely determined by $(A, \mathscr{C})$ if the characteristic is 0, as we have seen in Proposition 14, the *field of moduli* of $(A, \mathscr{C})$. Obviously, two polarized abelian varieties, isomorphic to each other, have the same field of moduli. We can define the field of moduli also in case of positive characteristics; for details we refer to [28], [36].

If the characteristic is 0, $(A, \mathscr{C})$ determines a point z on the Siegel's space of degree n, where n is the dimension of A. It is plausible that the field of moduli of $(A, \mathscr{C})$ is generated over Q by the values of certain Siegel's modular (or paramodular) functions (cf. Siegel [38]) at the point z; this is at least true for "generic" polarized abelian varieties $(A, \mathscr{C})$ (cf. [30] exposés 18–20).

PROPOSITION 15. *Let $\mathscr{C}$ be a polarization of an abelian variety. Then, there exists a divisor Y in $\mathscr{C}$ such that every divisor in $\mathscr{C}$ is algebraically equivalent to a multiple mY with a positive integer m.*

PROOF. Consider, for each $X \in \mathscr{C}$, the homomorphism φ_X of A into its Picard variety A^*. By Proposition 13, every X in $\mathscr{C}$ is non-degenerate, so that we have $\nu(\varphi_X) > 0$. Since the $\nu(\varphi_X)$ are integers, there exists a divisor Y in $\mathscr{C}$ such that $\nu(\varphi_Y) = \mathrm{Min}\{\nu(\varphi_X) | X \in \mathscr{C}\}$. We shall prove that Y has the property of our proposition. For every X in $\mathscr{C}$, by our definition, there exist two positive integers a and b such that aX is algebraically equivalent to bY; we have then $a\varphi_X = b\varphi_Y$. We can find two integers q and r such that $b = aq+r$, $0 \leqq r < a$. Assume that $r > 0$; then putting $Z = X - qY$, $\varphi_{aZ} = a\varphi_Z = a\varphi_X - aq\varphi_Y = r\varphi_Y = \varphi_{rY}$. This implies that aZ is algebraically equivalent to rY, and hence Z is contained in $\mathscr{C}$. By the relations $a\varphi_Z = r\varphi_Y$ and $r < a$, we get $\nu(\varphi_Z) < \nu(\varphi_Y)$; this is a contradiction; so r must be 0. We have then $b = aq$, and hence $\varphi_X = q\varphi_Y$. It follows that X is algebraically equivalent to qY; this completes the proof.

We call a divisor Y with the property of Proposition 15 a *basic polar divisor* of $\mathscr{C}$.

4. 3. Quotient of an abelian variety. We want to prove

PROPOSITION 16. *Let A be an abelian variety and G a finite group of automorphisms of A; let k be a field of definition for A and the elements of G. Then, there exist a projective variety W and a rational mapping F of A onto W, both defined over k, satisfying the following conditions:*

(K1) *F is everywhere defined on A;*

(K2) *$F(u) = F(v)$ if and only if there exists an element $\gamma \in G$ such that $u = \gamma(v)$;*

(K3) *if F' is a rational mapping of A into a variety W satisfying $F' = F' \circ \gamma$ for every $\gamma \in G$, then there exists a rational mapping Φ of W into W' such that $F' = \Phi \circ F$ and Φ is defined at $F(a)$ whenever F' is defined at a.*

PROOF. Here we borrow an idea from Serre [32], where quotient of a variety, which is not necessarily abelian, is treated in a little different form. We assume that A is a projective variety. This is possible by virtue of Propositions 11 and 12. For every point a of A, we can find a homogeneous polynomial $H(X)$ with coefficients in k, other than the constants, such that $H(\gamma(a)) \neq 0$ for every $\gamma \in G$. Put

$$B' = \{x \in A \mid H(x) \neq 0\}, \qquad B = \bigcap_{\gamma \in G} \gamma(B').$$

Then, B is an open set of A, in the sense of Zariski-topology, which is biregularly equivalent over k to an affine variety. By our choice of H, B contains the given point a; moreover, we have $\gamma(B) = B$ for every $\gamma \in G$. We obtain in this way a finite open covering $\{B_i\}$ of A such that each B_i is biregularly equivalent over k to an affine variety V_i and $\gamma(B_i) = B_i$ for every $\gamma \in G$. Let k' be an arbitrary extension of k, x a generic point of A over k', and ξ_i the point on V_i corresponding to x for each i. Now we fix our attention to one of the V_i, say V_1. Since A is non-singular, so is V_1; hence $k'[\xi_1]$ is integrally closed. As we have $\gamma(B_1) = B_1$, we can define the operation of the elements of G on the variety V_1. Every element γ of G determines an automorphism of $k'(x) = k'(\xi_1)$. We denote by u^γ the image of $u \in k'(x)$ by this automorphism. Moreover, since γ operates on V_1 and $k'[\xi_1]$ is integrally closed, this automorphism induces an automorphism of $k'[\xi_1]$. Denote by K, K', R, R' respectively the set of G-invariant elements of $k(x)$, $k'(x)$, $k[\xi_1]$, $k'[\xi_1]$. Then, it is easy to see that K and K' are respectively the quotient fields of R and R', and we have $R' = R \otimes_k k'$. Now let $(\xi_{1\lambda})$ be the coordinates of ξ_1, and η_μ the coefficients of the polynomials $P_\lambda(X) = \prod_\gamma (X - \xi_{1\lambda}{}^\gamma)$. Then we see that $k[\xi_1] \supset R \supset k[\eta]$ and $k[\xi_1]$ is integral over $k[\eta]$. As $k[\xi_1]$ is finitely generated as $k[\eta]$-module, the submodule R is also finitely generated. Hence there exists a finite set of elements (ζ_1) such that $R = k[\zeta_1]$; we have then $R' = k'[\zeta_1]$. Since $k'[\xi_1]$ is integrally closed and $R' = K' \cap k'[\xi_1]$, we see that $k'[\zeta_1]$ is integrally closed. We obtain in the same manner, for each i, a finite set (ζ_i) such that

$$K = k(\zeta_i), \qquad k[\zeta_i] = K \cap k[\xi_i], \qquad k'[\zeta_i] = K' \cap k'[\xi_i].$$

Let a be a point of B_1 and α the point on V_1 corresponding to a. We have obviously

$$[x \to a;\ k'] = [\xi_1 \to \alpha;\ k'],$$

where $[u \to v;\ k']$ denotes the specialization-ring of v in $k'(u)$ (cf. § 9.2). Let β be a specialization of ζ_1 over $\xi_1 \to \alpha$ ref. k'. We shall now prove

$$K' \cap [\xi_1 \to \alpha;\ k'] = [\zeta_1 \to \beta;\ k']. \tag{1}$$

First we observe that for every $\gamma \in G$,

$$K' \cap [\xi_1 \to \alpha;\ k'] = K' \cap [\xi_1 \to \gamma(\alpha);\ k']. \tag{2}$$

In fact, if u is an element of $K' \cap [\xi_1 \to \alpha;\ k']$, we have an expression $u = f(\xi_1)/g(\xi_1)$, where f and g are polynomials with coefficients in k' such that $g(\alpha) \neq 0$. As u is contained in K', we have $u = f(\xi_1{}^\gamma)/g(\xi_1{}^\gamma)$. Since the $\xi_{1\lambda}{}^\gamma$ are contained in $k[\xi_1]$, there exist polynomials h_λ with coefficients in k such that $\xi_{1\lambda}{}^\gamma = h_\lambda(\xi_1)$. Put

$$p(X) = f(\cdots, h_\lambda(X), \cdots), \qquad q(X) = g(\cdots, h_\lambda(X), \cdots).$$

Then we have $u = p(\xi_1)/q(\xi_1)$ and $q(\gamma^{-1}(\alpha)) = g(\alpha) \neq 0$. Hence u is contained in $K' \cap [\xi_1 \to \gamma^{-1}(\alpha);\ k']$; so we have

$$K' \cap [\xi_1 \to \alpha;\ k'] \subset K' \cap [\xi_1 \to \gamma^{-1}(\alpha);\ k'].$$

The inverse inclusion is similarly proved; so we obtain the equality (2). Now u being an element of $K' \cap [\xi_1 \to \alpha;\ k']$, let d be a specialization of u over $\zeta_1 \to \beta$ ref. k'. Extend this specialization to a specialization

$$(\xi_1, \zeta_1, u) \to (\alpha', \beta, d) \quad \text{ref. } k'.$$

As $k'[\xi_1]$ is integral over $k'[\zeta_1]$, α' must be finite. Consider the polynomial

$$M(T) = \prod_{\gamma}(\sum_{\lambda} \xi_{1\lambda}{}^{\gamma} T_{\lambda}).$$

We observe that the coefficients of $M(T)$ are contained in $k[\zeta_1]$, so that the specializations

$$(\xi_1, \zeta_1) \to (\alpha, \beta) \quad \text{ref. } k', \qquad (\xi_1, \zeta_1) \to (\alpha', \beta) \quad \text{ref. } k'$$

lead to the equality

$$\prod_{\gamma}(\sum_{\lambda} \gamma(\alpha)_{\lambda} T_{\lambda}) = \prod_{\gamma}(\sum_{\lambda} \gamma(\alpha')_{\lambda} T_{\lambda}),$$

where $\gamma(\alpha)_\lambda$ and $\gamma(\alpha')_\lambda$ denote respectively the λ-th coordinates of the points $\gamma(\alpha)$ and $\gamma(\alpha')$. This shows that there exists an element γ of G such that $\gamma(\alpha) = \alpha'$. By the relation (2), u is contained in $K' \cap [\xi_1 \to \alpha';\ k']$; so its specialization d must be finite. This implies that every element of $K' \cap [\xi_1 \to \alpha;\ k']$ is integral over $[\zeta_1 \to \beta;\ k']$. On the other hand, as $k'[\zeta_1]$ is integrally closed, $[\zeta_1 \to \beta;\ k']$ is integrally closed; this proves the equality (1). Now let W_i be the locus of ζ_i over k. Consider a specialization

$$(\zeta_1, \cdots, \zeta_h) \to (\beta_1, \cdots, \beta_h) \text{ ref. } k'.$$

Extend this to a specialization

$$(x, \xi_1, \cdots, \xi_h, \zeta_1, \cdots, \zeta_h) \to (a, \alpha_1, \cdots, \alpha_h, \beta_1, \cdots, \beta_h) \quad \text{ref. } k'.$$

Since $k'[\xi_i]$ is integral over $k'[\zeta_i]$ and $k'[\xi_i] \supset k'[\zeta_i]$, we see that, for every i, α_i is finite if and only if β_i is finite. As $\{B_i\}$ is a covering of A, at least one of the α_i is finite; and for such an i, we have

$$[x \to a; k'] = [\xi_i \to \alpha_i; k'],$$

$$K' \cap [\xi_i \to \alpha_i; k'] = [\zeta_i \to \beta_i; k'],$$

and hence

$$K' \cap [x \to a; k'] = [\zeta_i \to \beta_i; k']. \tag{3}$$

Therefore the specialization-ring $[\zeta_i \to \beta_i; k]$ does not depend on the choice of i, so far as β_i is finite. It follows that the affine varieties W_i determine an abstract variety W if we regard the ζ_i as corresponding generic points with respect to k. Denote by z the point on W whose representatives are the ζ_i, and by F the rational mapping of A onto W defined by $F(x) = z$ with respect to k. The equality (3) is then written in the form

$$K' \cap [x \to a;\ k'] = [z \to F(a);\ k']. \tag{4}$$

By our construction, F is everywhere defined on A and $F \circ \gamma = F$ for every $\gamma \in G$. We shall now prove that (W, F) satisfies the condition (K3). (W', F') being as in (K3), let k' be a field of definition for W' and F', containing k; let x be a generic point on A over k'. Put $F(x) = z$, $F'(x) = z'$. Since $F' \circ \gamma = F'$ for every $\gamma \in G$, $k'(z')$ is contained in $k'(z)$. Hence we obtain a rational mapping Φ of W into W' defined by $\Phi(z) = z'$ with respect to k'; we have then $F' = \Phi \circ F$. Now suppose that F' is defined at a point $a \in A$. Then we have

$$[x \to a; k'] \supset [z' \to F'(a); k'].$$

By the equality (4), we have

$$[z \to F(a); k'] \supset [z' \to F'(a); k'];$$

this proves that Φ is defined at $F(a)$. Therefore (W, F) satisfies (K3). We have thus constructed an abstract variety W and a rational mapping F, both defined over k, satisfying the conditions (K1), (K3) and the "if" part of (K2). It remains to prove the "only if" part of (K2) and realize W as a projective variety. For this purpose, take a generic point x on A over k and consider the Chow point y of the 0-dimensional cycle $\sum_{\gamma \in G} (\gamma(x))$ on A. Let W_1 be the locus of y over k and W_0 a projective normalization of W_1 with respect to k. Then we obtain a rational mapping f_1 of A onto W_1 defined by $f_1(x) = y$ with respect to k and a birational mapping f of W_0 onto W_1 defined by the normalization. Put $f_0 = f^{-1} \circ f_1$, $t = f_0(x)$. We have obviously $k(t) = K = k(z)$. Hence there exists a birational mapping Ψ of W onto W_0, defined over k, such that $\Psi(z) = t$. Let (a, b) be a specialization of (x, t) over k. As W_0 is a normalization of W_1 with respect to k, $[t \rightarrow b;\ k]$ is integrally closed. Using this fact, we can prove the equality

$$K \cap [x \rightarrow a; k] = [t \rightarrow b; k],$$

in the same way as in the proof of (1). Hence we have

$$[t \rightarrow b; k] = [z \rightarrow F(a); k].$$

It follows that W_0 and W are biregularly equivalent over k. Furthermore, it is easy to see that (W_1, f_1) and (W_0, f_0) satisfy (K2). This completes our proof.

The couple (W, F) is uniquely determined by the conditions (K1–3) up to biregular birational mappings. We call (W, F) a *quotient of A by G, defined over k.*

Remark 1. Notations and assumptions being as in (K3), let k' be a field of definition for W' and F', containing k. Then the rational mapping Φ is defined over k'. This is included in the above proof.

4. 4. Kummer varieties. By Weil [54], Matsusaka [28] we know

Proposition 17. *Every polarized abelian variety has only a finite number of automorphisms.*

Here we reproduce the proof of [54]. $\mathscr{C}$ being a polarization of an abelian variety A, take a divisor X in $\mathscr{C}$ and consider the involution $\alpha \rightarrow \alpha' = \varphi_X^{-1}\, {}^t\alpha \varphi_X$ of $\mathscr{A}_0(A)$. For every automorphism α of $(A, \mathscr{C})$, there exist two positive integers m and m' such that

$$m\, {}^t\alpha \varphi_X \alpha = m' \varphi_X$$

on account of the relation (7) of § 1.3. Taking the degree of both sides, we get $m = m'$, so that $\alpha\alpha' = 1_A$. Thus we obtain $\mathrm{tr}(\alpha\alpha') = 2n$ for every automorphism α of $(A, \mathscr{C})$, where n is the dimension of A.

Since $\mathrm{tr}(\alpha\alpha')$ is a positive non-degenerate quadratic form and $\mathscr{A}(A)$ is finitely generated over $\boldsymbol{Z}$, only a finite number of such α can exist.

$(A, \mathscr{C})$ being a polarized abelian variety, let G be the group of automorphisms of $(A, \mathscr{C})$; Proposition 17 asserts that G is finite. By a *Kummer variety* of $(A, \mathscr{C})$, we understand a quotient of A by G.

THEOREM 3. *Let $(A, \mathscr{C})$ be a polarized abelian variety and k_0 the field of moduli of $(A, \mathscr{C})$. Then there exists a Kummer variety (W, F) of $(A, \mathscr{C})$ satisfying the following conditions:*

(N1) *W is defined over k_0;*

(N2) *F is defined over every field of definition for $(A, \mathscr{C})$ containing k_0;*

(N3) *k being a field of definition for $(A, \mathscr{C})$ containing k_0, if σ is an isomorphism of k into a field and if η is an isomorphism of $(A, \mathscr{C})$ onto $(A^\sigma, \mathscr{C}^\sigma)$, then we have $F = F^\sigma \circ \eta$.*

We note that if $(A, \mathscr{C})$ is isomorphic to $(A^\sigma, \mathscr{C}^\sigma)$, then σ is the identity on k_0 by virtue of the property (M) of Theorem 2, so that $W^\sigma = W$ by the property (N1).

We shall call a Kummer variety (W, F) of $(A, \mathscr{C})$ satisfying the conditions (N1–3) a *normalized Kummer variety* of $(A, \mathscr{C})$, which is uniquely determined for $(A, \mathscr{C})$ up to biregular birational mappings defined over k_0, if A is defined over a separably generated extension of k_0.

We give a proof of Theorem 3 only in case where $(A, \mathscr{C})$ is defined over an algebraic number field; the same method is applicable to the general case; as for this, see Remark 2 at the end of the proof.

Let G be the group of automorphisms of $(A, \mathscr{C})$ and k a field of definition for $(A, \mathscr{C})$ and the elements of G; we assume that k is a finite Galois extension of $\boldsymbol{Q}$; this is possible by our restriction. Then, as is seen above, there exists a Kummer variety (W, F) defined over k. Let $\mathfrak{G}$ denote the Galois group of k over k_0. For every $\sigma \in \mathfrak{G}$, by virtue of the property (M) of k_0, there exists an isomorphism α_σ of $(A, \mathscr{C})$ onto $(A^\sigma, \mathscr{C}^\sigma)$. We see that $G^\sigma = \{\gamma^\sigma | \gamma \in G\}$ is the group of automorphisms of $(A^\sigma, \mathscr{C}^\sigma)$ and (W^σ, F^σ) is a Kummer variety of $(A^\sigma, \mathscr{C}^\sigma)$. Then $F^\sigma \circ \alpha_\sigma$ is a rational mapping of A onto W^σ which is everywhere defined on A; and for every $\gamma \in G$, we have

$(F^\sigma\circ\alpha_\sigma)\circ\gamma = F^\sigma\circ\alpha_\sigma$; in fact, as α_σ is an isomorphism of $(A, \mathscr{C})$ onto $(A^\sigma, \mathscr{C}^\sigma)$, there exists an element $\gamma' \in G^\sigma$ such that $\alpha_\sigma\circ\gamma = \gamma'\circ\alpha_\sigma$, so that $F^\sigma\circ\alpha_\sigma\circ\gamma = F^\sigma\circ\gamma'\circ\alpha_\sigma = F^\sigma\circ\alpha_\sigma$. Hence, by (K3), there exists a rational mapping β_σ of W onto W^σ such that $F^\sigma\circ\alpha_\sigma = \beta_\sigma\circ F$; and β_σ is everywhere defined on W. We obtain similarly a rational mapping β_σ' of W^σ onto W, everywhere defined on W^σ, such that $\beta_\sigma'\circ F^\sigma = F\circ\alpha_\sigma^{-1}$. It is easy to see that β_σ is birational and biregular, and $\beta_\sigma' = \beta_\sigma^{-1}$. The birational mapping β_σ is uniquely determined by σ and does not depend upon the choice of α_σ; in fact, for any other isomorphism α_σ' of $(A, \mathscr{C})$ on $(A^\sigma, \mathscr{C}^\sigma)$, there exists an element $\gamma \in G$ such that $\alpha_\sigma' = \alpha_\sigma\circ\gamma$; it follows that $F^\sigma\circ\alpha_\sigma' = F^\sigma\circ\alpha_\sigma$; this shows the uniqueness of β_σ. We can easily verify that β_σ is defined over k. Now σ and τ being two elements of $\mathfrak{G}$, we have $\beta_\sigma^\tau\circ F^\tau = F^{\sigma\tau}\circ\alpha_\sigma^\tau$ and $\beta_\tau\circ F = F^\tau\circ\alpha_\tau$ so that $\beta_\sigma^\tau\circ\beta_\tau\circ F = F^{\sigma\tau}\circ\alpha_\sigma^\tau\circ\alpha_\tau$. By the uniqueness, we have $\beta_\sigma^\tau\circ\beta_\tau = \beta_{\sigma\tau}$. Put $f_{\tau,\sigma} = \beta_\tau\circ\beta_\sigma^{-1}$ for every $\sigma \in \mathfrak{G}$, $\tau \in \mathfrak{G}$. Then we observe that the relations

$$f_{\tau,\rho} = f_{\tau,\sigma}\circ f_{\sigma,\rho}, \qquad f_{\tau\rho,\sigma\rho} = (f_{\tau,\sigma})^\rho$$

hold for every ρ, σ, $\tau \in \mathfrak{G}$. Hence, applying the results of Weil [55] to the present case, we obtain a variety W_0 and a birational biregular mapping φ of W_0 onto W such that: i) W_0 is defined over k_0; ii) φ is defined over k; iii) $f_{\tau,\sigma} = \varphi^\tau\circ(\varphi^\sigma)^{-1}$ for every σ, $\tau \in \mathfrak{G}$. Put $F_0 = \varphi^{-1}\circ F$; then (W_0, F_0) is clearly a Kummer variety of $(A, \mathscr{C})$ and F_0 is defined over k. We shall now show that (W_0, F_0) satisfies the conditions (N1–3). (N1) is just the property i). Let k' be a field of definition for $(A, \mathscr{C})$; then k' contains k_0 by virtue of Proposition 14. Let σ be an isomorphism of kk' onto a field which fixes every element of k_0; denote by the same letter σ the element of $\mathfrak{G}$ induced by σ. Then, for every isomorphism α_σ of $(A, \mathscr{C})$ onto $(A^\sigma, \mathscr{C}^\sigma)$, we have

$$F_0^\sigma\circ\alpha_\sigma = (\varphi^\sigma)^{-1}\circ F^\sigma\circ\alpha_\sigma = (\varphi^\sigma)^{-1}\circ\beta_\sigma\circ F = \varphi^{-1}\circ F = F_0;$$

This shows that F_0 satisfies (N3). In particular, if σ is the identity on k', we have $(A^\sigma, \mathscr{C}^\sigma) = (A, \mathscr{C})$, so that we can take $\alpha_\sigma = 1_A$; we have hence $F_0^\sigma = F_0$ for every isomorphism σ of kk' over k'. It follows that F_0 is defined over k'; so F_0 satisfies (N2).

REMARK 2. We can prove Theorem 3 without any condition for the fields of definition, using also the theory of [55]. In order to perform this, it is necessary to avoid inseparable field-extensions, since [55] deals with only separable or regular extensions. This is certainly possible by virtue of Proposition 4 of [36].

REMARK 3. We can take the variety W in Theorem 3 to be a projective variety; this is proved by means of Proposition 16 and [55].

CHAPTER II. ABELIAN VARIETIES WITH COMPLEX MULTIPLICATION.

5. STRUCTURE OF $\mathscr{A}_0(A)$.[1]

5. 1. Let $\mathfrak{R}$ be a simple algebra over Q and $\mathfrak{Z}$ the center of $\mathfrak{R}$; put $[\mathfrak{R}:\mathfrak{Z}]=f^2$, $[\mathfrak{Z}:Q]=d$. Then, $\mathfrak{R}$ has d inequivalent irreducible representations in the algebraic closure of Q, which are all of degree f. We call a representation S of $\mathfrak{R}$ in an extension of Q a *reduced representation* of $\mathfrak{R}$ if S is equivalent to the direct sum of those d irreducible representations. S being a reduced representation of $\mathfrak{R}$, the characteristic polynomial of $S(\alpha)$ has rational coefficients for every $\alpha \in \mathfrak{R}$. Put

$$N(\alpha) = \det S(\alpha), \ \mathrm{Tr}(\alpha) = \mathrm{tr}\, S(\alpha)$$

for $\alpha \in \mathfrak{R}$. We call $N(\alpha)$ and $\mathrm{Tr}(\alpha)$ the *reduced norm* and the *reduced trace* of α; these are independent of the choice of S.

LEMMA 1. *Let $\mathfrak{R}$ be a simple algebra over Q and S a representation of $\mathfrak{R}$ in an extension of Q. Suppose that for every $\alpha \in \mathfrak{R}$, the characteristic polynomial of $S(\alpha)$ has rational coefficients. Then S is equivalent to the sum of a multiple of a reduced representation of $\mathfrak{R}$ and a 0-representation.*

PROOF. Let the S_i, for $1 \leqq i \leqq d$, denote the inequivalent irreducible representations of $\mathfrak{R}$ in the algebraic closure L of Q. Then S is equivalent to the direct sum of representations $m_i S_i$ and a 0-representation, where the m_i denote the multiplicities. Let the σ_i, for $1 \leqq i \leqq d$, be all the isomorphisms of the center $\mathfrak{Z}$ of $\mathfrak{R}$ into L. Then we observe, after reordering, that $S_i(\alpha)$ is the diagonal matrix $\alpha^{\sigma_i} 1_f$

1) Some of the results of §§ 5–6 have their source in Lefschetz [27]. The reader will also find a more general structure-theory of $\mathscr{A}_0(A)$ in Albert [1, 2].

for $\alpha \in \mathfrak{Z}$, for every i. Hence, for every $\alpha \in \mathfrak{Z}$, the characteristic polynomial of $S(\alpha)$ is of the form $X^h \prod_i (X-\alpha^{\sigma_i})^{m_i}$. Our assumption implies that the m_i are the same; this proves our lemma.

PROPOSITION 1. *Let A be an abelian variety of dimension n and $\mathfrak{S}$ a commutative semi-simple subalgebra of $\mathscr{A}_0(A)$. Then we have*

$$[\mathfrak{S} : \boldsymbol{Q}] \leqq 2n.$$

If $[\mathfrak{S} : \boldsymbol{Q}] = 2n$, then the commutor of $\mathfrak{S}$ in $\mathscr{A}_0(A)$ coincides with $\mathfrak{S}$.

PROOF. Let the K_i denote the simple components of $\mathfrak{S}$; then, as $\mathfrak{S}$ is commutative, the K_i are fields. Put $[K_i : \boldsymbol{Q}] = d_i$. Let S_i be a reduced representation of K_i. Take a prime l other than the characteristic of the fields of definition for A, and consider an l-adic representation M_l of $\mathscr{A}_0(A)$. By Lemma 1, the restriction of M_l to K_i is equivalent to the direct sum of a multiple $m_i S_i$ of S_i and a 0-representation. Considering M_l on $\mathfrak{S}$, we see that M_l is equivalent to the direct sum of the $m_i S_i$ and a 0-representation. As M_l is faithful, every m_i must be positive. Hence we have $2n \geqq \sum_i m_i d_i \geqq \sum_i d_i = [\mathfrak{S} : \boldsymbol{Q}]$. This proves the first assertion. Now suppose that $2n = [\mathfrak{S} : \boldsymbol{Q}]$. Let $\mathfrak{S}'$ be the commutor of $\mathfrak{S}$ in $\mathscr{A}_0(A)$. We can find a matrix P with coefficients in the algebraic closure of $\boldsymbol{Q}_l$ such that $PM_l(\xi)P^{-1}$ is a diagonal matrix for every $\xi \in \mathfrak{S}$. As we have $[\mathfrak{S} : \boldsymbol{Q}] = 2n$, there exists an element α of $\mathfrak{S}$ such that the diagonal elements of $PM_l(\alpha)P^{-1}$ are distinct. For every $\eta \in \mathfrak{S}'$, $PM_l(\eta)P^{-1}$ commutes with $PM_l(\alpha)P^{-1}$, so that $PM_l(\eta)P^{-1}$ is a diagonal matrix for every $\eta \in \mathfrak{S}'$. This shows that $\mathfrak{S}'$ is a commutative semi-simple algebra. Then, applying to $\mathfrak{S}'$ what we have just proved for $\mathfrak{S}$, we get $[\mathfrak{S}' : \boldsymbol{Q}] \leqq 2n$; so we must have $\mathfrak{S} = \mathfrak{S}'$; this completes the proof.

PROPOSITION 2. *Let A be an abelian variety of dimension n; let $\mathfrak{R}$ be a simple subalgebra of $\mathscr{A}_0(A)$ and $\mathfrak{Z}$ the center of $\mathfrak{R}$; and put*

$$[\mathfrak{R} : \mathfrak{Z}] = f^2, \qquad [\mathfrak{Z} : \boldsymbol{Q}] = d.$$

Suppose that $\mathfrak{R}$ contains the identity element of $\mathscr{A}_0(A)$. Then fd divides $2n$; and putting $2n = fdm$, we have, for every $\alpha \in \mathfrak{R}$,

$$\nu(\alpha) = N(\alpha)^m, \qquad \mathrm{tr}(\alpha) = m\,\mathrm{Tr}(\alpha),$$

where $N(\alpha)$ *and* $\mathrm{Tr}(\alpha)$ *denote the reduced norm and trace of* $\alpha \in \mathfrak{R}$.

PROOF. Let S be a reduced representation of $\mathfrak{R}$. Take a prime l other than the characteristic and an l-adic representation M_l of $\mathscr{A}_0(A)$. By Lemma 1, the restriction of M_l to $\mathfrak{R}$ is equivalent to a multiple mS of S; so we have $2n = fdm$; and the characteristic polynomial of $M_l(\alpha)$ is the m-th power of that of $S(\alpha)$. This proves the proposition.

PROPOSITION 3. *Let A be an abelian variety of dimension n. If $\mathscr{A}_0(A)$ contains a field F of degree $2n$ over Q, then A is isogenous to a product $B\times\cdots\times B$ with a simple abelian variety B; the commutor of F in $\mathscr{A}_0(A)$ coincides with F; and, for every $\alpha \in F$, we have*

$$\nu(\alpha) = N_{F/Q}(\alpha), \qquad \mathrm{tr}(\alpha) = \mathrm{Tr}_{F/Q}(\alpha).$$

PROOF. By the results of n°55–6 of Weil [46], there exist simple abelian varieties $A_1, \cdots, A_s$ such that A is isogenous to the product

$$(A_1\times\cdots\times A_1)\times\cdots\times(A_s\times\cdots\times A_s)$$

and the A_i are not isogenous to each other. Let h_i be the number of the factor A_i occuring in the product, for each i. Then, denoting by $\mathfrak{R}_i$ the total matric ring of degree h_i over $\mathscr{A}_0(A_i)$, $\mathscr{A}_0(A_i\times\cdots\times A_i)$ is identified with $\mathfrak{R}_i$, and $\mathscr{A}_0(A)$ is identified with the direct sum of the $\mathfrak{R}_i$. Let ε_i denote the identity element of $\mathfrak{R}_i$ for each i. $F\varepsilon_i$ is not $\{0\}$ for at least one of the ε_i, say ε_1. Then, $F\varepsilon_1$ is isomorphic to F, since F is a field. We see that $F\varepsilon_1$ is a semi-simple commutative subalgebra of $\mathscr{A}_0(A_1\times\cdots\times A_1)$; hence, by Proposition 1, we have $[F:Q] \leqq 2h_1\cdot\dim(A_1)$. By the assumption $[F:Q] = 2n$, we must have $s = 1$ and A is isogenous to $A_1\times\cdots\times A_1$. This proves the first assertion of our proposition. The second assertion follows from Proposition 1 and the last from Proposition 2.

PROPOSITION 4. *The notations A, B and F being as in Proposition* 3, *let m be the dimension of B and h the number of the factor B in the product $B\times\cdots\times B$ which is isogenous to A. Let K be the center of $\mathscr{A}_0(B)$. Then, K is a subfield of F; and, if we put $[K:Q] = f$, $[\mathscr{A}_0(B):K] = g^2$, we have $2n = fgh$, $2m = fg$.*

PROOF. We first note that $\mathscr{A}_0(B)$ is a division algebra, since B is simple. $\mathscr{A}_0(A)$ is identified with the total matric ring of degree h over $\mathscr{A}_0(B)$; hence K is the center of $\mathscr{A}_0(A)$ and is contained in F by virtue of Proposition 3. We observe that $\mathscr{A}_0(A)$ is a central simple algebra over K and $[\mathscr{A}_0(A): K] = g^2h^2$. By a well-known theorem of ring theory, $[F: K] = 2n/f$ divides gh; and if we put $gh = [F: K]q$, the commutor of F in $\mathscr{A}_0(A)$ is an algebra of degree q^2 over F. By Proposition 3, we must have $q = 1$, so that $[F: K] = gh = 2n/f$ and hence $2m = fg$.

LEMMA 2. *Let K be an algebraic number field of finite degree; let ρ be an automorphism of K such that $\rho^2 = 1$ and K_0 the subfield of K consisting of all the elements of K fixed by ρ. Suppose that*

$$\mathrm{Tr}_{K/Q}(\xi\xi^\rho) > 0$$

for every element $\xi \neq 0$ in K. Then K_0 is a totally real field. If ρ is not the identity on K, K is a totally imaginary field, and, for every isomorphism τ of K into $\boldsymbol{C}$, $\xi^{\rho\tau}$ is the complex conjugate of ξ^τ.

PROOF. We have $\mathrm{Tr}_{K_0/Q}(\xi^2) > 0$ for every $\xi \neq 0$ in K_0. Let $\tau_1, \cdots, \tau_m$ denote all the isomorphisms of K_0 into $\boldsymbol{C}$. Assume that τ_1 is not real; then the complex conjugate of τ_1 coincides with one of the isomorphisms $\tau_2, \cdots, \tau_m$, say τ_2. We see that $K_0^{\tau_1}$ is dense in $\boldsymbol{C}$, so that there exists an element η in K_0 such that $\mathrm{Re}((\eta^2)^{\tau_1}) < -1$. By the approximation theorem, for any small positive number ε, we can find an element ξ in K_0 such that

$$|\xi^{\tau_1} - \eta^{\tau_1}| = |\xi^{\tau_2} - \eta^{\tau_2}| < \varepsilon, \ |\xi^{\tau_i}| < \varepsilon \quad (2 < i \leqq m).$$

If we take a sufficiently small ε, we have

$$\begin{aligned}\mathrm{Tr}_{K_0/Q}(\xi^2) &= \mathrm{Re}(\mathrm{Tr}_{K_0/Q}(\xi^2)) \\ &= \mathrm{Re}((\xi^2)^{\tau_1}) + \mathrm{Re}((\xi^2)^{\tau_2}) + \cdots + \mathrm{Re}((\xi^2)^{\tau_m}) < -2.\end{aligned}$$

This is a contradiction; hence K_0 must be totally real. Now suppose that ρ is not the identity. Then we have $[K: K_0] = 2$, so that there exists an element ζ of K such that $K = K_0(\zeta)$, $\zeta^2 \in K_0$, $\zeta^\rho = -\zeta$. For every element $\alpha \neq 0$ of K_0, we have

$$2\mathrm{Tr}_{K_0/Q}(\alpha^2\zeta^2) = -\mathrm{Tr}_{K/Q}((\alpha\zeta)(\alpha\zeta)^\rho) < 0.$$

Again by the approximation theorem, we can find, for each i, an element α of K_0 such that

$$|\alpha^{\tau_i}| > 1, \ |\alpha^{\tau_j}| < \varepsilon \quad (j \neq i)$$

for a sufficiently small positive number ε; we have then $(\alpha^2\zeta^2)^{\tau_i} < 0$; this shows that $-(\zeta^2)^{\tau_i}$ is positive. Hence $-\zeta^2$ is totally positive, so that $K = K_0(\zeta)$ is totally imaginary; and for every isomorphism τ of K into $\boldsymbol{C}$, ζ^τ is a purely imaginary number. Therefore, we have, for every α, $\beta \in K_0$,

$$(\alpha+\beta\zeta)^{\rho\tau} = (\alpha-\beta\zeta)^\tau = \alpha^\tau - \beta^\tau\zeta^\tau = \overline{\alpha^\tau + \beta^\tau\zeta^\tau} = \overline{(\alpha+\beta\zeta)^\tau},$$

where $\bar{z}$ denotes the complex conjugate of z; this completes our proof.

PROPOSITION 5. *Let B be a simple abelian variety and K the center of $\mathscr{A}_0(B)$. Then K is a totally real number field or a totally imaginary quadratic extension of a totally real number field.*

PROOF. In § 1.3, we have noted that $\mathscr{A}_0(B)$ has an involution $\xi \rightarrow \xi'$ with the property $\mathrm{tr}(\xi\xi') > 0$ for every $\xi \neq 0$ in $\mathscr{A}_0(B)$. As K is the center of $\mathscr{A}_0(B)$, the involution maps K onto itself; and by Proposition 2, we have $\mathrm{tr}(\xi) = m\mathrm{Tr}_{K/\boldsymbol{Q}}(\xi)$ for $\xi \in K$, for a suitable positive integer m. Hence we have $\mathrm{Tr}_{K/\boldsymbol{Q}}(\xi\xi') > 0$ for every $\xi \neq 0$ in K. Our proposition is then an immediate consequence of Lemma 2.

PROPOSITION 6. *Notations being as in Proposition* 4, *suppose that the characteristic of the fields of definition for A is zero. Then, we have $g = 1$ and $\mathscr{A}_0(B) = K$.*

PROOF. If the characteristic is 0, we can consider a rational representation of $\mathscr{A}_0(B)$, defined in § 3.2, which is of degree $2m$, m being the dimension of B. As $\mathscr{A}_0(B)$ is a division algebra, the degree of any rational representation of $\mathscr{A}_0(B)$ is divisible by $[\mathscr{A}_0(B) : \boldsymbol{Q}] = fg^2$. Hence, by the equality $2m = fg$, we must have $g = 1$; this implies $\mathscr{A}_0(B) = K$.

5. 2. CM-type. Let $\mathfrak{R}$ be an algebra over $\boldsymbol{Q}$, with an identity element 1. We understand by an *abelian variety of type* $(\mathfrak{R})$ a couple (A, ι) formed by an abelian variety A and an isomorphism ι of $\mathfrak{R}$

into $\mathscr{A}_0(A)$ such that $\iota(1) = 1_A$. When there is no fear of confusion, we write (A, ι) simply by A and identify an element α of $\mathfrak{R}$ with $\iota(\alpha)$.

Let F be an algebraic number field, (A, ι) an abelian variety of type (F) and n the dimension of A. By Proposition 2, $[F: Q]$ divides $2n$. We shall now investigate the structure of (A, ι) for which $[F: Q] = 2n$ holds, in case where the characteristic is 0. If the characteristic is 0, A is isomorphic to a complex torus, and we obtain a rational representation M and an analytic representation S of $\mathscr{A}_0(A)$, with respect to an analytic coordinate-system; M is of degree $2n$, and S is of degree n; M is equivalent to the direct sum of S and the complex conjugate $\bar{S}$ of S (cf. § 3.2). Let $\varphi_1, \cdots, \varphi_{2n}$ be all the isomorphisms of F into $\boldsymbol{C}$. Then, by Lemma 1, the representation M restricted to F is equivalent to the direct sum of the φ_i; hence S is equivalent to the direct sum of a half of $2n$ isomorphisms φ_i, say $\varphi_1, \cdots, \varphi_n$. Then $\bar{S}$ is equivalent to the direct sum of $\varphi_{n+1}, \cdots, \varphi_{2n}$, which is equal, as a whole, to $\bar{\varphi}_1, \cdots, \bar{\varphi}_n$. Therefore, we observe that there are no two isomorphisms among $\varphi_1, \cdots, \varphi_n$ which are complex conjugate of each other. Moreover, we see that F must be totally imaginary. $\{\varphi_1, \cdots, \varphi_n\}$ being thus determined, we say that (A, ι) is of type $(F; \{\varphi_1, \cdots, \varphi_n\})$. Recalling that S is equivalent to the representation of $\mathscr{A}_0(A)$ by invariant differential forms, we can find n invariant differential forms $\omega_1, \cdots, \omega_n$ of degree 1 on A such that, for every $\alpha \in F$,

$$\delta\iota(\alpha)\omega_i = \alpha^{\varphi_i}\omega_i \quad (1 \leqq i \leqq n).$$

Conversely, if there exist such ω_i, (A, ι) is of type $(F; \{\varphi_i\})$; and the ω_i form a basis of $\mathfrak{D}_0(A)$. We shall often use these facts afterwards.

Now let us consider the center K of $\mathscr{A}_0(A)$, which is also the center of $\mathscr{A}_0(B)$, where B is a simple abelian variety determined as in Proposition 3. Proposition 5 asserts that K is totally real or a totally imaginary quadratic extension of a totally real field. By Propositions 4 and 6, we have $[K: Q] = 2 \cdot \dim(B)$; so we can apply to B and K what we have proved for A and F; then we see that K must be totally imaginary. Let S' be an analytic representation of $\mathscr{A}_0(B)$. Then, as A is isogenous to the product of h copies of B, the restriction of S to K is equivalent to h times of S'. Hence the restriction of $\varphi_1,\cdots,\varphi_n$ to K yields exactly h times of $f/2$ isomorphisms $\psi_1,\cdots,\psi_{f/2}$ of K into $\boldsymbol{C}$, where $f=[K:\boldsymbol{Q}]$; and S' is equivalent to the direct sum of the ψ_j; there are no two isomorphisms among ψ_j which are complex conjugate of each other.

In general, for an algebraic number field F of degree $2n$ and n distinct isomorphisms φ_i of F into $\boldsymbol{C}$, we say that $(F;\ \{\varphi_1,\cdots,\varphi_n\})$ is a *CM-type* if there exists an abelian variety of dimension n of type $(F;\ \{\varphi_i\})$. The above discussion gives us a necessary condition for a CM-type.

THEOREM 1. *In order that $(F;\ \{\varphi_i\})$ is a CM-type, it is necessary and sufficient that F contains two subfields K and K_0 satisfying the following conditions.*

(CM1) *K_0 is totally real and K is a totally imaginary quadratic extension of K_0.*

(CM2) *There are no two isomorphisms among the φ_i which are complex conjugate of each other on K.*

The sufficiency will be proved in the following section (Theorem 3).

6. CONSTRUCTION OF ABELIAN VARIETIES WITH COMPLEX MULTIPLICATION.

6. 1. Analytic structure of an abelian variety of type $(F;\ \{\varphi_i\})$. $(A,\ \iota)$ being of type $(F;\ \{\varphi_i\})$, put

$$\mathfrak{r}=\iota^{-1}[\mathscr{A}(A)\cap\iota(F)];$$

then $\mathfrak{r}$ is a subring of F which is finitely generated over $\boldsymbol{Z}$ and $F=\boldsymbol{Q}\mathfrak{r}$; hence $\mathfrak{r}$ is a free $\boldsymbol{Z}$-module of rank $2n$, where $n=\dim A$. Take an analytic coordinate-system $(\boldsymbol{C}^n/D,\ \theta)$ of A and denote by S the analytic representation of $\mathscr{A}_0(A)$ with respect to θ. We see that $S(\iota(\alpha))$ is non-singular for every $\alpha\neq 0$ in F. As we have $S(\iota(\alpha))D\subset D$ for every α in $\mathfrak{r}$, D is considered as an $\mathfrak{r}$-module. Choose a vector $x_0\neq 0$ in D and put $D'=S(\iota(\mathfrak{r}))x_0$. Then the mapping $\alpha\rightarrow S(\iota(\alpha))x_0$ is an $\mathfrak{r}$-isomorphism of $\mathfrak{r}$ onto D'. Hence D' is of rank $2n$, so that there exists a positive integer g such that $gD\subset D'$. Fixing such a number g, we obtain an $\mathfrak{r}$-isomorphism $x \to \mu$ of D into $\mathfrak{r}$ by means of the relation

$$gx = S(\iota(\mu))x_0.$$

Let $\mathfrak{m}$ denote the image of this isomorphism; $\mathfrak{m}$ is then an ideal of $\mathfrak{r}$. Put $x_1 = g^{-1}x_0$; we have then

$$D = S(\iota(\mathfrak{m}))x_1.$$

We observe that $S(\iota(\alpha))D \subset D$ if and only if $\alpha\mathfrak{m} \subset \mathfrak{m}$; hence $\mathfrak{r}$ consists of all the elements $\alpha \in F$ such that $\alpha\mathfrak{m} \subset \mathfrak{m}$, namely $\mathfrak{r}$ is the "order" of the module $\mathfrak{m}$. Now, for a suitable choice of coordinate-system, $S(\iota(\alpha))$ is the diagonal matrix with the diagonal elements $\alpha^{\varphi_1}, \cdots, \alpha^{\varphi_n}$. Let $(b_1, \cdots, b_n)$ be the components of the vector x_1 with respect to this coordinate-system. Then D is the set of all vectors with the components $(\mu^{\varphi_1}b_1, \ldots, \mu^{\varphi_n}b_n)$ for $\mu \in \mathfrak{m}$. Assume that we have $b_i = 0$ for some i; then D is contained in a proper subspace of $\boldsymbol{C}^n$; this is a contradiction, since D is a discrete subgroup of $\boldsymbol{C}^n$ of rank $2n$. Therefore, we must have $b_i \neq 0$ for every i. Change the coordinate-system $(z_1, \cdots, z_n)$ for $(b_1^{-1}z_1, \cdots, b_n^{-1}z_n)$; we see that $S(\iota(\alpha))$ is expressed again by the same diagonal matrix as before with respect to this new system; and D is the set of all vectors with the components $(\mu^{\varphi_1}, \cdots, \mu^{\varphi_n})$ for $\mu \in \mathfrak{m}$. We have thus proved

THEOREM 2. *Let F be an algebraic number field of degree $2n$ and the φ_i, for $1 \leqq i \leqq n$, n distinct isomorphisms of F into $\boldsymbol{C}$; denote by $u(\alpha)$ the vector in $\boldsymbol{C}^n$ with the components $(\alpha^{\varphi_1}, \cdots, \alpha^{\varphi_n})$ for $\alpha \in F$, by $D(\mathfrak{m})$ the set of all vectors $u(\alpha)$ for α in a free $\boldsymbol{Z}$-module $\mathfrak{m}$ in F of rank $2n$, and by $S(\alpha)$ the diagonal matrix with the diagonal elements $\alpha^{\varphi_1}, \cdots, \alpha^{\varphi_n}$. If (A, ι) is an abelian variety of type $(F;\ \{\varphi_i\})$, then there exist a module $\mathfrak{m}$ and an isomorphism θ of A onto $\boldsymbol{C}^n/D(\mathfrak{m})$ by which $\iota(\alpha)$ corresponds to the linear transformation of $\boldsymbol{C}^n$ given by $S(\alpha)$ for every $\alpha \in F$; and if we denote by $\mathfrak{r}$ the set of all elements α in F such that $\alpha\mathfrak{m} \subset \mathfrak{m}$, we have*

$$\iota(\mathfrak{r}) = \iota(F) \cap \mathscr{A}(A).$$

COROLLARY. *Any two abelian varieties of the same CM-type are isogenous to each other.*

PROOF. If $\mathfrak{m}, \mathfrak{m}'$ are two free $\boldsymbol{Z}$-submodules of F of rank $2n$, then there exists a positive integer g such that $g\mathfrak{m} \subset \mathfrak{m}'$; we have then $gD(\mathfrak{m}) \subset D(\mathfrak{m}')$. Hence $x \to gx$ gives a homomorphism of $\boldsymbol{C}^n/D(\mathfrak{m})$ onto $\boldsymbol{C}^n/D(\mathfrak{m}')$; this proves the assertion.

REMARK. The homomorphism $x \to gx$ commutes obviously with the operation of F.

6. 2. Construction. We shall now prove that the existence of the fields K and K_0 satisfying (CM 1, 2) is sufficient for $(F; \{\varphi_i\})$ to be a CM-type.

THEOREM 3. *The notations F, φ_i, $D(\mathfrak{m})$, $S(\alpha)$ being the same as in Theorem 2, suppose that F contains two subfields K, K_0 satisfying the conditions* (CM 1, 2) *of Theorem* 1. *Then, for every free* $\boldsymbol{Z}$*-submodule* $\mathfrak{m}$ *of F of rank $2n$, $\boldsymbol{C}^n/D(\mathfrak{m})$ is isomorphic to an abelian variety A, and, for every $\alpha \in F$, the linear transformation of $\boldsymbol{C}^n$ given by $S(\alpha)$ corresponds to an element of $\mathscr{A}_0(A)$; if we denote this element by $\iota(\alpha)$, (A, ι) is of type $(F; \{\varphi_i\})$. Moreover, if F does not coincide with K, A is not simple.*

PROOF. Take a basis $\{\alpha_1, \cdots, \alpha_{2n}\}$ of $\mathfrak{m}$ over $\boldsymbol{Z}$; then $2n$ vectors $u(\alpha_1), \cdots, u(\alpha_{2n})$ form a basis of $D(\mathfrak{m})$ over $\boldsymbol{Z}$. In order that $D(\mathfrak{m})$ is discrete in $\boldsymbol{C}^n$, it is sufficient that the $u(\alpha_i)$ are linearly independent over $\boldsymbol{R}$; this is equivalent to that the matrix of degree $2n$ with the columns $(\alpha_i^{\varphi_1}, \cdots, \alpha_i^{\varphi_n}, \overline{\alpha_i^{\varphi_1}}, \cdots, \overline{\alpha_i^{\varphi_n}})$, for $1 \leqq i \leqq 2n$, is non-singular. The latter is the case, since the α_i form a basis of F over $\boldsymbol{Q}$ and $2n$ isomorphisms φ_i, $\bar{\varphi}_i$ give all the isomorphisms of F into $\boldsymbol{C}$. Hence $\boldsymbol{C}^n/D(\mathfrak{m})$ is a complex torus. We shall now prove that $\boldsymbol{C}^n/D(\mathfrak{m})$ has a structure of abelian variety. It is sufficient to show this for a certain $\mathfrak{m}$, because, for every two free $\boldsymbol{Z}$-submodules $\mathfrak{m}$ and $\mathfrak{m}'$ of F, $D(\mathfrak{m})$ and $D(\mathfrak{m}')$ are commensurable to each other. Put $[K_0 : \boldsymbol{Q}] = m$, $[F : K] = h$; we have then $n = mh$, $[K : \boldsymbol{Q}] = 2m$. Let $\mathfrak{n}$ be a free $\boldsymbol{Z}$-submodule of K of rank $2m$ and $\{\gamma_1, \cdots, \gamma_h\}$ a basis of F over K; put

$$\mathfrak{m} = \mathfrak{n}\gamma_1 + \cdots + \mathfrak{n}\gamma_h,$$

$$\Delta_\lambda = \{u(\beta) \mid \beta \in \mathfrak{n}\gamma_\lambda\}.$$

Then $D(\mathfrak{m})$ is the sum of $\Delta_1, \cdots, \Delta_h$, and each Δ_λ has $2m$ generators which are linearly independent over $\boldsymbol{R}$. Denote by V_λ the subspace of $\boldsymbol{C}^n$ generated over $\boldsymbol{R}$ by these $2m$ vectors. Then it is easy to see that $\boldsymbol{C}^n/D(\mathfrak{m})$ is isomorphic to the direct product of the V_λ/Δ_λ as real analytic manifold. We shall now show that the V_λ are complex vector subspaces of $\boldsymbol{C}^n$. Let $\psi_1, \cdots, \psi_k$ be the distinct isomorphisms of K into $\boldsymbol{C}$ induced by the φ_i. By virtue of the conditions (CM1, 2), we see that $k = m$ and the φ_i are all the isomorphisms of F into $\boldsymbol{C}$ inducing the ψ_j on K. Denote by $v(\beta)$, for $\beta \in K$, the vector of $\boldsymbol{C}^m$ whose components are $\beta^{\psi_1}, \cdots, \beta^{\psi_m}$, and by Δ the set of all vectors $v(\beta)$ for $\beta \in \mathfrak{n}$. Then, applying to Δ what we have proved above, we see that Δ is a discrete subgroup of $\boldsymbol{C}^m$ and $\boldsymbol{C}^m/\Delta$ is a complex torus. If $\{\beta_1, \cdots, \beta_{2m}\}$ is a basis of $\mathfrak{n}$ over $\boldsymbol{Z}$, $2m$ vectors $v(\beta_t)$ give a basis of $\boldsymbol{C}^m$ over $\boldsymbol{R}$. The linear mapping $x \to \sqrt{-1}x$ of $\boldsymbol{C}^m$ onto itself, regarded as an $\boldsymbol{R}$-linear mapping, determines a matrix (c_{st}) of degree $2m$ with real coefficients with respect to the basis $\{v(\beta_t)\}$:

$$(1) \qquad \sqrt{-1}\,\beta_t^{\psi_j} = \sum_{s=1}^{2m} c_{st}\beta_s^{\psi_j} \qquad (1 \leqq j \leqq m,\ 1 \leqq t \leqq 2m).$$

Now we see that the vectors $(\gamma_\lambda^{\varphi_1}\beta_t^{\varphi_1}, \ldots, \gamma_\lambda^{\varphi_n}\beta_t^{\varphi_n})$, for $1 \leqq t \leqq 2m$, form a basis of V_λ over $\boldsymbol{R}$. As every φ_i induces one of the ψ_j on K, we find, multiplying (1) by $\gamma_\lambda^{\varphi_i}$,

$$(2) \qquad \sqrt{-1}\;\gamma_\lambda^{\varphi_i}\beta_t^{\varphi_i} = \sum_{s=1}^{2m} c_{st}\gamma_\lambda^{\varphi_i}\beta_s^{\varphi_i} \qquad (1 \leqq i \leqq n,\ 1 \leqq t \leqq 2m).$$

This implies $\sqrt{-1}\,V_\lambda \subset V_\lambda$ for every λ, so that V_λ is a complex subspace of $\boldsymbol{C}^n$ of dimension m; and it can be easily verified that $\boldsymbol{C}^n/D(\mathfrak{m})$ is isomorphic, as complex manifold, to the direct product of the complex tori V_λ/Δ_λ. Moreover, if we correspond $v(\beta_t)$ to $u(\gamma_\lambda\beta_t)$, we obtain an $\boldsymbol{R}$-isomorphism η_λ of $\boldsymbol{C}^m$ onto V_λ; we see easily $\eta_\lambda(\Delta) = \Delta_\lambda$. By the relations (1) and (2), we have $\sqrt{-1}\,\eta_\lambda = \eta_\lambda\sqrt{-1}$, so that η_λ gives a complex analytic isomorphism of $\boldsymbol{C}^m/\Delta$ onto V_λ/Δ_λ. It follows that $\boldsymbol{C}^n/D(\mathfrak{m})$ is complex analytically isomorphic to the direct product of h copies of $\boldsymbol{C}^m/\Delta$. Hence, if we show that $\boldsymbol{C}^m/\Delta$ has a structure of abelian variety, $\boldsymbol{C}^n/D(\mathfrak{m})$ has also a structure of abelian variety. We prove this in constructing a non-degenerate Riemann form on $\boldsymbol{C}^m/\Delta$. By the condition (CM1), there exists an element ζ in K such that

$K = K_0(\zeta)$ and $\zeta^2 \in K_0$; as K is totally imaginary, $-\zeta^2$ must be totally positive. We can take ζ in such a way that

$$\mathrm{Im}(\zeta^{\phi_j}) > 0 \qquad (1 \leqq j \leqq m).$$

In fact, if this is not so, we choose an element α of K_0 such that $\alpha^{\phi_j}\mathrm{Im}(\zeta^{\phi_j}) > 0$ for $1 \leqq j \leqq m$, and adopt $\alpha\zeta$ in place of ζ. Now, z, w being two vectors of $\boldsymbol{C}^m$ with the components $(z_1, \cdots, z_m)$ and $(w_1, \cdots, w_m)$, we define an $\boldsymbol{R}$-bilinear form $E(z, w)$ on $\boldsymbol{C}^m$ by

$$E(z, w) = \sum_{j=1}^{m} \zeta^{\phi_j}(z_j\bar{w}_j - \bar{z}_j w_j).$$

We see easily $E(z, w) = -E(w, z)$, and

$$E(z, \sqrt{-1}\, w) = -\sqrt{-1} \sum_{j=1}^{m} \zeta^{\phi_j}(z_j\bar{w}_j + \bar{z}_j w_j).$$

Hence $E(z, \sqrt{-1}\, w)$ is a symmetric form and is positive non-degenerate since the ζ^{ϕ_j} are purely imaginary and we have $\mathrm{Im}(\zeta^{\phi_j}) > 0$. Denoting by ρ the automorphism of K over K_0, other than the identity, we have $\zeta^{\rho} = -\zeta$ and $\xi^{\rho\phi_i} = \overline{\xi^{\phi_i}}$ for every ξ in K (cf. Lemma 2 of § 5. 1 and its proof). By means of these relations, we have, for every α, β in K,

$$E(v(\alpha), v(\beta)) = \mathrm{Tr}_{K/Q}(\zeta\alpha\beta^{\rho}).$$

We can find a positive integer g such that all elements of $g\zeta\mathfrak{m}\mathfrak{m}^{\rho}$ are algebraic integers; then the values of $gE(z, w)$ on $\Delta \times \Delta$ are integers. Thus we obtain a non-degenerate Riemann form $gE(z, w)$ on $\boldsymbol{C}^m/\Delta$. This proves that $\boldsymbol{C}^n/D(\mathfrak{m})$ has a structure of abelian variety. The rest of our theorem is almost obvious.

Notations being as above, denote by $T(\xi)$ for $\xi \in K$ the diagonal matrix with the diagonal elements $\xi^{\phi_1}, \cdots, \xi^{\phi_m}$. Then, by virtue of the relation $\xi^{\rho\phi_i} = \overline{\xi^{\phi_i}}$, we have

$$E(z, T(\xi)w) = E(T(\xi^{\rho})z, w)$$

for every $\xi \in K$. Thus we have proved the first part of the following theorem.

Theorem 4. *Let K_0 be a totally real field of degree m, K a totally imaginary quadratic extension of K_0 and ρ the automorphism of K over*

K_0 other than the identity; let $(K; \{\psi_i\})$ be a CM-type and $\mathfrak{n}$ a free $\boldsymbol{Z}$-submodule of K of rank $2m$. Denote by $v(\beta)$ for $\beta \in K$ the vector of $\boldsymbol{C}^m$ with the components $\beta^{\psi_1}, \cdots, \beta^{\psi_m}$, by $T(\beta)$ the diagonal matrix with the diagonal elements $\beta^{\psi_1}, \cdots, \beta^{\psi_m}$, and by $D(\mathfrak{n})$ the set of all vectors $v(\beta)$ for $\beta \in \mathfrak{n}$. Let ζ be a number of K such that $-\zeta^2$ is a totally positive element of K_0 and $\mathrm{Im}(\zeta^{\psi_i}) > 0$ for every i. Put, for two vectors $z = (z_1, \cdots, z_m)$ and $w = (w_1, \cdots, w_m)$ of $\boldsymbol{C}^m$,

$$E(z, w) = \sum_{i=1}^{m} \zeta^{\psi_i}(z_i\bar{w}_i - \bar{z}_i w_i).$$

Then, for a suitable positive integer g, the form gE is a non-degenerate Riemann form on $\boldsymbol{C}^m/D(\mathfrak{n})$; and we have

$$E(z, T(\xi)w) = E(T(\xi^\rho)z, w) \tag{3}$$

for every ξ in K. Conversely, every non-degenerate Riemann form on $\boldsymbol{C}^m/D(\mathfrak{n})$ satisfying (3) *is obtained from an element ζ of K in this manner. If $\boldsymbol{C}^m/D(\mathfrak{n})$ is simple, every Riemann form on $\boldsymbol{C}^m/D(\mathfrak{n})$, other than* 0, *is non-degenerate and satisfies the relation* (3).

PROOF. We have only to prove the second and the last assertions; we first prove the last. As is remarked in § 1.3 and § 3.3, for every non-degenerate Riemann form $E(z, w)$, we obtain an involution $\Lambda \rightarrow \Lambda'$ of $\mathscr{A}_0(\boldsymbol{C}^m/D(\mathfrak{n}))$ by the relation

$$E(z, \Lambda w) = E(\Lambda' z, w).$$

If $\boldsymbol{C}^m/D(\mathfrak{n})$ is simple, every Riemann form on it, other than 0, is non-degenerate, and $\mathscr{A}_0(\boldsymbol{C}^m/D(\mathfrak{n}))$ coincides with $T(K)$ by virtue of Proposition 6; so the involution corresponds to an automorphism τ of K; we have namely $T(\xi)' = T(\xi^\tau)$; and we have $\mathrm{Tr}_{K/\boldsymbol{Q}}(\xi\xi^\tau) > 0$ for every $\xi \neq 0$ in K. By Lemma 2, if we denote by K_1 the subfield of K consisting of the elements fixed by τ, K_1 is totally real and $[K : K_1] = 2$. As K_0 and K_1 are totally real, we must have $K_0 = K_1$, and hence $\tau = \rho$; so E satisfies (3). Now we prove the second assertion. If E is a Riemann form, the mapping $\xi \rightarrow E(v(\xi), v(1))$ is a $\boldsymbol{Q}$-linear mapping of K into $\boldsymbol{Q}$, so that there exists an element ζ of K such that $E(v(\xi), v(1)) = \mathrm{Tr}_{K/\boldsymbol{Q}}(\zeta\xi)$ for every $\xi \in K$. Suppose that E

satisfies (3). We have then

$$E(v(\xi),\ v(\eta)) = E(v(\xi),\ T(\eta)v(1)) = E(T(\eta^\rho)v(\xi),\ v(1))$$
$$= E(v(\eta^\rho\xi),\ v(1)) = \mathrm{Tr}_{K/Q}(\zeta\xi\eta^\rho).$$

Since E is alternating, we have

$$\mathrm{Tr}_{K/Q}(\zeta\xi\eta^\rho) = -\mathrm{Tr}_{K/Q}(\zeta\xi^\rho\eta) = -\mathrm{Tr}_{K/Q}(\zeta^\rho\xi\eta^\rho);$$

this implies $\zeta = -\zeta^\rho$. Hence $-\zeta^2 = \zeta\zeta^\rho$ is contained in K_0 and $K = K_0(\zeta)$. As K is totally imaginary, $-\zeta^2$ must be totally positive. By the same argument as in the proof of Lemma 2, we find $\xi^{\rho\phi_i} = \overline{\xi^{\phi_i}}$ for every $\xi \in K$, so that

$$E(v(\xi),\ v(\eta))) = \mathrm{Tr}_{K/Q}(\zeta\xi\eta^\rho) = \sum_{i=1}^{m} \zeta^{\phi_i}(\xi^{\phi_i}\overline{\eta^{\phi_i}} - \overline{\xi^{\phi_i}}\eta^{\phi_i}).$$

Since the vectors $v(\xi)$ for $\xi \in K$ form a dense subset of $\boldsymbol{C}^m$, we have

$$E(z,\ w) = \sum_{i=1}^{m} \zeta^{\phi_i}(z_i\bar{w}_i - \bar{z}_i w_i)$$

on $\boldsymbol{C}^m \times \boldsymbol{C}^m$. The inequality $\mathrm{Im}(\zeta^{\phi_i}) > 0$ follows from the fact that $E(z,\ \sqrt{-1}\,z) = -2\sqrt{-1}\sum_{i=1}^{m}\zeta^{\phi_i}|z_i|^2$ is a positive form. This completes our proof.

We can give another expression for the form E on $D(\mathfrak{n}) \times D(\mathfrak{n})$. Let $\{\gamma_1,\ \gamma_2\}$ be a basis of K over K_0; put

$$\eta = \zeta(\gamma_1\gamma_2{}^\rho - \gamma_1{}^\rho\gamma_2);$$

then we have $\eta^\rho = \eta$, so that η is an element of K_0. For $\alpha_1,\ \alpha_2,\ \beta_1,\ \beta_2 \in K_0$, we have

$$\mathrm{Tr}_{K/K_0}(\zeta(\alpha_1\gamma_1 + \alpha_2\gamma_2)(\beta_1\gamma_1 + \beta_2\gamma_2)^\rho) = \eta(\alpha_1\beta_2 - \alpha_2\beta_1).$$

Hence we obtain

$$E(v(\alpha_1\gamma_1 + \alpha_2\gamma_2),\ v(\beta_1\gamma_1 + \beta_2\gamma_2)) = \mathrm{Tr}_{K_0/Q}(\eta(\alpha_1\beta_2 - \alpha_2\beta_1)).$$

6. 3. Picard variety. Notations being as in Theorem 4, let A be an abelian variety isomorphic to $\boldsymbol{C}^m/D(\mathfrak{n})$; we fix an isomorphism θ of A onto $\boldsymbol{C}^m/D(\mathfrak{n})$ and denote by $\iota(\alpha)$ for $\alpha \in K$ the element of $\mathscr{A}_0(A)$ corresponding to $T(\alpha)$; then $(A,\ \iota)$ is of type $(K;\ \{\psi_\nu\})$. We shall now consider a Picard variety A^* of A. Recall the form $\langle z, w \rangle$ on $\boldsymbol{C}^m$ introduced in § 3.3. We have

$$\langle z, w \rangle = \sum_{\nu=1}^{m} (z_\nu \bar{w}_\nu + \bar{z}_\nu w_\nu)$$

for any two vectors z, w with the coordinates z_ν w_ν, so that for every $\xi,\ \eta \in K$,

$$\langle v(\xi),\ v(\eta) \rangle = \mathrm{Tr}_{K/Q}(\xi\eta^\rho). \tag{4}$$

Let $(\boldsymbol{C}^m/D^*,\ \theta^*)$ be the dual of $(\boldsymbol{C}^m/D(\mathfrak{n}),\ \theta)$, defined in § 3.3, which is an analytic representation of A^*; D^* is the set of vectors z such that $\langle z, w \rangle \in \boldsymbol{Z}$ for every $w \in D(\mathfrak{n})$; we see then easily that every vector in D^* is of the form $v(\xi)$ for $\xi \in K$. Hence if we denote by $\mathfrak{n}^*$ the set of elements $\xi \in K$ such that

$$\mathrm{Tr}_{K/Q}(\xi\mathfrak{n}^\rho) \in \boldsymbol{Z},$$

we find $D^* = D(\mathfrak{n}^*)$ on account of (4). Thus the dual of $\boldsymbol{C}^m/D(\mathfrak{n})$ is given by $\boldsymbol{C}^m/D(\mathfrak{n}^*)$. By the relation (4), we see

$$\langle T(\alpha)v(\xi),\ v(\eta) \rangle = \langle v(\xi),\ T(\alpha^\rho)v(\eta) \rangle.$$

Since the vectors $v(\xi)$ for $\xi \in K$ form a dense subset in $\boldsymbol{C}^m$, we have

$$\langle T(\alpha)z,\ w \rangle = \langle z,\ T(\alpha^\rho)w \rangle$$

for every $\alpha \in K$. This shows that $T(\alpha^\rho)$ is the analytic representation of the element ${}^t\iota(\alpha)$ of $\mathscr{A}_0(A^*)$ with respect to θ^*. Put, for $\alpha \in K$,

$$\iota^*(\alpha) = {}^t\iota(\alpha^\rho). \tag{5}$$

Then we see that ι^* is an isomorphism of K into $\mathscr{A}_0(A^*)$; and $\iota^*(\alpha)$ is represented by $T(\alpha)$. It follows that $(A^*,\ \iota^*)$ is of type $(K;\ \{\psi_\nu\})$. Now let $E(z,\ w)$ be the Riemann form on $\boldsymbol{C}^m/D(\mathfrak{n})$ obtained from an element ζ of K, as in Therem 4, and X a divisor on A corresponding to E. Since we have

$$E(z,\ w) = \langle T(\zeta)z,\ w \rangle,$$

the homomorphism φ_X of A into A^* corresponds to the mapping of $\boldsymbol{C}^m/D(\mathfrak{n})$ onto $\boldsymbol{C}^m/D(\mathfrak{n}^*)$ given by $T(\zeta)$. We see easily that

$$\varphi_X\iota(\alpha) = \iota^*(\alpha)\varphi_X$$

for every $\alpha \in K$.

7. TRANSFORMATIONS AND MULTIPLICATIONS.

7. 1. Definitions. Let $\mathfrak{R}$ be an algebra over $\boldsymbol{Q}$ with an identity element 1. We shall understand by a *lattice* in $\mathfrak{R}$ a free $\boldsymbol{Z}$-submodule of $\mathfrak{R}$ of rank $[\mathfrak{R}:\boldsymbol{Q}]$. We call a subring $\mathfrak{o}$ of $\mathfrak{R}$ an *order* in $\mathfrak{R}$ if it is a lattice in $\mathfrak{R}$ and contains the identity element of $\mathfrak{R}$. Let $\mathfrak{a}$ be a lattice in $\mathfrak{R}$; let $\mathfrak{o}_r$ (resp. $\mathfrak{o}_l$) be the set of all ellements α of $\mathfrak{R}$ such that $\mathfrak{a}\alpha \subset \mathfrak{a}$ (resp. $\alpha\mathfrak{a} \subset \mathfrak{a}$). Then, $\mathfrak{o}_r$ and $\mathfrak{o}_l$ are orders in $\mathfrak{R}$. We call $\mathfrak{o}_r$ (resp. $\mathfrak{o}_l$) the *right* (resp. *left*) *order* of $\mathfrak{a}$.

$\mathfrak{R}$ being as above, let (A, ι) be an abelian variety of type $(\mathfrak{R})$. Recall that ι is an isomorphism of $\mathfrak{R}$ into $\mathscr{A}_0(A)$ such that $\iota(1)$ is the identity 1_A of $\mathscr{A}_0(A)$. Put

$$\mathfrak{r} = \iota^{-1}[\mathscr{A}(A) \cap \iota(R)].$$

It is easy to see that $\mathfrak{r}$ is an order in $\mathfrak{R}$. $\mathfrak{r}$ is called the *order* of (A, ι). We say that (A, ι) is defined over a field k if k is a field of definition for A and every element of $\iota(\mathfrak{r})$. Let (A', ι') be another abelian variety of type $(\mathfrak{R})$. A homomorphism (resp. an isomorphism) λ of A into A' is called a *homomorphism* (resp. an *isomorphism*) of (A, ι) into (A', ι'), or an $\mathfrak{R}$-*homomorphism* (resp. $\mathfrak{R}$-*isomorphism*) of A into A', if it satisfies

$$\lambda\iota(\alpha) = \iota'(\alpha)\lambda$$

for every $\alpha \in \mathfrak{R}$. An *endomorphism* or an *automorphism* of (A, ι) is similarly defined.

Let (A, ι) and (A', ι') be abelian varieties of type $(\mathfrak{R})$; let $\mathfrak{r}$ be the order of (A, ι) and $\mathfrak{a}$ a lattice in $\mathfrak{R}$ contained in $\mathfrak{r}$. A homomorphism λ of (A, ι) onto (A', ι') is called an $\mathfrak{a}$-*multiplication of* (A, ι) *onto* (A', ι') if there exist a field k of definition for (A, ι), (A', ι') and λ, and a generic point x of A over k, such that $k(\lambda x)$ is the composite of all the fields $k(\iota(\alpha)x)$ for $\alpha \in \mathfrak{a}$. We note that if λ is an $\mathfrak{a}$-multiplication, then, for any field of definition k_1 for (A, ι), (A', ι') and λ, and for any generic point y of A over k_1, $k_1(\lambda y)$ is the composite of all the fields $k_1(\iota(\alpha)y)$ for $\alpha \in \mathfrak{a}$. It is easy to see that every $\mathfrak{a}$-multiplication is an $\mathfrak{r}\mathfrak{a}$-multiplication. (A', ι') is called an $\mathfrak{a}$-*transform* of (A, ι) if there exists an $\mathfrak{a}$-multiplication λ of (A, ι) onto (A', ι'). We call also the system $(A', \iota'; \lambda)$ an $\mathfrak{a}$-transform of (A, ι). By our definition, every $\mathfrak{a}$-transform of (A, ι) is of the same dimension as (A, ι) and every $\mathfrak{a}$-multiplication is an isogeny.

PROPOSITION 7. *Let $\mathfrak{R}$ be an algebra over $\boldsymbol{Q}$ with an identity element and (A, ι) an abelian variety of type $(\mathfrak{R})$; let $\mathfrak{r}$ be the order of (A, ι) and $\mathfrak{a}$ a lattice in $\mathfrak{R}$ contained in $\mathfrak{r}$. Then, there exists an $\mathfrak{a}$-transform $(A', \iota'; \lambda)$ of (A, ι); $(A', \iota'; \lambda)$ is uniquely determined by (A, ι) and $\mathfrak{a}$ up to an $\mathfrak{R}$-isomorphism; and the order of (A', ι') contains the right order of $\mathfrak{a}$. Moreover, if k is a field of definition for (A, ι), we can find (A', ι') and λ so that they are defined over k.*

PROOF. The uniqueness follows immediately from our definition. Let k be a field of definition for (A, ι) and x a generic point of A over k. Take a basis $\{\alpha_1, \cdots, \alpha_d\}$ of $\mathfrak{a}$ over $\boldsymbol{Z}$. Let A' denote the locus of $\iota(\alpha_1)x \times \cdots \times \iota(\alpha_d)x$ over k in the product of d copies of A. Then, A' is an abelian variety with the origin $0 \times \cdots \times 0$, where 0 denotes the origin of A. Define a rational mapping λ of A onto A' by

$$\lambda x = \iota(\alpha_1)x \times \cdots \times \iota(\alpha_d)x$$

with respect to k; then λ is a homomorphism of A onto A'. We see easily that $k(\lambda x)$ is the composite of the fields $k(\iota(\alpha)x)$ for $\alpha \in \mathfrak{a}$, since $\{\alpha_1, \cdots, \alpha_d\}$ is a basis of $\mathfrak{a}$ over $\boldsymbol{Z}$. Let $\mathfrak{r}'$ be the right order of $\mathfrak{a}$. Let β be an element of $\mathfrak{r}'$. Put $\beta_i = \alpha_i\beta$; then the β_i are contained in $\mathfrak{a}$. We can find a positive integer g such that $g\beta \in \mathfrak{r}$. Let y be a point of A such that $gy = x$; we have then

$$\iota(\beta_1)x \times \cdots \times \iota(\beta_d)x = \lambda(\iota(g\beta)y),$$

so that the point $\iota(\beta_1)x \times \cdots \times \iota(\beta_d)x$ is contained in A'. Since the elements β_i are contained in $\mathfrak{a}$, the field $k(\iota(\beta_1)x, \cdots, \iota(\beta_d)x)$ is contained in $k(\lambda x)$. Hence we can define a rational mapping μ of A' into itself by $\mu(\lambda x) = \iota(\beta_1)x \times \cdots \times \iota(\beta_d)x$, with respect to k. μ is an endomorphism of A', since it maps the origin onto the origin. Denote this endomorphism μ by $\iota'(\beta)$. We have then

$$\iota'(\beta)\lambda x = \iota(\alpha_1\beta)x \times \cdots \times \iota(\alpha_d\beta)x.$$

It follows from this relation that $\beta \to \iota'(\beta)$ is an isomorphism of $\mathfrak{r}'$ into $\mathscr{A}(A')$; and $\iota'(1)$ is the identity element of $\mathscr{A}(A')$; so (A', ι') is an abelian variety of type $(\mathfrak{R})$ and the order of (A', ι') contains $\mathfrak{r}'$. If α is contained in $\mathfrak{r} \cap \mathfrak{r}'$, we have $\iota'(\alpha)\lambda x = \lambda\iota(\alpha)x$ by our construction. This completes our proof.

Notations being as in Proposition 7, we denote by $\mathfrak{g}(\mathfrak{a}, A)$, or simply by $\mathfrak{g}(\mathfrak{a})$, the set of points t on A such that $\iota(\alpha)t = 0$ for every $\alpha \in \mathfrak{a}$.

PROPOSITION 8. *The notations* $\mathfrak{R}$, (A, ι), $\mathfrak{r}$, $\mathfrak{a}$ *being as in Proposition* 7, *let* $(A', \iota'; \lambda)$ *be an* $\mathfrak{a}$*-transform of* (A, ι) *and* k *a field of definition for* (A, ι), (A', ι') *and* λ. *Then, for every point* t *on* A, *the field* $k(\lambda t)$ *is the composite of all the fields* $k(\iota(\alpha)t)$ *for* $\alpha \in \mathfrak{a}$; *and the kernel of* λ *is* $\mathfrak{g}(\mathfrak{a}, A)$.

PROOF. By the uniqueness, it is sufficient to prove our conclusion for the $\mathfrak{a}$-transform $(A', \iota'; \lambda)$ constructed in the proof of Proposition 7; but this is easily seen by the relation $\lambda t = \iota(\alpha_1)t \times \cdots \times \iota(\alpha_d)t$.

(A, ι) and $\mathfrak{r}$ being as above, let α be a regular element of $\mathfrak{R}$ contained in $\mathfrak{r}$. Define an isomorphism ι' of $\mathfrak{R}$ into $\mathscr{A}_0(A)$ by $\iota'(\gamma) = \iota(\alpha\gamma\alpha^{-1})$. Then, we see easily that $\iota(\alpha)$ is an $\mathfrak{r}\alpha$-multiplication of (A, ι) onto (A, ι'). If $\mathfrak{R}$ is commutative, we have of course $(A, \iota) = (A, \iota')$.

PROPOSITION 9. *The notations* $\mathfrak{R}$, (A, ι), $\mathfrak{r}$, $\mathfrak{a}$ *being as in Proposition* 7, *let* $\mathfrak{r}_1$ *be the right order of* $\mathfrak{a}$, *and* $\mathfrak{b}$ *a lattice in* $\mathfrak{R}$ *contained in* $\mathfrak{r}_1$. *Let* $(A_1, \iota_1; \lambda)$ *be an* $\mathfrak{a}$*-transform of* (A, ι) *and* $(A_2, \iota_2; \mu)$ *a* $\mathfrak{b}$*-transform of* (A_1, ι_1). *Then,* $(A_2, \iota_2; \mu\lambda)$ *is an* $\mathfrak{a}\mathfrak{b}$*-transform of* (A, ι).

PROOF. $\mu\lambda$ is obviously an $\mathfrak{R}$-homomorphism of A onto A_2. Let k be a field of definition for (A, ι), (A_1, ι_1), (A_2, ι_2), λ, μ; take a generic point x of A over k and put $y = \lambda x$. Then $k(\mu y)$ is the composite of the fields $k(\iota_1(\beta)y)$ for $\beta \in \mathfrak{b}$. We can find a positive integer m such that $m\mathfrak{b} \subset \mathfrak{r}$ and a point z of A such that $mz = x$. We have then $\iota_1(\beta)y = \lambda\iota(m\beta)z$, and, by Proposition 8, $k(\lambda\iota(m\beta)z)$ is the composite of the fields $k(\iota(\alpha)\iota(m\beta)z)$ for $\alpha \in \mathfrak{a}$. As we have $\mathfrak{a}\mathfrak{b} \subset \mathfrak{a}\mathfrak{r}_1 \subset \mathfrak{a}$, $\alpha\beta$ is contained in $\mathfrak{r}$, so that we have $\iota(\alpha)\iota(m\beta)z = \iota(\alpha\beta)x$ for every $\alpha \in \mathfrak{a}$,

$\beta \in \mathfrak{b}$. Hence $k(\mu\lambda x)$ is the composite of the fields $k(\iota(\alpha\beta)x)$ for $\alpha \in \mathfrak{a}$ and $\beta \in \mathfrak{b}$. Since $\mathfrak{ab}$ is generated by the elements $\alpha\beta$, this proves that $\mu\lambda$ is an $\mathfrak{ab}$-multiplication.

7. 2. From now on, we assume that $\mathfrak{R}$ *is a simple algebra over* Q[2] and denote by $N(\xi)$ the reduced norm of $\xi \in \mathfrak{R}$ (cf. § 5.1). We first recall the ideal-theory in $\mathfrak{R}$; for details we refer to Deuring [7]. An order $\mathfrak{o}$ in $\mathfrak{R}$ is said to be *maximal* if there is no order containing $\mathfrak{o}$ other than itself. Let $\mathfrak{a}$ be a lattice in $\mathfrak{R}$ and $\mathfrak{o}$ an order in $\mathfrak{R}$. We call $\mathfrak{a}$ a *right* (resp. *left*) $\mathfrak{o}$-*ideal* if we have $\mathfrak{ao} \subset \mathfrak{a}$ (resp. $\mathfrak{oa} \subset \mathfrak{a}$). $\mathfrak{a}$ is said to be *normal* if both its right and left orders are maximal; it is known that if one of the left and right orders of $\mathfrak{a}$ is maximal, then $\mathfrak{a}$ is normal. $\mathfrak{a}$ and $\mathfrak{b}$ being normal lattices in $\mathfrak{R}$, the product $\mathfrak{ab}$ is said to be *proper* if the right order of $\mathfrak{a}$ coincides with the left order of $\mathfrak{b}$. The set of all normal lattices in $\mathfrak{R}$ form a groupoid $\mathfrak{G}$ with respect to the operation of proper product; the maximal orders are the units of $\mathfrak{G}$ and the inverse of $\mathfrak{a}$ is given by

$$\mathfrak{a}^{-1} = \{\xi \mid \xi \in \mathfrak{R},\ \mathfrak{a}\xi\mathfrak{a} \subset \mathfrak{a}\}.$$

$\mathfrak{o}_r$ and $\mathfrak{o}_l$ being the right and left orders of a lattice $\mathfrak{a}$ in $\mathfrak{R}$, if we have $\mathfrak{a} \subset \mathfrak{o}_r$, then $\mathfrak{a} \subset \mathfrak{o}_l$, and conversely; we call such $\mathfrak{a}$ *integral*. If $\mathfrak{a}$ is integral and normal, the numbers of elements in the factor modules $\mathfrak{o}_r/\mathfrak{a}$ and $\mathfrak{o}_l/\mathfrak{a}$ are the same; we denote this number by $N_1(\mathfrak{a})$. Let $\mathfrak{Z}$ be the center of $\mathfrak{R}$; and put

$$[\mathfrak{R} : \mathfrak{Z}] = f^2, \quad [\mathfrak{Z} : Q] = d. \tag{1}$$

Then, we can prove that $N_1(\mathfrak{a})$ is the f-th power of a positive integer; we put $N(\mathfrak{a}) = N_1(\mathfrak{a})^{1/f}$. We can define $N(\mathfrak{a})$ in a natural manner for every normal lattice in $\mathfrak{R}$ which is not necessarily integral; and if the product $\mathfrak{ab}$ is proper, we have

$$N(\mathfrak{ab}) = N(\mathfrak{a})N(\mathfrak{b}).$$

2) For our principal aim in Chap IV, it is sufficient to consider the case where $\mathfrak{R}$ is an algebraic number field and $2(\dim A) = [\mathfrak{R} : Q]$; so the reader who is interested only in this case may dispense with the trouble of considering the general case.

If ξ is a regular element in $\mathfrak{R}$, we have, for every maximal order $\mathfrak{o}$,

$$N(\mathfrak{o}\xi) = N(\xi\mathfrak{o}) = |N(\xi)|.$$

Now consider an abelian variety (A, ι) of type $(\mathfrak{R})$. Let n be the dimension of A and f, d be as in (1). Then, by Proposition 2, fd divides $2n$; putting $2n = mfd$, we call m the *index* of (A, ι). (A, ι) is said to be *principal* if the order of (A, ι) is maximal. By Proposition 7, if (A, ι) is principal, then, for every integral left $\mathfrak{o}$-ideal $\mathfrak{a}$, an $\mathfrak{a}$-transform of (A, ι) is also principal. In the following treatment, (A, ι), (A', ι') etc. will denote abelian varieties of type $(\mathfrak{R})$ which are assumed to be principal.

PROPOSITION 10. *Let $\mathfrak{o}$ be the order of (A, ι) and $\mathfrak{a}$ an integral left $\mathfrak{o}$-ideal; let $(A_1, \iota_1; \lambda_{\mathfrak{a}})$ be an $\mathfrak{a}$-transform of (A, ι). Then we have*

$$\nu(\lambda_{\mathfrak{a}}) = N(\mathfrak{a})^m,$$

where m is the index of (A, ι).

PROOF. Let $\mathfrak{o}'$ be the right order of $\mathfrak{a}$. Then we can find an integral left $\mathfrak{o}'$-ideal $\mathfrak{b}$ such that $\mathfrak{a}\mathfrak{b}$ is a principal ideal $\mathfrak{o}\gamma$ and $(N(\mathfrak{b}), \nu(\lambda_{\mathfrak{a}})) = 1$ (cf. [7] VI, Satz 27). Let $(A_2, \iota_2; \lambda_{\mathfrak{b}})$ be a $\mathfrak{b}$-transform of (A_1, ι_1); then $(A_2, \iota_2; \lambda_{\mathfrak{b}}\lambda_{\mathfrak{a}})$ is an $\mathfrak{o}\gamma$-transform of (A, ι) by virtue of Proposition 9. On the other hand, putting $\iota'(\alpha) = \iota(\gamma\alpha\gamma^{-1})$ for $\alpha \in \mathfrak{R}$, we see that $(A, \iota'; \iota(\gamma))$ is an $\mathfrak{o}\gamma$-transform of (A, ι). Hence there exists an isomorphism η of (A_2, ι_2) onto (A, ι') such that $\eta\lambda_{\mathfrak{b}}\lambda_{\mathfrak{a}} = \iota(\gamma)$. It follows that

$$\nu(\lambda_{\mathfrak{b}})\nu(\lambda_{\mathfrak{a}}) = \nu(\iota(\gamma)).$$

By Proposition 2, we have $\nu(\iota(\gamma)) = N(\gamma)^m = N(\mathfrak{a})^m N(\mathfrak{b})^m$, so that

$$\nu(\lambda_{\mathfrak{a}})\nu(\lambda_{\mathfrak{b}}) = N(\mathfrak{a})^m N(\mathfrak{b})^m. \tag{2}$$

Since $\nu(\lambda_{\mathfrak{a}})$ is prime to $N(\mathfrak{b})$, $\nu(\lambda_{\mathfrak{a}})$ must divide $N(\mathfrak{a})^m$. Applying this result to $\mathfrak{b}$, we see that $\nu(\lambda_{\mathfrak{b}})$ divides $N(\mathfrak{b})^m$. Therefore the equality (2) shows $\nu(\lambda_{\mathfrak{a}}) = N(\mathfrak{a})^m$.

PROPOSITION 11. *Let $\mathfrak{o}$ be the order of (A, ι); let $\mathfrak{a}$ and $\mathfrak{b}$ be integral left $\mathfrak{o}$-ideals. Let $(A_1, \iota_1; \lambda_{\mathfrak{a}})$ and $(A_2, \iota_2; \lambda_{\mathfrak{b}})$ be respectively an $\mathfrak{a}$-transform and a $\mathfrak{b}$-transform of (A, ι). Then the following three conditions are equivalent to each other.*

1) $\mathfrak{a} \supset \mathfrak{b}$.

2) *There exist a field of definition k for (A, ι), (A_1, ι_1), (A_2, ι_2), $\lambda_{\mathfrak{a}}$, $\lambda_{\mathfrak{b}}$ and a generic point x of A over k such that $k(\lambda_{\mathfrak{a}}x) \supset k(\lambda_{\mathfrak{b}}x)$.*

3) *There exists a homomorphism μ of (A_1, ι_1) onto (A_2, ι_2) such that $\mu\lambda_{\mathfrak{a}} = \lambda_{\mathfrak{b}}$.*

PROOF. It is easy to see that $1) \Rightarrow 2) \Longleftrightarrow 3)$. Suppose that $\mathfrak{a} \not\supset \mathfrak{b}$; and put $\mathfrak{c} = \mathfrak{a}+\mathfrak{b}$. We have then $\mathfrak{c} \supsetneqq \mathfrak{a}$, so that $N(\mathfrak{c}) < N(\mathfrak{a})$. Hence, if $\lambda_{\mathfrak{c}}$ is a $\mathfrak{c}$-multiplication of (A, ι), we have $k(\lambda_{\mathfrak{c}}x) \supsetneqq k(\lambda_{\mathfrak{a}}x)$ by virtue of Proposition 10. On the other hand, as we have $\mathfrak{c} = \mathfrak{a}+\mathfrak{b}$, the field $k(\lambda_{\mathfrak{c}}x)$ is the composite of $k(\lambda_{\mathfrak{a}}x)$ and $k(\lambda_{\mathfrak{b}}x)$; so we must have $k(\lambda_{\mathfrak{a}}x) \not\supset k(\lambda_{\mathfrak{b}}x)$. This proves $2) \Rightarrow 1)$.

PROPOSITION 12. *Notations being as in Proposition* 11, *let g be a positive integer such that $g\mathfrak{a}^{-1}\mathfrak{b}$ is integral. Then, there exists a $(g\mathfrak{a}^{-1}\mathfrak{b})$-multiplication μ of (A_1, ι_1) onto (A_2, ι_2) such that $\mu\lambda_{\mathfrak{a}} = g\lambda_{\mathfrak{b}}$.*

PROOF. Put $\mathfrak{c} = g\mathfrak{a}^{-1}\mathfrak{b}$. Let $(A_3, \iota_3; \lambda_{\mathfrak{c}})$ be a $\mathfrak{c}$-transform of (A_1, ι_1). Then, as both (A_2, ι_2) and (A_3, ι_3) are $g\mathfrak{b}$-transforms of (A, ι), we obtain an isomorphism η of (A_3, ι_3) onto (A_2, ι_2) such that $\eta\lambda_{\mathfrak{c}}\lambda_{\mathfrak{a}} = g\lambda_{\mathfrak{b}}$. We see easily that $\eta\lambda_{\mathfrak{c}}$ is a $\mathfrak{c}$-multiplication; this proves our proposition.

Now we impose the following condition on our abelian varieties of type $(\mathfrak{R})$.

(C) *If $\mathfrak{Z}$ denotes the center of $\mathfrak{R}$, the commutor of $\iota(\mathfrak{Z})$ in $\mathscr{A}_0(A)$ is contained in $\iota(\mathfrak{R})$.*

This is trivially satisfied if $\iota(\mathfrak{R}) = \mathscr{A}_0(A)$. If the index of (A, ι) is 1, (A, ι) satisfies (C). In fact, the degrees f and d being as in (1), $\mathfrak{R}$ contains a subfield $\mathfrak{F}$ such that $[\mathfrak{F}:\mathfrak{Z}] = f$. If (A, ι) is of index 1, we have $2\dim(A) = [\mathfrak{F}:Q]$. By Proposition 3, $\mathscr{A}_0(A)$ must be simple; and if we denote by $\mathfrak{K}$ the center of $\mathscr{A}_0(A)$, $\iota(\mathfrak{F})$ contains $\mathfrak{K}$. It follows that $\iota(\mathfrak{Z})$ contains $\mathfrak{K}$. As we have $[\mathscr{A}_0(A):\iota(\mathfrak{F})] = [\iota(\mathfrak{F}):\mathfrak{K}]$ and $[\mathfrak{R}:\mathfrak{F}] = [\mathfrak{F}:\mathfrak{Z}]$, we get $[\mathscr{A}_0(A):\iota(\mathfrak{R})] = [\iota(\mathfrak{Z}):\mathfrak{K}]$. Let $\mathfrak{L}$ be the commutor of $\iota(\mathfrak{Z})$ in $\mathscr{A}_0(A)$; then $\mathfrak{L}$ contains $\iota(\mathfrak{R})$; and by a property of central simple algebra we have $[\mathscr{A}_0(A):\mathfrak{L}] = [\iota(\mathfrak{Z}):\mathfrak{K}]$. This shows $\mathfrak{L} = \iota(\mathfrak{R})$. Hence (A, ι) satisfies (C).

We note that if (A, ι) satisfies (C), every $\mathfrak{a}$-transform of (A, ι), for an integral lattice $\mathfrak{a}$, satisfies (C).

PROPOSITION 13. *Suppose that* (A, ι) *satisfies* (C). *Let* $\mathfrak{o}$ *be the order of* (A, ι) *and* $\mathfrak{a}$ *an integral left* $\mathfrak{o}$*-ideal; let* $(A_1, \iota_1; \lambda_{\mathfrak{a}})$ *be an* $\mathfrak{a}$*-transform of* (A, ι). *Denote by* ι^* *and* ι_1^* *the restrictions of* ι *and* ι_1 *to the center* $\mathfrak{Z}$ *of* $\mathfrak{R}$. *Then, every homomorphism of* (A, ι^*) *onto* (A_1, ι_1^*) *is a* $\mathfrak{c}$*-multiplication of* (A, ι) *for an integral left* $\mathfrak{o}$*-ideal* $\mathfrak{c}$. *Moreover, the set of all homomorphisms of* (A, ι^*) *into* (A_1, ι_1^*) *coincides with* $\lambda_{\mathfrak{a}}\cdot\iota(\mathfrak{a}^{-1})$.

PROOF. Take a positive integer g such that $g\mathfrak{a}^{-1}$ is integral and put $\mathfrak{b} = g\mathfrak{a}^{-1}$. By Proposition 12, there exists a $\mathfrak{b}$-multiplication $\lambda_{\mathfrak{b}}$ of (A_1, ι_1) onto (A, ι) such that $\lambda_{\mathfrak{b}}\lambda_{\mathfrak{a}} = g1_A$; we fix $\mathfrak{b}$ and $\lambda_{\mathfrak{b}}$. Let μ be a homomorphism of (A, ι^*) into (A_1, ι_1^*). Then, $\mu\lambda_{\mathfrak{b}}$ is an endomorphism of (A_1, ι_1^*). On account of (C), $\mu\lambda_{\mathfrak{b}}$ must be of the form $\iota_1(\gamma)$ for an element $\gamma \in \mathfrak{o}_1$, where $\mathfrak{o}_1$ denotes the left order of $\mathfrak{b}$. Applying Proposition 11 to the ideals $\mathfrak{b}$ and $\mathfrak{o}_1\gamma+\mathfrak{b}$, we see that $\gamma \in \mathfrak{b}$. Now suppose that μ is an isogeny; then γ must be a regular element of $\mathfrak{R}$. Put $\mathfrak{c} = \mathfrak{b}^{-1}\gamma$; let $(A_2, \iota_2; \lambda_{\mathfrak{c}})$ be a $\mathfrak{c}$-transform of (A, ι). By the same argument as in the proof of Proposition 10, we obtain an isomorphism η of A_2 onto A_1 such that $\eta\lambda_{\mathfrak{c}}\lambda_{\mathfrak{b}} = \iota_1(\gamma) = \mu\lambda_{\mathfrak{b}}$. As $\lambda_{\mathfrak{b}}$ is an isogeny, we have $\eta\lambda_{\mathfrak{c}} = \mu$. It follows that μ is a $\mathfrak{c}$-multiplication; this proves the first assertion. Now let $\mathfrak{H}$ denote the module of homomorphisms of (A, ι^*) into (A_1, ι_1^*). We have proved above $\mathfrak{H}\cdot\lambda_{\mathfrak{b}} \subset \iota_1(\mathfrak{b})$. Let β be an element of $\mathfrak{b}$. If k is a field of definition for (A, ι), (A_1, ι_1) and $\lambda_{\mathfrak{b}}$, and x is a generic point of A_1 over k, we have $k(\lambda_{\mathfrak{b}}x) \supset k(\iota_1(\beta)x)$. Hence there exists a homomorphism λ of A into A_1 such that $\lambda\lambda_{\mathfrak{b}} = \iota_1(\beta)$. We see easily that λ commutes with the operation of $\mathfrak{Z}$. This shows $\mathfrak{H}\cdot\lambda_{\mathfrak{b}} = \iota_1(\mathfrak{b})$. Multiplying by $\lambda_{\mathfrak{a}}$ this relation, we get $\mathfrak{H}\cdot g1_A = \iota_1(\mathfrak{b})\lambda_{\mathfrak{a}} = g\cdot\lambda_{\mathfrak{a}}\cdot\iota(\mathfrak{a}^{-1})$, so that $\mathfrak{H} = \lambda_{\mathfrak{a}}\cdot\iota(\mathfrak{a}^{-1})$; this completes our proof.

PROPOSITION 14. *Notations and assumptions being as in Proposition* 13, *let* $\mathfrak{b}$ *be an integral left* $\mathfrak{o}$*-ideal and* $(A_2, \iota_2; \lambda_{\mathfrak{b}})$ *be a* $\mathfrak{b}$*-transform of* (A, ι); *denote by* ι_2^* *the restriction of* ι_2 *to* $\mathfrak{Z}$. *Then,* (A_1, ι_1^*) *is isomorphic to* (A_2, ι_2^*) *if and only if there exists a regular element* γ *of* $\mathfrak{R}$ *such that* $\mathfrak{a} = \mathfrak{b}\gamma$.

PROOF. Let $\mathfrak{H}_i$ denote, for $i = 1, 2$, the set of all homomorphisms of (A, ι^*) into (A_i, ι_i^*). The $\mathfrak{H}_i$ are considered as right $\mathfrak{o}$-modules. If (A_1, ι_1^*) is isomorphic to (A_2, ι_2^*), $\mathfrak{H}_1$ must be $\mathfrak{o}$-isomorphic to $\mathfrak{H}_2$. By Proposition 13, this amounts to saying that $\mathfrak{a}^{-1}$ is isomorphic to $\mathfrak{b}^{-1}$ as right $\mathfrak{o}$-modules; this implies that $\mathfrak{a}$ and $\mathfrak{b}$ are isomorphic as left $\mathfrak{o}$-modules. This proves the "only if" part of our proposition. Conversely, suppose that there exists a regular element γ in $\mathfrak{R}$ such that $\mathfrak{a}\gamma = \mathfrak{b}$. Take a positive integer g such that $g\gamma$ is contained in the right order of $\mathfrak{a}$. Then, by the same argument as in the proof of Proposition 10, we can find an isomorphism η of A_1 onto A_2 such that $\eta\iota_1(g\gamma)\lambda_{\mathfrak{a}} = g\lambda_{\mathfrak{b}}$. It is easy to see that η commutes with the operation of $\mathfrak{Z}$. This proves the "if" part.

7. 3. Now we consider the case where $\mathfrak{R}$ is an algebraic number field F. In this case the condition (C) is reduced to the following form.

(C′) *The commutor of* $\iota(F)$ *in* $\mathscr{A}_0(A)$ *is* $\iota(F)$ *itself.*

This is satisfied if $\iota(F) = \mathscr{A}_0(A)$ or if (A, ι) is of index 1.

Assuming the condition (C′) to be satisfied, we give the following definition: c being an ideal-class of F, we call (A', ι') a c-transform of (A, ι) if (A', ι') is an $\mathfrak{a}$-*transform* of (A, ι) for some integral ideal $\mathfrak{a}$ in c; if that is so, for *every* integral ideal $\mathfrak{c}$ in c, (A', ι') is a $\mathfrak{c}$-transform of (A, ι). Let c and d be ideal-classes of F; let $(A_{\mathfrak{b}}, \iota_{\mathfrak{b}})$ and (A_d, ι_d) be respectively a c-transform and a d-transform of (A, ι). Then, by Proposition 12, (A_d, ι_d) is a $c^{-1}d$-transform of (A_c, ι_c). Furthermore, by Proposition 14, (A_c, ι_c) and (A_d, ι_d) are isomorphic if and only if $c = d$.

7. 4. Let us consider the case of characteristic 0. $(F; \{\varphi_i\})$ being a CM-type, let (A, ι) be an abelian variety of type $(F; \{\varphi_i\})$; by our definition, (A, ι) is of index 1. By Theorem 2, (A, ι) is represented by a complex torus $\boldsymbol{C}^n/D(\mathfrak{a})$ for a free $\boldsymbol{Z}$-submodule $\mathfrak{a}$ of rank $2n$ in F, notations being as in that theorem. We observe that (A, ι) is principal if and only if $\mathfrak{a}$ is an ideal (not necessarily integral) of F. It is easy to see that, for every ideal-class c of F, a c-transform of (A, ι) is also of type $(F; \{\varphi_i\})$.

PROPOSITION 15. *Notations being as in Theorem 2, let $\mathfrak{a}$ and $\mathfrak{b}$ be two ideals of F; let (A_1, ι_1) and (A_2, ι_2) be abelian varieties of type $(F; \{\varphi_i\})$, respectively represented by the complex tori $\boldsymbol{C}^n/D(\mathfrak{a})$ and $\boldsymbol{C}^n/D(\mathfrak{b})$. If γ is an element of $\mathfrak{a}^{-1}\mathfrak{b}$ other than 0, the diagonal matrix $S(\gamma)$ with the diagonal elements $\gamma^{\varphi_1}, \cdots, \gamma^{\varphi_n}$ represents a $(\gamma\mathfrak{b}^{-1}\mathfrak{a})$-multiplication of (A_1, ι_1) into (A_2, ι_2); conversely, every homomorphism of (A_1, ι_1) onto (A_2, ι_2) corresponds to some $S(\gamma)$ such that $\gamma \in \mathfrak{a}^{-1}\mathfrak{b}$.*

PROOF. If $\gamma \in \mathfrak{a}^{-1}\mathfrak{b}$, we have $S(\gamma)D(\mathfrak{a}) \subset D(\mathfrak{b})$, so that $S(\gamma)$ gives a homomorphism of $\boldsymbol{C}^n/D(\mathfrak{a})$ into $\boldsymbol{C}^n/D(\mathfrak{b})$. Hence $S(\gamma)$ represents a homomorphism λ of A_1 into A_2. Since λ commutes with the operation of F, λ is a homomorphism of (A_1, ι_1) into (A_2, ι_2). Suppose that $\gamma \neq 0$. We see easily that the kernel $\mathfrak{g}(\lambda)$ of λ corresponds to $D(\gamma^{-1}\mathfrak{b})/D(\mathfrak{a})$ and

$$D(\gamma^{-1}\mathfrak{b}) = \{u \mid u \in \boldsymbol{C}^n, \ S(\alpha)u \in D(\mathfrak{a}) \text{ for every } \alpha \in \gamma\mathfrak{a}\mathfrak{b}^{-1}\}.$$

This implies $\mathfrak{g}(\lambda) = \mathfrak{g}(\gamma\mathfrak{a}\mathfrak{b}^{-1}, A_1)$. By Proposition 8, it follows that λ is a $(\gamma\mathfrak{a}\mathfrak{b}^{-1})$-multiplication of (A_1, ι_1) onto (A_2, ι_2). The last assertion of our proposition follows from this and Proposition 13.

PROPOSITION 16. *Let (A, ι) and (A', ι') be two abelian varieties which are principal and of the same CM-type $(F; \{\varphi_i\})$. Then (A', ι') is a c-transform of (A, ι) for an ideal-class c of F.*

This is an easy consequence of Proposition 15. Furthermore, on account of Proposition 14, we obtain

PROPOSITION 17. *Let $(F; \{\varphi_i\})$ be a CM-type and h the number of ideal-classes of F. Then, there are exactly h abelian varieties of type $(F; \{\varphi_i\})$, which are principal and not isomorphic to each other.*

7. 5. Ideal-section points. Now coming back to the case of arbitrary characteristic, denote by $\mathfrak{o}$ the ring of integers in the number field F; let (A, ι) be an abelian variety of type (F), which is principal. Let $\mathfrak{a}$ be an ideal of $\mathfrak{o}$ and $(A', \iota'; \lambda_{\mathfrak{a}})$ an $\mathfrak{a}$-transform of (A, ι). We observe that $\nu_i(\lambda_{\mathfrak{a}})$ and $\nu_s(\lambda_{\mathfrak{a}})$ depends only upon (A, ι) and $\mathfrak{a}$, and not on the choice of $(A', \iota'; \lambda_{\mathfrak{a}})$; so we denote them by $N_i(\mathfrak{a}, A)$ and $N_s(\mathfrak{a}, A)$. Let c be an ideal-class of F and (A_c, ι_c) a c-transform of

(A, ι). Then we have

$$N_i(\mathfrak{a}, A) = N_i(\mathfrak{a}, A_c), \; N_s(\mathfrak{a}, A) = N_s(\mathfrak{a}, A_c).$$

In fact, let $(A_c', \iota_c'; \lambda_{\mathfrak{a}}')$ be an $\mathfrak{a}$-transform of (A_c, ι_c). Take an integral ideal $\mathfrak{b}$ in the class c, prime to the characteristic p; let $\lambda_{\mathfrak{b}}$ and $\lambda_{\mathfrak{b}}'$ be respectively $\mathfrak{b}$-multiplications of (A, ι) onto (A_c, ι_c) and of (A', ι') onto (A_c', ι_c'). Then both $\lambda_{\mathfrak{b}}'\lambda_{\mathfrak{a}}$ and $\lambda_{\mathfrak{a}}'\lambda_{\mathfrak{b}}$ are $\mathfrak{ab}$-multiplications of (A, ι) onto (A_c', ι_c'); so there exists an automorphism η of (A_c', ι_c') such that $\lambda_{\mathfrak{b}}'\lambda_{\mathfrak{a}} = \eta\lambda_{\mathfrak{a}}'\lambda_{\mathfrak{b}}$. We have then $\nu_i(\lambda_{\mathfrak{b}}')\nu_i(\lambda_{\mathfrak{a}}) = \nu_i(\lambda_{\mathfrak{a}}')\nu_i(\lambda_{\mathfrak{b}})$. By our assumption that $\mathfrak{b}$ is prime to p, the degree $\nu(\lambda_{\mathfrak{b}}) = \nu(\lambda_{\mathfrak{b}}') = N(\mathfrak{b})^m$ is prime to p, where m denotes the index of (A, ι); hence we have $\nu_i(\lambda_{\mathfrak{b}}) = \nu_i(\lambda_{\mathfrak{b}}') = 1$, so that $\nu_i(\lambda_{\mathfrak{a}}) = \nu_i(\lambda_{\mathfrak{a}}')$. This proves the above relations.

Now let $\mathcal{S} = \{(A, \iota)\}$ be a system of abelian varieties of type (F), whose members are transforms of each other by ideals of $\mathfrak{o}$. Then, $N_i(\mathfrak{a}, A)$ and $N_s(\mathfrak{a}, A)$ for $(A, \iota) \in \mathcal{S}$ does not depend on the choice of (A, ι); so we denote them by $N_i(\mathfrak{a}, \mathcal{S})$ and $N_s(\mathfrak{a}, \mathcal{S})$ or simply by $N_i(\mathfrak{a})$ and $N_s(\mathfrak{a})$ when we fix our attention to a given system $\mathcal{S}$. We can easily verify

$$N_i(\mathfrak{a})N_s(\mathfrak{a}) = N(\mathfrak{a})^m,$$

m denoting the index of the members of $\mathcal{S}$, and

$$N_i(\mathfrak{ab}) = N_i(\mathfrak{a})N_i(\mathfrak{b}), \; N_s(\mathfrak{ab}) = N_s(\mathfrak{a})N_s(\mathfrak{b}).$$

If $\lambda_{\mathfrak{a}}$ is an $\mathfrak{a}$-multiplication of (A, ι), $\nu_s(\lambda_{\mathfrak{a}})$ is the order of the kernel $\mathfrak{g}(\lambda_{\mathfrak{a}})$ of $\lambda_{\mathfrak{a}}$. As we have $\mathfrak{g}(\lambda_{\mathfrak{a}}) = \mathfrak{g}(\mathfrak{a}, A)$, this shows that $N_s(\mathfrak{a})$ is the order of $\mathfrak{g}(\mathfrak{a}, A)$; in particular, if $\mathfrak{a}$ is prime to the characteristic of the fields of definition for A, we get $N_i(\mathfrak{a}) = 1$, and hence $\mathfrak{g}(\mathfrak{a}, A)$ is of order $N(\mathfrak{a})^m$.

PROPOSITION 18. *Let* $\mathfrak{a}$ *and* $\mathfrak{b}$ *be ideals of* $\mathfrak{o}$. *Then we have*

$$\mathfrak{g}(\mathfrak{a}+\mathfrak{b}, A) = \mathfrak{g}(\mathfrak{a}, A) \cap \mathfrak{g}(\mathfrak{b}, A),$$

$$\mathfrak{g}(\mathfrak{a} \cap \mathfrak{b}, A) = \mathfrak{g}(\mathfrak{a}, A) + \mathfrak{g}(\mathfrak{b}, A).$$

Moreover, if $\mathfrak{a}$ *is prime to* $\mathfrak{b}$, $\mathfrak{g}(\mathfrak{ab}, A)$ *is the direct sum of* $\mathfrak{g}(\mathfrak{a}, A)$ *and* $\mathfrak{g}(\mathfrak{b}, A)$.

PROOF. The first equality is obvious. We see easily that

$$\mathfrak{g}(\mathfrak{a} \cap \mathfrak{b}, A) \supset \mathfrak{g}(\mathfrak{a}, A)+\mathfrak{g}(\mathfrak{b}, A).$$

By an elementary theorem of group-theory, the order of $\mathfrak{g}(\mathfrak{a}, A)+\mathfrak{g}(\mathfrak{b}, A)$ is equal to

$$[\mathfrak{g}(\mathfrak{a}, A):\{0\}]\,[\mathfrak{g}(\mathfrak{b}, A):\{0\}]/[\mathfrak{g}(\mathfrak{a}, A) \cap \mathfrak{g}(\mathfrak{b}, A):\{0\}].$$

As we have $\mathfrak{g}(\mathfrak{a}+\mathfrak{b}, A) = \mathfrak{g}(\mathfrak{a}, A) \cap \mathfrak{g}(\mathfrak{b}, A)$, this number is equal to $N_s(\mathfrak{a})N_s(\mathfrak{b})N_s(\mathfrak{a}+\mathfrak{b})^{-1}$. On the other hand, by means of the relation $\mathfrak{a}\mathfrak{b} = (\mathfrak{a} \cap \mathfrak{b})(\mathfrak{a}+\mathfrak{b})$, we have $N_s(\mathfrak{a})N_s(\mathfrak{b})N_s(\mathfrak{a}+\mathfrak{b})^{-1} = N_s(\mathfrak{a} \cap \mathfrak{b})$. Hence both sides of the above inclusion-relation have the same order; this proves the second equality. If $\mathfrak{a}$ is prime to $\mathfrak{b}$, we have $\mathfrak{a} \cap \mathfrak{b} = \mathfrak{a}\mathfrak{b}$ and $\mathfrak{a}+\mathfrak{b} = \mathfrak{o}$, so that

$$\mathfrak{g}(\mathfrak{a}, A) \cap \mathfrak{g}(\mathfrak{b}, A) = \mathfrak{g}(\mathfrak{o}, A) = \{0\}.$$

This implies the last assertion.

PROPOSITION 19. *Let $\mathfrak{p}$ be a prime ideal of $\mathfrak{o}$. Then, $N_i(\mathfrak{p})$ and $N_s(\mathfrak{p})$ are powers of $N(\mathfrak{p})$. In particular, if (A, ι) is of index* 1, *we have $N_i(\mathfrak{p}) = 1$ or $N_s(\mathfrak{p}) = 1$.*

PROOF. We can easily verify that $\mathfrak{g}(\mathfrak{p}, A)$ is invariant under the operation of $\mathfrak{o}$; moreover, $\mathfrak{g}(\mathfrak{p}, A)$ is considered as an $(\mathfrak{o}/\mathfrak{p})$-module. Since $\mathfrak{p}$ is a prime ideal, $\mathfrak{o}/\mathfrak{p}$ is a finite field with $N(\mathfrak{p})$ elements; and $\mathfrak{g}(\mathfrak{p}, A)$ is a vector space over the field $\mathfrak{o}/\mathfrak{p}$. This proves the first assertion. If (A, ι) is of index 1, we must have $N_i(\mathfrak{p})N_s(\mathfrak{p}) = N(\mathfrak{p})$; this proves the second assertion.

As an example, we shall determine $N_i(\mathfrak{a})$ in the case of dimension 1. Suppose that $[F:Q] = 2$ and (A, ι) is of dimension 1; then the index of (A, ι) is 1. Let k be a field of definition for (A, ι). If the characteristic of k is 0, we have $N_i(\mathfrak{a}) = 1$ for every $\mathfrak{a}$; so there is no problem. Suppose that k is of characteristic $p \neq 0$. If $\mathfrak{a}$ is prime to p, we have $N_i(\mathfrak{a}) = 1$; so we have only to consider $N_i(\mathfrak{p})$ for the prime ideals $\mathfrak{p}$ dividing p. Since F is of degree 2, there can occur three cases:

i) $(p) = \mathfrak{p}_1\mathfrak{p}_2,\ \mathfrak{p}_1 \neq \mathfrak{p}_2,$

ii) $(p) = \mathfrak{p}$,

iii) $(p) = \mathfrak{p}^2$,

where $\mathfrak{p}_1$, $\mathfrak{p}_2$ and $\mathfrak{p}$ denote prime ideals of F. By Proposition 7 of § 2, we have $N_i((p)) = \nu_i(p1_A) = p$ or p^2. Hence, in the cases ii) and iii), we must have $N_i(\mathfrak{p}) > 1$; so by Proposition 19, we have $N_i(\mathfrak{p}) = N(\mathfrak{p})$, $\nu_i(p1_A) = p^2$. By the same reason, in the case i), we can not have $N_i(\mathfrak{p}_1) = N_i(\mathfrak{p}_2) = 1$. Assume that $N_i(\mathfrak{p}_1) = N_i(\mathfrak{p}_2) = p$. Let λ_1 and λ_2 be respectively a $\mathfrak{p}_1$-multiplication and a $\mathfrak{p}_2$-multiplication of (A, ι). Then, as A is of dimension 1, if x is a generic point of A over k, the fields $k(\lambda_1 x)$ and $k(\lambda_2 x)$ must be contained in $k(x^p)$. On the other hand, as we have $\mathfrak{o} = \mathfrak{p}_1 + \mathfrak{p}_2$, the field $k(x)$ is the composite of $k(\lambda_1 x)$ and $k(\lambda_2 x)$; we have thus arrived at a contradiction. Hence we must have $N_i(\mathfrak{p}_\alpha) = 1$ for one of $\mathfrak{p}_1$ and $\mathfrak{p}_2$, say $\mathfrak{p}_1$. Then, we have $N_i(\mathfrak{p}_2) = p$ and hence $\nu_i(p1_A) = p$. This completes the analysis of the case i).

Returning to the general case, we call a point t of $\mathfrak{g}(\mathfrak{a}, A)$ a *proper* $\mathfrak{a}$*-section point* on A if $\iota(\alpha)t = 0$ implies $\alpha \in \mathfrak{a}$.

PROPOSITION 20. *(A, ι) being principal and of index* 1, *let $\mathfrak{m}$ be an ideal of $\mathfrak{o}$ and t a proper $\mathfrak{m}$-section point of A. Then, for every point t' of $\mathfrak{g}(\mathfrak{m})$, there exists an element α of $\mathfrak{o}$ such that $t' = \iota(\alpha)t$; and the mapping $\alpha \rightarrow \iota(\alpha)t$ gives an $\mathfrak{o}$-isomorphism of $\mathfrak{o}/\mathfrak{m}$ onto $\mathfrak{g}(\mathfrak{m})$. The point $\iota(\alpha)t$ is a proper $\mathfrak{m}$-section point on A if and only if α is prime to $\mathfrak{m}$.*

PROOF. It is easy to see that the mapping $\alpha \rightarrow \iota(\alpha)t$ is an $\mathfrak{o}$-homomorphism of $\mathfrak{o}$ into $\mathfrak{g}(\mathfrak{m})$; as t is a proper $\mathfrak{m}$-section point, the kernel of this homomorphism is $\mathfrak{m}$. Hence the module $\mathfrak{o}/\mathfrak{m}$ is isomorphic to a submodule of $\mathfrak{g}(\mathfrak{m})$. On the other hand, $\mathfrak{o}/\mathfrak{m}$ is of order $N(\mathfrak{m})$ and the order of $\mathfrak{g}(\mathfrak{m})$ is $N_s(\mathfrak{m})$, which is not greater than $N(\mathfrak{m})$. It follows that the mapping $\alpha \rightarrow \iota(\alpha)t$ is an isomorphism of $\mathfrak{o}/\mathfrak{m}$ onto $\mathfrak{g}(\mathfrak{m})$; all the assertions easily follow from this fact.

PROPOSITION 21. *(A, ι) and $\mathfrak{m}$ being as in Proposition* 20, *there exists a proper $\mathfrak{m}$-section point on A if and only if $N_i(\mathfrak{m}, A) = 1$. In particular, if $\mathfrak{m}$ is prime to the characteristic of the fields of definition for A, there exists a proper $\mathfrak{m}$-section point.*

PROOF. By Proposition 20, if there exists a proper $\mathfrak{m}$-section point, then the order of $\mathfrak{g}(\mathfrak{m})$ is equal to $N(\mathfrak{m})$, so that $N_i(\mathfrak{m}) = 1$. Conversely, suppose that $N_i(\mathfrak{m}) = 1$. Let $\mathfrak{m} = \mathfrak{p}_1^{e_1} \cdots \mathfrak{p}_r^{e_r}$ be the factorization of $\mathfrak{m}$ into prime ideals $\mathfrak{p}_u$. By Proposition 18, $\mathfrak{g}(\mathfrak{m})$ is the direct sum of the $\mathfrak{g}(\mathfrak{p}_u^{e_u})$. We have clearly $N_i(\mathfrak{p}_u) = 1$, and hence $\mathfrak{g}(\mathfrak{p}_u^f)$ is of order $N(\mathfrak{p}_u^f)$. Therefore, we can find a point t_u in $\mathfrak{g}(\mathfrak{p}_u^{e_u})$ which is not contained in $\mathfrak{g}(\mathfrak{p}_u^{e_u-1})$. Let α be an element of $\mathfrak{o}$ such that $\iota(\alpha)t_u = 0$. Put $\alpha\mathfrak{o}+\mathfrak{p}_u^{e_u} = \mathfrak{p}_u^f$; then we see that t_u is contained in $\mathfrak{g}(\mathfrak{p}_u^f)$, so that $e_u = f$; this implies that α is contained in $\mathfrak{p}_u^{e_u}$. Hence t_u is a proper $\mathfrak{p}_u^{e_u}$-section point. Put $t = t_1 + \cdots + t_r$. Then we can easily verify that t is a proper $\mathfrak{m}$-section point. This proves our proposition.

PROPOSITION 22. *(A, ι) being principal and of index 1, let $\mathfrak{h}$ be a finite subgroup of A, such that $\iota(\mathfrak{o})\mathfrak{h} \subset \mathfrak{h}$. Then, there exists an ideal $\mathfrak{a}$ of $\mathfrak{o}$ such that $\mathfrak{h} = \mathfrak{g}(\mathfrak{a}, A)$.*

PROOF. Let $\{t_1, \cdots, t_h\}$ be a system of generators of $\mathfrak{h}$ over $\iota(\mathfrak{o})$. Let $\mathfrak{a}_u$, for each u, denote the set of elements $\alpha \in \mathfrak{o}$ such that $\iota(\alpha)t_u = 0$. Then, $\mathfrak{a}_u$ is an ideal of $\mathfrak{o}$ and t_u is a proper $\mathfrak{a}_u$-section point. Hence, by Proposition 20, we have $\mathfrak{g}(\mathfrak{a}_u) = \iota(\mathfrak{o})t_u$. Putting $\mathfrak{a} = \mathfrak{a}_1 \cap \cdots \cap \mathfrak{a}_h$, we obtain, by Proposition 18,

$$\mathfrak{g}(\mathfrak{a}) = \mathfrak{g}(\mathfrak{a}_1) + \cdots + \mathfrak{g}(\mathfrak{a}_h) = \iota(\mathfrak{o})t_1 + \cdots + \iota(\mathfrak{o})t_h = \mathfrak{h}.$$

This proves our proposition.

PROPOSITION 23. *Let (A, ι) and $(A' \iota')$ be abelian varieties of type (F), which are principal and of index 1. Let λ be a homomorphism of (A, ι) onto (A', ι') such that $\nu_i(\lambda) = 1$. Then, λ is an $\mathfrak{a}$-multiplication of (A, ι) onto (A', ι') for an ideal $\mathfrak{a}$ of $\mathfrak{o}$.*

PROOF. Put $\mathfrak{h} = \mathfrak{g}(\lambda)$ and apply the argument of the proof of Proposition 22 to this case. We obtain then $\mathfrak{g}(\lambda) = \mathfrak{g}(\mathfrak{a}, A)$; moreover by Proposition 21, we have $N_i(\mathfrak{a}_u) = 1$ for each u, so that $N_i(\mathfrak{a}) = 1$. Hence, if $(A_1, \iota_1; \lambda_{\mathfrak{a}})$ is an $\mathfrak{a}$-transform of (A, ι), we have $\nu_i(\lambda_{\mathfrak{a}}) = 1$. The equality $\mathfrak{g}(\lambda) = \mathfrak{g}(\mathfrak{a}, A)$ shows that λ and $\lambda_{\mathfrak{a}}$ have the same kernel. It follows from this and the relation $\nu_i(\lambda) = \nu_i(\lambda_{\mathfrak{a}}) = 1$ that there exists an isomorphism η of A' onto A_1 such that $\eta\lambda = \lambda_{\mathfrak{a}}$. Since both λ and $\lambda_{\mathfrak{a}}$ are $\mathfrak{o}$-homomorphisms, η is an $\mathfrak{o}$-isomorphism. This proves that $(A', \iota'; \lambda)$ is an $\mathfrak{a}$-transform of (A, ι).

PROPOSITION 24. *Let $\mathfrak{m}$ be an ideal of $\mathfrak{o}$ and c an ideal-class of F. Assuming (A, ι) to be principal and of index 1, let (A', ι') be a c-transform of (A, ι) and t a proper $\mathfrak{m}$-section point on A. Then, for every t' in $\mathfrak{g}(\mathfrak{m}, A')$, there exist an ideal $\mathfrak{a}$ in c and an $\mathfrak{a}$-multiplication $\lambda_{\mathfrak{a}}$ of (A, ι) onto (A', ι') such that $t' = \lambda_{\mathfrak{a}} t$; and $\lambda_{\mathfrak{a}} t$ is a proper $(\mathfrak{a}, \mathfrak{m})^{-1}\mathfrak{m}$-section point of A'. In particular, $\lambda_{\mathfrak{a}} t$ is a proper $\mathfrak{m}$-section point of A' if and only if $\mathfrak{a}$ is prime to $\mathfrak{m}$; and $\lambda_{\mathfrak{a}} t = 0$ if and only if $\mathfrak{a} \subset \mathfrak{m}$.*

PROOF. Let $\mathfrak{a}$ be an ideal in c and $\lambda_{\mathfrak{a}}$ an $\mathfrak{a}$-multiplication of (A, ι) onto (A', ι'). We first prove that $\lambda_{\mathfrak{a}} t$ is a proper $(\mathfrak{a}, \mathfrak{m})^{-1}\mathfrak{m}$-section point on A'. Take an integral ideal $\mathfrak{b}$ in the class c^{-1}, prime to $\mathfrak{m}$, and a $\mathfrak{b}$-multiplication $\lambda_{\mathfrak{b}}$ of (A', ι') onto (A, ι). Then there exists an element γ of $\mathfrak{o}$ such that $\lambda_{\mathfrak{b}}\lambda_{\mathfrak{a}} = \iota(\gamma)$ and $\mathfrak{a}\mathfrak{b} = \gamma\mathfrak{o}$. If we have $\iota'(\mu)\lambda_{\mathfrak{a}} t = 0$ for an element $\mu \in \mathfrak{o}$, we have $\iota(\mu\gamma)t = 0$, so that $\mu\gamma \in \mathfrak{m}$, namely $\mu\mathfrak{a}\mathfrak{b} \subset \mathfrak{m}$. As $\mathfrak{b}$ is prime to $\mathfrak{m}$, we get $\mu\mathfrak{a} \subset \mathfrak{m}$; this shows that $\mu \in (\mathfrak{a}, \mathfrak{m})^{-1}\mathfrak{m}$. Conversely, if we have $\mu \in (\mathfrak{a}, \mathfrak{m})^{-1}\mathfrak{m}$, then $\mu\mathfrak{a} \subset \mathfrak{m}$ and hence $\mu\gamma \in \mu\mathfrak{a}\mathfrak{b} \subset \mathfrak{m}$, so that $\lambda_{\mathfrak{b}}\iota'(\mu)\lambda_{\mathfrak{a}} t = 0$; this shows that $\iota'(\mu)\lambda_{\mathfrak{a}} t \in \mathfrak{g}(\mathfrak{b}, A')$. On the other hand, as t is contained in $\mathfrak{g}(\mathfrak{m}, A)$, we have clearly $\iota'(\mu)\lambda_{\mathfrak{a}} t \in \mathfrak{g}(\mathfrak{m}, A')$. Since $\mathfrak{b}$ is prime to $\mathfrak{m}$, the intersection of $\mathfrak{g}(\mathfrak{b}, A')$ and $\mathfrak{g}(\mathfrak{m}, A')$ must be $\{0\}$; it follows that $\iota'(\mu)\lambda_{\mathfrak{a}} t = 0$. We have thus proved that $\iota'(\mu)\lambda_{\mathfrak{a}} t = 0$ if and only if μ is contained in $(\mathfrak{a}, \mathfrak{m})^{-1}\mathfrak{m}$, namely, $\lambda_{\mathfrak{a}} t$ is a proper $(\mathfrak{a}, \mathfrak{m})^{-1}\mathfrak{m}$-section point. In particular, $\lambda_{\mathfrak{a}} t$ is a proper $\mathfrak{m}$-section point if and only if $\mathfrak{a}$ is prime to $\mathfrak{m}$; and $\lambda_{\mathfrak{a}} t = 0$ if and only if $\mathfrak{a} \subset \mathfrak{m}$. Now fix an integral ideal $\mathfrak{c}$ in c, prime to $\mathfrak{m}$, and a $\mathfrak{c}$-multiplication $\lambda_{\mathfrak{c}}$ of (A, ι) onto (A', ι'). Then $\lambda_{\mathfrak{c}} t$ is a proper $\mathfrak{m}$-section point; hence, for every t' in $\mathfrak{g}(\mathfrak{m}, A')$, there exists, by Proposition 20, an element α of $\mathfrak{o}$ such that $t' = \iota'(\alpha)\lambda_{\mathfrak{c}} t$. This proves the first assertion of our proposition, since $\iota'(\alpha)\lambda_{\mathfrak{c}}$ is an $\alpha\mathfrak{c}$-multiplication of (A, ι) onto (A', ι'). The rest of the proposition is already proved.

7. 6. Let (A, ι) be an abelian variety of type (F), defined over a field k, and σ an isomorphism of k onto a field k^{σ}. Let $\mathfrak{r}$ be the order of (A, ι). Put, for every $\alpha \in \mathfrak{r}$, $\iota^{\sigma}(\alpha) = \iota(\alpha)^{\sigma}$ (cf. § 1.5); then ι^{σ} is uniquely extended to an isomorphism of F into $\mathscr{A}_0(A^{\sigma})$ which we denote also by ι^{σ}. We obtain thus an abelian variety $(A^{\sigma}, \iota^{\sigma})$ of type (F), defined over k^σ; $\mathfrak{r}$ is the order of (A^σ, ι^σ). Let $\mathfrak{a}$ be an ideal of $\mathfrak{r}$ and $(A_1, \iota_1; \lambda)$ an $\mathfrak{a}$-transform of (A, ι), defined over k. Then, we see easily that $(A_1^\sigma, \iota_1^\sigma; \lambda^\sigma)$ is an $\mathfrak{a}$-transform of (A^σ, ι^σ). If (A, ι) is principal, so is (A^σ, ι^σ); and if t is a proper $\mathfrak{a}$-section point on A, rational over k, then t^σ is a proper $\mathfrak{a}$-section point on A^σ. Now suppose that k is of characteristic $p \neq 0$. Then, for every power $q = p^f$ with $f > 0$, we obtain an abelian variety (A^q, ι^q) of type (F); let π be the q-th power homomorphism of A onto A^q, defined in § 1.5. We see easily that $\pi\iota(\alpha) = \iota^q(\alpha)\pi$ for every $\alpha \in F$, so that π is a homomorphism of (A, ι) onto (A^q, ι^q). In particular, if (A, ι) is defined over a finite field with q elements, the q-th power endomorphism π of A is an endomorphism of (A, ι); hence, if further (A, ι) satisfies the condition (C′) of § 7.3, there exists an element γ of $\mathfrak{r}$ such that $\pi = \iota(\gamma)$.

8. THE DUAL OF A CM-TYPE.

The purpose of this section is to investigate the algebraic structure of a CM-type. For the sake of simplicity, we assume that the fields appearing in this section are all containd in the field $\boldsymbol{C}$ of complex numbers.

8. 1. Group-theoretic characterization of CM-types. We begin with

LEMMA 3. *Let L be a Galois extension of Q, G the Galois group of L over Q and ρ the element of G such that ξ^ρ is the complex conjugate of ξ for every $\xi \in L$. Let K and K_0 be two subfields of L such that $[K: K_0] = 2$, and H, H_0 be respectively the subgroups of G corresponding to K, K_0. Then, the following two conditions are equivalent.*

i) *K_0 is totally real and K is totally imaginary.*

ii) *$H_0 = H \cup H\sigma\rho\sigma^{-1}$ for every $\sigma \in G$.*

If these conditions are satisfied, we have $\rho H\tau = H\tau\rho = \sigma\rho\sigma^{-1}H\tau = H\tau\sigma\rho\sigma^{-1}$ for every $\sigma \in G$, $\tau \in G$.

PROOF. If σ is an element of G, the subfields K_0^σ, K^σ of L correspond to the subgroups $\sigma^{-1}H_0\sigma$, $\sigma^{-1}H\sigma$ of G. If K_0 is totally real and K is totally imaginary, then K_0^σ is a real field and K^σ is an imaginary field, so that ρ fixes every element of K_0^σ and does not fix some element of K^σ. Hence we have $\rho \in \sigma^{-1}H_0\sigma$ and $\rho \notin \sigma^{-1}H\sigma$, so that $\sigma\rho\sigma^{-1} \in H_0$ and $\sigma\rho\sigma^{-1} \notin H$. By the assumption $[K:K_0] = 2$, we have $[H_0:H] = 2$; it follows that $H_0 = H \cup H\sigma\rho\sigma^{-1}$. Conversely, if the relation $H_0 = H \cup H\sigma\rho\sigma^{-1}$ holds for every $\sigma \in G$, we can easily see, following up the above argument in the opposite direction, that K_0 is totally real and K is totally imaginary. Now suppose that the conditions i) and ii) are satisfied. Then, we see that both $H\sigma\rho\sigma^{-1}$ and $\sigma\rho\sigma^{-1}H$ are equal to the set $H_0 - H$ for every $\sigma \in G$. We have hence

$$\rho H = H\rho = \sigma\rho\sigma^{-1}H = H\sigma\rho\sigma^{-1}.$$

It follows that $\rho H\sigma = H\sigma\rho$. Let μ be an element of G. Then, K^μ is totally imaginary and K_0^μ is totally real; and the subgroup $\mu^{-1}H\mu$ of G corresponds to K^μ. Therefore, applying the formula $\rho H\sigma = H\sigma\rho$ to $\mu^{-1}H\mu$, we have $\rho(\mu^{-1}H\mu)\sigma = (\mu^{-1}H\mu)\sigma\rho$. Transform this by the inner automorphism $\gamma \to \mu\gamma\mu^{-1}$ and put $\tau = \mu\sigma\mu^{-1}$. We have then $\mu\rho\mu^{-1}H\tau = H\tau\mu\rho\mu^{-1}$. This completes the proof.

PROPOSITION 25. *Let F be an extension of $\boldsymbol{Q}$ of degree $2n$, $\{\varphi_1, \cdots, \varphi_n\}$ a set of n distinct isomorphisms of F into $\boldsymbol{C}$. Let L be a Galois extension of $\boldsymbol{Q}$ containing F, and G the Galois group of L over $\boldsymbol{Q}$. Denote by ρ the element of G such that ξ^ρ is the complex conjugate of ξ for every $\xi \in L$, and by S the set of all the elements of G inducing some φ_i on F. Then, $(F; \{\varphi_i\})$ is a CM-type if and only if we have*

(1) $$G = S \cup S\sigma\rho\sigma^{-1}, \quad S\sigma\rho\sigma^{-1} = \sigma\rho\sigma^{-1}S$$

for every $\sigma \in G$.

PROOF. If $(F; \{\varphi_i\})$ is a CM-type, then, by Theorem 1 of § 5, F has two subfields K and K_0 satisfying the conditions (CM1, 2) in that theorem. L, G, ρ, S being as in our proposition, let H be the subgroup of G corresponding to F. Let $\{\psi_1, \cdots, \psi_m\}$ be the set of all distinct isomorphisms of K into $\boldsymbol{C}$ obtained by restricting φ_i to K. Then there are no two members of $\{\psi_j\}$ which are complex conjugate of each other; and it is easy to see that $\{\psi_j\}$ gives the set of all distinct isomorphisms of K_0 into $\boldsymbol{C}$. It follows that $[K_0:\boldsymbol{Q}] = m$. We observe also that $\{\varphi_i\}$ is the set of all the isomorphisms of F into $\boldsymbol{C}$ inducing some ψ_j on K. Hence S is the set of all the elements of G inducing some ψ_j on K. Take, for every j, an element τ_j of G inducing ψ_j on K. Then we have $S = \cup H\tau_j$. Every element of G coincides with τ_j or $\tau_j\rho$ on K. Hence we have

$$G = \bigcup_j (H\tau_j \cup H\tau_j\rho) = S \cup S\rho.$$

By Lemma 3, we have $\rho H\tau_j = H\tau_j\rho = \sigma\rho\sigma^{-1}H\tau_j = H\tau_j\sigma\rho\sigma^{-1}$; it follows that $\rho S = S\rho = \sigma\rho\sigma^{-1}S = S\sigma\rho\sigma^{-1}$. Thus we have proved the "only if" part of our proposition. Conversely, suppose that the relation (1) holds for every $\sigma \in G$. Put $\rho' = \sigma\rho\sigma^{-1}$. As the number of the elements in S is the half of the order of G, the sets S and $\rho'S = S\rho'$ have no common element and $\rho'S = G - S$. Put

$$H' = \{\gamma \mid \gamma \in G, \gamma S = S\}.$$

We have then, $\rho'H'\rho S = \rho'H'\rho'S = \rho'H'S\rho' = \rho'S\rho' = \rho'\rho'S = S$, so that we have $\rho'H'\rho \subset H'$, $\rho'H'\rho' \subset H'$. It follows from this that $\rho'H' = H'\rho' = H'\rho$. Since S does not coincide with ρS, the element ρ is not contained in H'. Put now

$$H_0' = H' \cup H'\rho.$$

We can easily verify that H_0' is a subgroup of G and $[H_0' : H'] = 2$; and we have $H_0' = H' \cup H'\sigma\rho\sigma^{-1}$ for every $\sigma \in G$. Hence, if we denote by K' and K_0' the subfields of L corresponding to H' and H_0', respectively, K' is totally imaginary and K_0' is totally real by virtue of Lemma 3. If γ is an element of G leaving invariant every element of F, then every element of γS coincides with one of the φ_i on F, so that we have $\gamma S \subset S$ and hence $\gamma \in H'$; this implies $F \supset K'$. As we have $H'S = S$, S is expressed as a join of cosets: $S = \cup H'\mu_\alpha$. We see that $\{\mu_\alpha\}$ gives the half of the isomorphisms of K' into $\boldsymbol{C}$; and $H'\mu_\alpha\rho$ does not coincide with any $H'\mu_\beta$, since S and $S\rho$ have no common element; in other words, for any α and β, μ_α does not coincide with the complex conjugate of μ_β on K'; namely, the system $\{K', K_0', \{\varphi_i\}\}$ satisfies the conditions (CM1, 2) of Theorem 1. Hence $(F; \{\varphi_i\})$ is a CM-type. This completes the proof.

8. 2. Primitive CM-types. We call a CM-type *primitive* if the abelian varieties of that type are simple; recall that any two abelian varieties of the same CM-type are isogenous to each other (Corollary of Theorem 2). The following proposition is a criterion for the primitiveness of a CM-type.

PROPOSITION 26. *$(F; \{\varphi_i\})$ being a CM-type, let L, G, ρ, S, be as in Proposition 25 and H_1 the subgroup of G corresponding to F. Put*

$$H' = \{\gamma \mid \gamma \in G, \gamma S = S\}.$$

Then, $(F; \{\varphi_i\})$ is primitive if and only if $H_1 = H'$.

PROOF. Using the same notations as in the proof of Proposition 25, we see that F contains the field K' corresponding to H'. If $(F; \{\varphi_i\})$ is primitive, we must have $F = K'$ by virtue of Theorem 3 of § 6, so that $H_1 = H'$. If $(F; \{\varphi_i\})$ is not primitive, F contains two subfields K and K_0, satisfying the conditions (CM1, 2) of Theorem 1, such that $F \neq K$; this follows from the discussion in § 5.2. Denoting by H the subgroup of G corresponding to K, there exist elements τ_j of G such that $S = \bigcup H\tau_j$, as is seen in the proof of Proposition 25. We have then $HS = S$, and hence $H \subset H'$. By the relation $F \supsetneqq K$, we have $H \supsetneqq H_1$, so that $H_1 \neq H'$; this completes the proof.

We shall now give another criterion with no use of Galois group. If $(K; \{\varphi_i\})$ is a primitive CM-type, Theorem 3 of § 6 shows that K is a totally imaginary quadratic extension of a totally real field K_0. We have seen in the proof of that theorem that there exists an element ζ of K such that $K = K_0(\zeta)$, $-\zeta^2$ is totally positive and $\mathrm{Im}(\zeta^{\varphi_i}) > 0$ for every i. Conversely, suppose a totally real field K_0 and a totally positive element η of K_0 to be given; let ζ be a number such that $-\zeta^2 = \eta$; and put $K = K_0(\zeta)$. Let $\{\varphi_i\}$ be the set of all the isomorphisms φ of K into $\boldsymbol{C}$ such that $\mathrm{Im}(\zeta^\varphi) > 0$. Then it can be easily seen that $(K; \{\varphi_i\})$ is a CM-type. We shall denote this CM-type by $K_0((\zeta))$. We have $K_0((\zeta)) = K_0((\zeta'))$ if and only if ζ/ζ' is a totally positive element of K_0.

PROPOSITION 27. *$K_0((\zeta))$ is primitive if and only if the following two conditions are satisfied:*

i) $K_0(\zeta) = \boldsymbol{Q}(\zeta)$;

ii) *for any conjugate* ζ' *of* ζ *other than* ζ *itself, over* $\boldsymbol{Q}$, ζ'/ζ *is not totally positive.*

PROOF. First we note that ζ'/ζ'' is totally real for any two conjugates ζ' and ζ'' of ζ over $\boldsymbol{Q}$, since ζ' and ζ'' are purely imaginary numbers. Put $F = K = K_0(\zeta)$; let $\{\varphi_i\}$ be the set of all the isomorphisms φ of F into $\boldsymbol{C}$ such that $\operatorname{Im}(\zeta^\varphi) > 0$. Define L, G, ρ, S for $(F; \{\varphi_i\})$ as in Proposition 25 and denote by H the subgroup of G corresponding to K; put $H' = \{\gamma \mid \gamma \in G, \ \gamma S = S\}$. Then we see easily that $S = \{\sigma \mid \sigma \in G, \ \operatorname{Im}(\zeta^\sigma) > 0\}$. If $\gamma \in H'$, we have $\gamma\sigma \in S$ for every $\sigma \in S$, so that $\operatorname{Im}(\zeta^{\gamma\sigma}) > 0$ for every $\sigma \in S$. As $\zeta^{\gamma\sigma}/\zeta^\sigma$ is real, we see $\zeta^{\gamma\sigma}/\zeta^\sigma > 0$. If $\sigma \notin S$, then $\sigma \in S\rho$, $\gamma\sigma \in \gamma S\rho = S\rho$, and hence $\gamma\sigma \notin S$, so that $\operatorname{Im}(\zeta^{\gamma\sigma}) < 0$, $\operatorname{Im}(\zeta^\sigma) < 0$. Thus we have $\zeta^{\gamma\sigma}/\zeta^\sigma > 0$ for every $\sigma \in G$, namely ζ^γ/ζ is totally positive. Conversely, if ζ^γ/ζ is totally positive for an element γ of G, $\operatorname{Im}(\zeta^{\gamma\sigma})$ has the same sign as $\operatorname{Im}(\zeta^\sigma)$ for every $\sigma \in G$; it follows that $\gamma S = S$. Therefore, H' is the set of all the elements $\gamma \in G$ such that ζ^γ/ζ is totally positive. By Proposition 26, $K_0((\zeta)) = (K; \{\varphi_i\})$ is primitive if and only if $H' = H$. Our proposition is an immediate consequence of these facts.

8. 3. Now we define the dual of a *CM*-type.

PROPOSITION 28. *$(F; \{\varphi_i\})$, L, G, ρ, S, being the same as in Proposition* 26, *put*

$$S^* = \{\sigma^{-1} | \sigma \in S\}, \qquad H^* = \{\gamma \,|\, \gamma \in G, \gamma S^* = S^*\}.$$

Let K^* be the subfield of L corresponding to H^* and $\{\psi_j\}$ the set of all the isomorphisms of K^* into $\boldsymbol{C}$ obtained from the elements of S^*. Then, $(K^*; \{\psi_j\})$ is a primitive CM-type and we have

$$K^* = \boldsymbol{Q}(\sum_i \xi^{\varphi_i} | \xi \in F).$$

$(K^*; \{\psi_j\})$ is determined only by $(F; \{\varphi_i\})$ and independent of the choice of L.

PROOF. Let σ be an element of G. Then, by the relation (1) of Proposition 25, we have $G = S^* \cup S^*\sigma\rho\sigma^{-1}$, $S^*\sigma\rho\sigma^{-1} = \sigma\rho\sigma^{-1}S^*$. We see easily that S^* is the set of all the elements of G inducing on K^* some

ψ_j and $\{\psi_j\}$ is the half of all the isomorphisms of K^* into $\boldsymbol{C}$. Hence, by Proposition 25, $(K^*; \{\psi_j\})$ is a CM-type, and is primitive by virtue of Proposition 26. Let γ be an element of H^*. We have then $\gamma^{-1}S^* = S^*$, so that $S\gamma = S$; hence $\{\varphi_1\gamma,\cdots,\varphi_n\gamma\}$ coincides with $\{\varphi_1,\cdots,\varphi_n\}$ as a whole. We have therefore $(\sum_i \xi^{\varphi_i})^\gamma = \sum_i \xi^{\varphi_i}$ for every $\xi \in F$. Conversely, suppose that an element γ of G fixes $\sum_i \xi^{\varphi_i}$ for every $\xi \in F$. Then, we have for every integer a,

$$\sum_i (\xi^{\varphi_i\gamma})^a = \sum_i (\xi^a)^{\varphi_i\gamma} = \sum_i (\xi^a)^{\varphi_i} = \sum_i (\xi^{\varphi_i})^a.$$

By an elementary theorem of algebra, we see that $\{\xi^{\varphi_1\gamma},\cdots,\xi^{\varphi_n\gamma}\}$ coincides with $\{\xi^{\varphi_1},\cdots,\xi^{\varphi_n}\}$ as a whole; this shows that $\{\varphi_1,\cdots,\varphi_n\}$ coincides with $\{\varphi_1\gamma,\cdots,\varphi_n\gamma\}$ on F as a whole; in other words we have $S\gamma = S$, so that $\gamma \in H^*$. Thus we have proved that H^* is the set of all the elements of G leaving invariant every element of $\boldsymbol{Q}(\sum_i \xi^{\varphi_i} | \xi \in F)$; this implies $K^* = \boldsymbol{Q}(\sum_i \xi^{\varphi_i} | \xi \in F)$. The last assertion of our proposition follows easily from the definition.

We call the CM-type $(K^*; \{\psi_j\})$ of the above proposition the *dual* of $(F; \{\varphi_i\})$. By the proposition, the dual of every CM-type is primitive. If a CM-type $(F; \{\varphi_i\})$ is primitive, then $(F; \{\varphi_i\})$ coincides with the dual of its dual; this follows immediately from Propositions 26 and 28. For every type $(F; \{\varphi_i\})$, we can find two subfields K and K_0 of F satisfying the conditions (CM1, 2) of Theorem 1. Let $\{\chi_j\}$ be the set of distinct isomorphisms of K into $\boldsymbol{C}$ induced by the φ_i. Then it is easy to see that $(K; \{\chi_j\})$ is a CM-type; and we observe that $(F; \{\varphi_i\})$ and $(K; \{\chi_j\})$ have the same dual; this is also an immediate consequence of the definition.

PROPOSITION 29. *Let $(F; \{\varphi_i\})$ be a CM-type and $(K^*; \{\psi_j\})$ the dual of $(F; \{\varphi_i\})$; denote by ρ the automorphism of $\boldsymbol{C}$ which correponds to $\xi \in \boldsymbol{C}$ its complex conjugate. Let α be an element of K^*; put $\beta = \prod_j \alpha^{\psi_j}$. Then, β is contained in F; and we have $\beta\beta^\rho = N_{K^*/\boldsymbol{Q}}(\alpha)$. Let further $\mathfrak{a}$ be an ideal of K^*; put $\mathfrak{b} = \prod_j \mathfrak{a}^{\psi_j}$. Then, $\mathfrak{b}$ is an ideal of F; and we have $\mathfrak{b}\mathfrak{b}^\rho = N_{K^*/\boldsymbol{Q}}(\mathfrak{a})$.*

Proof. Define L, G, S as before. Let H be the subgroup of G corresponding to F. Then, by the definition of S, we have $HS = S$, so that $S^*H = S^*$, if we define S^* as in Proposition 28. It follows that, for every $\sigma \in H$, $\{\psi_j\sigma\}$ coincides with $\{\psi_j\}$ as a whole. Hence we have $\beta^\sigma = \prod \alpha^{\psi_j\sigma} = \prod \alpha^{\psi_j} = \beta$ for every $\sigma \in H$; so β is contained in F. As we have $G = S^* \cup S^*\rho$, $\{\psi_j, \psi_j\rho\}$ gives the set of all distinct isomorphisms of K^* into $\boldsymbol{C}$; this proves the relation $\beta\beta^\rho = N_{K^*/\boldsymbol{Q}}(\alpha)$. Now, as for the assertions concerning ideals, it is sufficient to prove it in case where $\mathfrak{a}$ is an integral ideal. Take a non-zero element α of K^*, divisible by $\mathfrak{a}$. We can find an element γ of K^* divisible by $\mathfrak{a}$ such that $\gamma\mathfrak{a}^{-1}$ is prime to $N_{K^*/\boldsymbol{Q}}(\alpha)$. Put $\beta = \prod_j \alpha^{\psi_j}$ and $\delta = \prod_j \gamma^{\psi_j}$. Then, by what we have already proved, β and δ are contained in F. Put $\mathfrak{b} = \prod_j \mathfrak{a}^{\psi_j}$; it is clear that both β and δ are divisible by $\mathfrak{b}$. As $\gamma\mathfrak{a}^{-1}$ is prime to $N_{K^*/\boldsymbol{Q}}(\alpha)$, we see that $\delta\mathfrak{b}^{-1}$ is prime to β. It follows that $\mathfrak{b}$ is the greatest common divisor of β and δ; this proves that $\mathfrak{b}$ is an ideal of F. The relation $\mathfrak{b}\mathfrak{b}^\rho = N_{K^*/\boldsymbol{Q}}(\mathfrak{b})$ is proved by the same argument as for $\beta\beta^\rho = N_{K^*/\boldsymbol{Q}}(\alpha)$.

8. 4. Examples. We shall now give some examples of CM-type.

(1) First we consider a CM-type $(F; \{\varphi_i\})$ such that F is a Galois extension of $\boldsymbol{Q}$. We can take F itself as L of Proposition 25; the subgroup of the Galois group G corresponding to F is then the subgroup consisting only of the identity; and we have $S = \{\varphi_1, \cdots, \varphi_n\}$, $S^* = \{\varphi_1^{-1}, \cdots, \varphi_n^{-1}\}$, where we consider the φ_i as elements of G. Hence, if F is abelian over $\boldsymbol{Q}$, the subgroup H^* defined in Proposition 28 coincides with the subgroup $H' = \{\gamma | \gamma \in G, \ \gamma S = S\}$. If moreover $(F; \{\varphi_i\})$ is primitive, H' must be the identity-subgroup, so that the field corresponding to H^* is F. Thus we get the following result: if F is abelian over $\boldsymbol{Q}$ and if $(F; \{\varphi_i\})$ is primitive, the dual of $(F; \{\varphi_i\})$ is $(F; \{\varphi_i^{-1}\})$. In the classical case, F is an imaginary quadratic field; so the dual is the same as itself.

Now we give an example of a primitive CM-type $(F; \{\varphi_i\})$ where F is a cyclotomic field. Let p be an odd prime and $\zeta = e^{2\pi i/p}$. The automorphisms of $\boldsymbol{Q}(\zeta)$ are given by $\zeta \to \zeta^a$ for the integers a such that $1 \leqq a \leqq p-1$. Put $n = (p-1)/2$ and denote by φ_i the automorphism

$\zeta \to \zeta^i$ for $i = 1, \cdots, n$. Then we see that there are no two automorphisms among φ_i which are complex conjugate of each other; and $\boldsymbol{Q}(\zeta)$ is totally imaginary quadratic extension of the totally real field $\boldsymbol{Q}(\zeta+\zeta^{-1})$. Hence $(\boldsymbol{Q}(\zeta); \{\varphi_i\})$ is a CM-type. Let γ be an automorphism of $\boldsymbol{Q}(\zeta)$ such that $\{\gamma\varphi_1, \cdots, \gamma\varphi_n\} = \{\varphi_1, \cdots, \varphi_n\}$; let a be an integer such that $\zeta^\gamma = \zeta^a$. Then, $\{1 \cdot a, \cdots, n \cdot a \bmod (p)\}$ coincides with $\{1, \cdots, n \bmod (p)\}$ as a whole, so that we have

$$1 \cdot a + \cdots + n \cdot a \equiv 1 + \cdots + n \mod (p).$$

As $1 + \cdots + n = (p^2-1)/8$ is relatively prime to p, we have $a \equiv 1 \bmod (p)$, so that γ is the identity. Therefore, our CM-type $(\boldsymbol{Q}(\zeta); \{\varphi_i\})$ is primitive.

There can exist many CM-types with the same field F. Consider for example $F = \boldsymbol{Q}(\zeta)$ with $p = 13$. We normalize $S = \{\varphi_1, \cdots, \varphi_n\}$ taking the identity as φ_1. Then, we obtain 32 CM-types $(F; \{\varphi_i\})$. By an easy calculation, we see that two of them are non-primitive and the remaining primitive 30 CM-types are divided into 5 families in the following way: each family consists of 6 types; and any two types belong to the same family if and only if they are transformed onto each other by an automorphism of F. We can similarly treat the case where F is cyclic over $\boldsymbol{Q}$.

(2) Let K_0 be a real quadratic field and ξ a number such that $-\xi^2$ is a totally positive number of K_0. Then we obtain a CM-type $K_0((\xi))$. Put $K = K_0(\xi)$. For the sake of simplicity, suppose $\mathrm{Im}(\xi) > 0$; this amounts to assuming that S contains the identity. If K is a Galois extension of $\boldsymbol{Q}$, the Galois group G is an abelian group of degree 4, so that G is cyclic or the product of two cyclic groups of order 2.

a) The case where G is the product of two cyclic groups of order 2. Denoting by ρ the element of G such that α^ρ is the complex conjugate of α for every $\alpha \in K$, the subgroup of G corresponding to K_0 is $\{1, \rho\}$. Put $S = \{1, \sigma\}$. Then we have $G = \{1, \sigma, \rho, \sigma\rho\}$; and the elements γ such that $\gamma S = S$ form the subgroup $\{1, \sigma\}$. Hence $K_0((\xi))$ is not primitive. Let K^* be the subfield of K corresponding to the subgroup $\{1, \sigma\}$. Then we see that K^* is an imaginary quadratic field, K is the composite of K_0 and K^*, and the dual of $K_0((\xi))$ is $(K^*, \{1\})$.

b) The case where G is cyclic. ρ and $S=\{1, \sigma\}$ being as above, we have $G=\{1, \sigma, \sigma^2=\rho, \sigma^3\}$. We see that there is no element γ other than the identity such that $\gamma S=S$, so that the CM-type $K_0((\xi)) =(K;\ \{1, \sigma\})$ is primitive. The dual is $(K;\ \{1, \sigma^{-1}\})$ by the result of (1). We can easily verify that $K_0((\xi^\sigma))=(K;\ \{1, \sigma^{-1}\})$.

c) The case where K is not Galois over $\boldsymbol{Q}$ (The case of Hecke [20]). Put $K_0((\xi))=(K;\ \{1, \varphi\})$. As K_0 is a real quadratic field, there exists a positive integer d such that $K_0=\boldsymbol{Q}(\sqrt{d})$; and $-\xi^2$ is expressed in the form $-\xi^2=x+y\sqrt{d}$, where x and y are rational numbers; as $-\xi^2$ is totally positive, we have $x+y\sqrt{d}>0$, $x-y\sqrt{d}>0$, and $\xi=\sqrt{x+y\sqrt{d}}\, i$, $\xi^\varphi=\sqrt{x-y\sqrt{d}}\, i$. We see that four elements $\pm\xi$, $\pm\xi^\varphi$ are the conjugates of ξ over $\boldsymbol{Q}$. As K is not Galois over $\boldsymbol{Q}$, ξ^φ is not contained in K, so that $K_0(\xi^\varphi)\neq K_0(\xi)$. Put $d'=x^2-y^2d$; then, we have $d'>0$. On the other hand, we have $d'=(\xi\xi^\varphi)^2$; hence $\sqrt{d'}$ is not contained in K_0, since we have $K_0(\xi^\varphi) \neq K_0(\xi)$. Therefore, $\boldsymbol{Q}(\sqrt{d'})$ is a real quadratic field different from $\boldsymbol{Q}(\sqrt{d})=K_0$. Put now $L=\boldsymbol{Q}(\xi, \xi^\varphi)$; then we see that L is Galois over $\boldsymbol{Q}$, $L=K(\sqrt{d'})$ and hence $[L:\boldsymbol{Q}]=8$. The Galois group of L over $\boldsymbol{Q}$ consists of eight automorphisms which map the couple (ξ, ξ^φ) onto $(\pm\xi, \pm\xi^\varphi)$, $(\pm\xi, \mp\xi^\varphi)$, $(\pm\xi^\varphi, \pm\xi)$, $(\pm\xi^\varphi, \mp\xi)$. Denote by σ and τ respectively the elements of G which send (ξ, ξ^φ) onto $(\xi^\varphi, -\xi)$ and (ξ^φ, ξ). Then we see that $\sigma^2=\rho$, $\sigma^4=\tau^2=1$, $\tau\sigma=\sigma^3\tau$ and G is generated by σ and τ. We can easily verify that the subgroup of G corresponding to $K=\boldsymbol{Q}(\xi)$ is $\{1, \sigma\tau\}$ and $S=\{1, \sigma, \tau, \sigma\tau\}$; moreover, we have $\{1, \sigma\tau\}=\{\gamma | \gamma\in G, \gamma S=S\}$, which proves that $(K;\{1, \varphi\})$ is primitive. If we define H^* as in Proposition 28, then we have $H^*=\{1, \tau\}$; and the subfield of L corresponding to H^* is $\boldsymbol{Q}(\xi+\xi^\varphi)$. As we have $S^*=H^*\cup H^*\sigma\tau$, the dual of $(\boldsymbol{Q}(\xi), \{1, \varphi\})$ is $(\boldsymbol{Q}(\xi+\xi^\varphi), \{1, \sigma\tau\})$; the latter is also written as $\boldsymbol{Q}(\sqrt{d'})((\xi+\xi^\varphi))$.

8. 5. Fields of definition for (A, ι).

PROPOSITION 30. *Let $(F;\ \{\varphi_i\})$ be a CM-type and $(K^*;\ \{\psi_j\})$ its dual; let (A, ι) be an abelian variety of type $(F;\ \{\varphi_i\})$ and k a field of* *definition for A. Then, if every element of $\iota(F) \cap \mathscr{A}(A)$ is defined over k, we have $k \supset K^*$; conversely, if $k \supset K^*$ and if $(F; \{\varphi_i\})$ is primitive, every element of $\mathscr{A}(A)$ is defined over k.*

PROOF. Let S be a representation of $\mathscr{A}_0(A)$ by invariant differential forms on A. Then, for every $\xi \in F$, $\xi^{\varphi_1}, \cdots, \xi^{\varphi_n}$ are the characteristic roots of $S(\iota(\xi))$. Suppose that every element of $\iota(F) \cap \mathscr{A}(A)$ is defined over k. Then we can find a basis of invariant differential forms on A with respect to which $S(\iota(\xi))$ has coefficients in k for every $\xi \in F$ (cf. § 2.8); hence the trace of $S(\iota(\xi))$ is contained in k, namely, we have $\sum_i \xi^{\varphi_i} \in k$ for every $\xi \in F$. This proves $k \supset K^*$. Conversely, suppose that $k \supset K^*$ and $(F; \{\varphi_i\})$ is primitive, namely A is simple. Then, by Proposition 6 of § 5.1, $\mathscr{A}_0(A)$ coincides with $\iota(F)$. Let σ be an isomorphism of $\boldsymbol{C}$ into itself which is the identity on k; we have then $A^\sigma = A$. Our proposition is proved if we show that $\lambda^\sigma = \lambda$ for every $\lambda \in \mathscr{A}(A)$. First we see that $\lambda \to \lambda^\sigma$ gives an automorphism of $\mathscr{A}_0(A)$. As we have $\mathscr{A}_0(A) = \iota(F)$, there exists an automorphism τ of F such that $\iota(\xi^\tau) = \iota(\xi)^\sigma$ for every $\xi \in F$. As is remarked in § 5.2, we can find n invariant differential forms $\omega_1, \cdots, \omega_n$ on A such that for every $\xi \in F$,

$$\delta\iota(\xi)\omega_i = \xi^{\varphi_i}\omega_i \quad (1 \leqq i \leqq n). \tag{2}$$

We have then $\delta\iota(\xi)^\sigma\omega_i^\sigma = \xi^{\varphi_i\sigma}\omega_i^\sigma$ $(1 \leqq i \leqq n)$; this shows that $S(\iota(\xi)^\sigma)$ has the characteristic roots $\xi^{\varphi_1\sigma}, \cdots, \xi^{\varphi_n\sigma}$. On the other hand, $S(\iota(\xi^\tau))$ has the characteristic roots $\xi^{\tau\varphi_1}, \cdots, \xi^{\tau\varphi_n}$; so, $\{\xi^{\varphi_1\sigma}, \cdots, \xi^{\varphi_n\sigma}\}$ coincides with $\{\xi^{\tau\varphi_1}, \cdots, \xi^{\tau\varphi_n}\}$ as a whole. Since we have assumed $k \supset K^*$, σ fixes every element of K^*; hence, for every $\xi \in F$, we have $\sum \xi^{\varphi_i\sigma} = (\sum \xi^{\varphi_i})^\sigma = \sum \xi^{\varphi_i}$; so by the same argument as in the proof of Proposition 28, we see that $\{\xi^{\varphi_1\sigma}, \cdots, \xi^{\varphi_n\sigma}\}$ coincides with $\{\xi^{\varphi_1}, \cdots, \xi^{\varphi_n}\}$ as a whole. Consequently, $\{\xi^{\varphi_1}, \cdots, \xi^{\varphi_n}\}$ coincides with $\{\xi^{\tau\varphi_1}, \cdots, \xi^{\tau\varphi_n}\}$ as a whole; this implies that $\{\varphi_1, \cdots, \varphi_n\}$ coincides with $\{\tau\varphi_1, \cdots, \tau\varphi_n\}$ as a whole. Now define L, G, S as in Proposition 25; and let H_1 denote the subgroup of G corresponding to F. Take an element of G inducing τ on F, and denote it again by τ. Then as τ gives an automorphism of F, we have $\tau H_1 = H_1\tau$. Take for every i an element γ_i of G inducing

φ_i on F. We have then $S = \bigcup_i H_1\gamma_i$. The above result shows that $\{H_1\tau\gamma_1, \cdots, H_1\tau\gamma_n\}$ coincides with $\{H_1\gamma_1, \cdots, H_1\gamma_n\}$ as a whole. We have therefore,

$$S = \bigcup_i H_1\gamma_i = \bigcup_i H_1\tau\gamma_i = \bigcup_i \tau H_1\gamma_i = \tau S.$$

By our assumption that $(F; \{\varphi_i\})$ is primitive, τ must be contained in H_1 by virtue of Proposition 26. This proves that τ is the identity on F; so we have $\iota(\xi)^\sigma = \iota(\xi)$ for every $\xi \in F$; this completes the proof.

PROPOSITION 31. *Let $(F; \{\varphi_i\})$ be a CM-type and $(K^*; \{\psi_j\})$ its dual; let (A, ι) be an abelian variety of type $(F; \{\varphi_i\})$ and k a field of definition for (A, ι). Let σ be an isomorphism of k into $\boldsymbol{C}$. Then, σ fixes every element of K^* if and only if there exists a homomorphism of (A, ι) onto (A^σ, ι^σ).*

PROOF. We note that k must contain K^* by virtue of Proposition 30. Extend σ to an isomorphism of $\boldsymbol{C}$ into itself and denote it again by σ. Take n invariant differential forms ω_i on A for which the relation (2) holds for every $\xi \in F$. Then, the ω_i^σ form a basis of invariant differential forms on A^σ; and we have $\delta\iota^\sigma(\xi)\omega_i^\sigma = \xi^{\varphi_i\sigma}\omega_i^\sigma$. This shows that (A^σ, ι^σ) is of type $(F; \{\varphi_i\sigma\})$. Suppose that there exists a homomorphism λ of (A, ι) onto (A^σ, ι^σ). By Theorem 1 of § 2, $\delta\lambda$ is an isomorphism of $\mathfrak{D}_0(A^\sigma)$ onto $\mathfrak{D}_0(A)$; putting $\omega_i' = (\delta\lambda)^{-1}\omega_i$, we see easily $\delta\iota^\sigma(\xi)\omega_i' = \xi^{\varphi_i}\omega_i'$ for every $\xi \in F$. Hence (A^σ, ι^σ) is of type $(F; \{\varphi_i\})$. It follows that $\{\varphi_i\sigma\}$ coincides with $\{\varphi_i\}$ as a whole; so we have, for every $\xi \in F$, $(\sum \xi^{\varphi_i})^\sigma = \sum \xi^{\varphi_i\sigma} = \sum \xi^{\varphi_i}$; namely, σ leaves invariant every element of K^*. This proves the "if" part of the proposition. Conversely, suppose that σ leaves invariant every element of K^*; then, by the same argument as in the proof of Proposition 28, we see that $\{\varphi_i\sigma\}$ coincides with $\{\varphi_i\}$ as a whole; so (A^σ, ι^σ) is of the same type $(F; \{\varphi_i\})$ as (A, ι). By Corollary of Theorem 2 of § 6 and Remark below it, we can obtain a homomorphism of (A, ι) onto (A^σ, ι^σ). This completes our proof.

CHAPTER III. REDUCTION OF CONSTANT FIELDS.

The aim of §§ 9–12 is to complement the theory of reduction modulo $\mathfrak{p}$ of algebraic varieties, given in [33], with a particular interest in abelian varieties, toward the later use. We will first recall definitions and results from the general theory with a slight modification, and then proceed to the main subject. For omitted proofs in § 9, we refer to [33].

9. REDUCTION OF VARIETIES AND CYCLES.

9. 1. Places. Let K be a field. We denote by K_∞ the join $K \cup \{\infty\}$ of the set K and one additional element ∞; and we define, besides the operation in K, the operation in K_∞ as follows:

$$a \pm \infty = \infty, \ a/\infty = 0 \quad \text{for } a \in K,$$
$$a \cdot \infty = a/0 = \infty \quad \text{for } a \in K_\infty, \ a \neq 0.$$

Let k and k' be two fields; we call a mapping φ of k_∞ onto k'_∞ a *place* of k if it satisfies

$$\varphi(a+b) = \varphi(a)+\varphi(b), \ \varphi(ab) = \varphi(a)\varphi(b);$$

k' is called the *residue field* of φ. Put

$$\mathfrak{o} = \{x \mid x \in k, \ \varphi(x) \neq \infty\},$$
$$\mathfrak{p} = \{x \mid x \in k, \ \varphi(x) = 0\}.$$

Then $\mathfrak{o}$ is a valuation ring of k, $\mathfrak{p}$ is the maximal ideal of $\mathfrak{o}$ and $\mathfrak{o}/\mathfrak{p}$ is isomorphic to k'; so we denote the place also by $\mathfrak{p}$ and $\varphi(x)$ by $\mathfrak{p}(x)$. If there is no fear of confusion, we denote $\mathfrak{p}(x)$ by $\tilde{x}$; similarly, the residue field is denoted by $\mathfrak{p}(k)$ or $\tilde{k}$. We call $\mathfrak{o}$ the *ring of* $\mathfrak{p}$*-integers*. If $F(X)$ is a polynomial with coefficients in $\mathfrak{o}$, $\tilde{F}(X)$ or $F_\mathfrak{p}(X)$ denotes the polynomial whose coefficients are the images of the corresponding coefficients of F by $\mathfrak{p}$. The following lemma is fundamental and well-known. A proof is given in Weil [49].

LEMMA 1. *Let S be a subring of a field k, containing the identity of k. Then, every homomorphism of S into a field k', which maps the identity of k onto the identity of k', is extended to a place of k whose residue field is contained in the algebraic closure of k'.*

We call a place $\mathfrak{p}$ of a field k *trivial* if $\mathfrak{p}$ is the identity mapping of k onto itself. We say that a place $\mathfrak{p}_1$ of a field k_1 is an *extension* of a place $\mathfrak{p}$ of a field k if $k_1 \supset k$ and $\mathfrak{p}_1(a) = \mathfrak{p}(a)$ for every $a \in k$.

9. 2. Specializations over a place. For the sake of simplicity, we fix two universal domains $\boldsymbol{K}$ and $\tilde{\boldsymbol{K}}$ with the same or different characteristics and deal only with the places defined on a subfield of $\boldsymbol{K}$ taking values in $\tilde{\boldsymbol{K}}_\infty$; this restriction is kept until the end of § 11. We denote by P^n, $\tilde{P}^n$, S^n, $\tilde{S}^n$ respectively the projective spaces and affine spaces, of dimension n, defined with respect to $\boldsymbol{K}$ and $\tilde{\boldsymbol{K}}$. Let $(x) = (x_1, \cdots, x_n)$ be a set of n elements in $\boldsymbol{K}_\infty$ and $(\xi) = (\xi, \cdots, \xi_n)$ a set of n elements in $\tilde{\boldsymbol{K}}_\infty$. We say that (ξ) is a *specialization* of (x) over a place $\mathfrak{p}$ of a field k, and write

$$(x) \rightarrow (\xi) \text{ ref. } \mathfrak{p},$$

if there exists an extension $\mathfrak{p}'$ of $\mathfrak{p}$ such that $\mathfrak{p}'(x_i) = \xi_i$ for every i. When $\mathfrak{p}$ is trivial, we write $(x) \rightarrow (\xi)$ ref. k. If the x_i are contained in k_∞, then (x) has the only specialization over $\mathfrak{p}$, which we denote by $\mathfrak{p}(x)$ or $(\tilde{x})$. We can easily verify

$$(x) \rightarrow (x') \text{ ref. } k,\ (x') \rightarrow (\xi) \text{ ref. } \mathfrak{p} \quad \Rightarrow \quad (x) \rightarrow (\xi) \text{ ref. } \mathfrak{p},$$

$$(x) \rightarrow (\xi) \text{ ref. } \mathfrak{p},\ (\xi) \rightarrow (\xi') \text{ ref. } \tilde{k} \quad \Rightarrow \quad (x) \rightarrow (\xi') \text{ ref. } \mathfrak{p}.$$

If we have $(x) \rightarrow (\xi)$ ref. $\mathfrak{p}$ and (y) is a set of elements in $\boldsymbol{K}_\infty$, then there exists a set of elements (η) in $\tilde{\boldsymbol{K}}_\infty$ such that $(x, y) \rightarrow (\xi, \eta)$ ref. $\mathfrak{p}$. This is an immediate consequence of Lemma 1.

We call a set of elements in $\boldsymbol{K}_\infty$ or $\tilde{\boldsymbol{K}}_\infty$ *finite* if it does not contain ∞; so, if (x) is finite, (x) is considered as a point of S^n, and the same for $\tilde{S}^n$. Let (ξ) be a specialization of (x) over a place $\mathfrak{p}$ of a field k. Then, if (ξ) is finite, so is (x). Assuming (ξ) to be finite, we denote by $[(x) \rightarrow (\xi); \mathfrak{p}]$ (or $[(x) \rightarrow (\xi); k]$, if $\mathfrak{p}$ is trivial,) the set of elements of the form $a(x)/b(x)$ in $k(x)$, where a and b are polynomials in $\mathfrak{o}[X]$

such that $\tilde{b}(\xi) \neq 0$, $\mathfrak{o}$ being the ring of $\mathfrak{p}$-integers. It is easy to see that $[(x) \to (\xi); \mathfrak{p}]$ is a local ring having $k(x)$ as its quotient field.

9. 3. Reduction of affine varieties. We call a place $\mathfrak{p}$ *discrete* if the ring of $\mathfrak{p}$-integers is a discrete valuation ring of rank 1. The theory in [33] concerns the reduction of varieties or cycles with respect to a discrete place. It is not difficult to extend the theory to non-discrete places, as is indicated in the appendix of [36], by means of the following lemma, which is a restatement of Proposition 26 of [33].

LEMMA 2. *Let $\mathfrak{p}$ be a discrete place of a field k and (ξ) a specialization of (x) over $\mathfrak{p}$. Then there exists a discrete place $\mathfrak{p}_1$ of $k(x)$, which is an extension of $\mathfrak{p}$, such that $\mathfrak{p}_1(x) = (\xi)$.*

COROLLARY. *Let $\mathfrak{p}$ be a place (not necessarily discrete) and (ξ) a specialization of (x) over $\mathfrak{p}$. Then there exist a field k_1 containing (x) and a discrete place $\mathfrak{p}_1$ of k_1 such that $\mathfrak{p}_1(x) = (\xi)$.*

PROOF. Let k_0 be the prime field contained in k and $\mathfrak{p}_0$ the restriction of $\mathfrak{p}$ to k_0; then we see that $\mathfrak{p}_0$ is discrete and (ξ) is a specialization of (x) over $\mathfrak{p}_0$. Hence by Lemma 2, there exists a discrete place $\mathfrak{p}_1$ of $k_0(x)$ such that $\mathfrak{p}_1(x) = (\xi)$.

In the present treatment, however, we restrict ourselves to discrete places, in order to avoid the complication arising from the generalization; therefore, from now on, *a place or an extension of a place means a discrete one*, except when the contrary is specifically stated.

Let k be a field, $\mathfrak{p}$ a place of k, and $\mathfrak{o}$ the ring of $\mathfrak{p}$-integers. Until the end of § 11, we use these notations always in this sense. Now let V be an algebraic set in the affine space S^n, defined over k. Denote by $\mathfrak{A}$ the set of polynomials $F(X)$ in $\mathfrak{o}[X]$ such that $F(x) = 0$ for every $(x) \in V$; then $\mathfrak{A}$ is an ideal of $\mathfrak{o}[X]$. We denote by $\mathfrak{p}(V)$ or $\tilde{V}$ the set of points (ξ) in $\tilde{S}^n$ such that $\tilde{F}(\xi) = 0$ for all $F \in \mathfrak{A}$. $\mathfrak{p}(V)$ is clearly an algebraic set defined over $\tilde{k}$. We can prove

$$\mathfrak{p}(V) = \{(\alpha) \mid (\alpha) \in \tilde{S}^n,\ (a) \to (\alpha) \text{ ref. } \mathfrak{p} \text{ for some } (a) \in V\}.$$

We call $\mathfrak{p}(V)$ *the reduction of V modulo* $\mathfrak{p}$. In general, $\mathfrak{X}$ being an algebro-geometric object defined with respect to k, we call the algebro-geometric object obtained by considering $\mathfrak{X}$ modulo $\mathfrak{p}$ (for which a precise definition will be given in each case) the *reduction of* $\mathfrak{X}$ *modulo* $\mathfrak{p}$, and denote it by $\mathfrak{p}(\mathfrak{X})$ or $\tilde{\mathfrak{X}}$. Let $\mathfrak{p}'$ be an extension of $\mathfrak{p}$; then we can easily verify $\mathfrak{p}(V) = \mathfrak{p}'(V)$. We have also $\mathfrak{p}(\mathfrak{X}) = \mathfrak{p}'(\mathfrak{X})$ for every algebro-geometric object $\mathfrak{X}$, whose reduction modulo $\mathfrak{p}$ is to be defined later. The following relations can be easily verified:

$$\mathfrak{p}(V \cup W) = \mathfrak{p}(V) \cup \mathfrak{p}(W), \qquad \mathfrak{p}(V \cap W) \subset \mathfrak{p}(V) \cap \mathfrak{p}(W),$$
$$\mathfrak{p}(V \times W) = \mathfrak{p}(V) \times \mathfrak{p}(W).$$

It may happen that $\tilde{V}$ is an empty set even if V is not empty. If the components of V are all of the same dimension r, and if $\tilde{V}$ is not empty, then the components of $\tilde{V}$ are all of dimension r.

We shall now define the reduction of cycles in S^n modulo $\mathfrak{p}$. We begin with the cycles of dimension 0. Let Y be a cycle of dimension 0 in S^n, rational over k; let $Y = \sum_{i=1}^{s} m_i a_i$ be its reduced expression, where the m_i are rational integers and the a_i are points of S^n. Consider a specialization

$$(a_1, \cdots, a_s) \to (\alpha_1, \cdots, \alpha_s) \text{ ref. } \mathfrak{p}$$

and remove those α_i having ∞ as one of their coordinates. Then the sum $\sum' m_i \alpha_i$ of the remaining α_i gives a cycle in $\tilde{S}^n$; and it can be proved that this cycle is uniquely determined by Y and $\mathfrak{p}$, and does not depend upon the choice of the above specialization. We call the cycle the *reduction of* Y *modulo* $\mathfrak{p}$ and denote it by $\mathfrak{p}(Y)$ or $\tilde{Y}$.

Now consider a cycle Z in S^n, of dimension r, rational over k. Let t_{ij}, for $1 \leqq i \leqq r$, $0 \leqq j \leqq n$, be $r(n+1)$ independent variables over k, and $\tilde{t}_{ij}$, for $1 \leqq i \leqq r$, $0 \leqq j \leqq n$, be $r(n+1)$ independent variables over $\tilde{k}$. Let L and $\tilde{L}$ denote the linear varieties defined respectively by

$$\sum_{j=1}^{n} t_{ij} X_j - t_{i0} = 0 \quad (1 \leqq i \leqq r),$$
$$\sum_{j=1}^{n} \tilde{t}_{ij} X_j - \tilde{t}_{i0} = 0 \quad (1 \leqq i \leqq r).$$

Then the intersection-product $Z\cdot L$ is defined and is a cycle of dimension 0 in S^n, rational over $k(t_{ij})$. We see that the specialization $(t_{ij}) \to (\tilde{t}_{ij})$ ref. $\mathfrak{p}$ gives a discrete extension $\mathfrak{p}'$ of $\mathfrak{p}$ in $k(t_{ij})$; so we can consider $\mathfrak{p}'(Z\cdot L)$. Now, it can be proved that there exists a cycle $\tilde{Z}$ of dimension r in $\tilde{S}^n$, rational over $\tilde{k}$, such that $\tilde{Z}\cdot\tilde{L} = \mathfrak{p}'(Z\cdot L)$; and such a cycle $\tilde{Z}$ is uniquely determined by Z and $\mathfrak{p}$. We call $\tilde{Z}$ the *reduction of Z modulo* $\mathfrak{p}$ and denote it by $\mathfrak{p}(Z)$. If Z is positive, the components of $\tilde{Z}$ are the components of the reduction of the support of Z.

Let V be an algebraic variety of dimension r in S^n, defined over k and α a point of $\tilde{V}$. We say that α is *simple* on V if there exist $n-r$ polynomials $F_1(X),\cdots, F_{n-r}(X)$ in $\mathfrak{o}[X]$, vanishing on V, such that

$$\operatorname{rank}(\partial\tilde{F}_i/\partial X_j(\alpha)) = n-r.$$

Let $\mathfrak{U}$ be a subvariety of $\tilde{V}$; we say that $\mathfrak{U}$ is *simple* on V if $\mathfrak{U}$ has a point which is simple on V. If x is a generic point of V over k and if a point ξ of $\tilde{V}$ is simple on V, then $[x \to \xi;\, \mathfrak{p}]$ is a regular local ring, so that it is integrally closed.[3] Let $\mathfrak{V}$ be a component of $\tilde{V}$. Then, $\mathfrak{V}$ is simple on V if and only if $\mathfrak{V}$ is of multiplicity 1 in the cycle $\mathfrak{p}(V)$. Suppose that a component $\mathfrak{V}$ of $\tilde{V}$ is simple on V; then, a point ξ of $\mathfrak{V}$ is simple on V if and only if ξ is simple on $\mathfrak{V}$; if x is generic on V over k and ξ is generic on $\mathfrak{V}$ over the algebraic closure of $\tilde{k}$, then $[x \to \xi;\, \mathfrak{p}]$ is a discrete valuation ring of rank 1 and every prime element of $\mathfrak{o}$ is a prime element of $[x \to \xi;\, \mathfrak{p}]$.

Let V and W be two affine varieties, defined over k, and T a birational correspondence between V and W, defined over k. Let $x\times y$ be a generic point of T over k and ξ a point of $\tilde{V}$. We say that T is *regular* at ξ if the coordinates of y are all contained in $[x \to \xi;\, \mathfrak{p}]$; if that is so, there exists one and only one point η on $\tilde{W}$ such that $\xi\times\eta \in \tilde{T}$. Let $\mathfrak{p}'$ be an extension of $\mathfrak{p}$; then T is regular at a point ξ of V with respect to $\mathfrak{p}$ if and only if T is so with respect to $\mathfrak{p}'$.

---

3) The proof in [33] of this fact is based on Proposition 17 of that paper, which the author considered as a simple translation of Proposition 19 of Weil [44] Chap. V. It is not easy, however, to prove the former proposition by the same argument as in the proof of the latter. A complete proof is given in Appendix of [24].

$\xi\times\eta$ being a point in $\tilde{T}$, we say that ξ and η are *regularly corresponding points* by T if T is regular at ξ and at η.

9. 4. Reduction of abstract varieties. Let $[V_\alpha;\ F_\alpha;\ T_{\beta\alpha}]$ be an abstract variety, defined over k; let, for each α, $\mathfrak{F}_\alpha$ be an algebraic subset in $\tilde{V}_\alpha$, other than $\tilde{V}_\alpha$, defined over $\tilde{k}$, containing $\tilde{F}_\alpha$. We call the system

$$[V_\alpha;\ F_\alpha;\ \mathfrak{F}_\alpha;\ T_{\beta\alpha}]$$

a $\mathfrak{p}$-*variety* if the following condition is satisfied:

(V) *If ξ is a point in $\tilde{V}_\alpha-\mathfrak{F}_\alpha$ and η is a point in $\tilde{V}_\beta-\mathfrak{F}_\beta$ such that $\xi\times\eta$ is in $\tilde{T}_{\beta\alpha}$, then ξ and η are regularly corresponding points by $T_{\beta\alpha}$.*

$V=[V_\alpha;F_\alpha;\mathfrak{F}_\alpha;T_{\beta\alpha}]$ being a $\mathfrak{p}$-variety, let $[U_{\alpha(\lambda)};F_{\alpha(\lambda)}\cap U_{\alpha(\lambda)};R_{\mu\lambda}]$ be a subvariety of $[V_\alpha;\ F_\alpha;\ T_{\beta\alpha}]$, defined over k. Then the system

$$[U_{\alpha(\lambda)};\ F_{\alpha(\lambda)}\cap U_{\alpha(\lambda)};\ \mathfrak{F}_{\alpha(\lambda)}\cap \tilde{U}_{\alpha(\lambda)};\ R_{\mu\lambda}]$$

defines a $\mathfrak{p}$-variety, which we call a subvariety of the $\mathfrak{p}$-variety V. Let $W=[W_\gamma;G_\gamma;\mathfrak{G}_\gamma;S_{\delta\gamma}]$ be another $\mathfrak{p}$-variety and $[V_\alpha\times W_\gamma;\ H_{\alpha\gamma};\ U_{\beta\delta,\alpha\gamma}]$ the product-variety of the abstract varieties $[V_\alpha;\ F_\alpha;\ T_{\beta\alpha}]$ and $[W_\gamma;\ G_\gamma;\ S_{\delta\gamma}]$. Put $\mathfrak{H}_{\alpha\gamma}=(\mathfrak{F}_\alpha\times\tilde{W}_\gamma)\cup(\tilde{V}_\alpha\times\mathfrak{G}_\gamma)$. Then the system $[V_\alpha\times W_\gamma;\ H_{\alpha\gamma};\ \mathfrak{H}_{\alpha\gamma};\ U_{\beta\delta,\alpha\gamma}]$ defines a $\mathfrak{p}$-variety which will be called the product variety of the $\mathfrak{p}$-varieties V and W. Every projective variety defined over k defines a uniquely determined $\mathfrak{p}$-variety with empty $\mathfrak{F}_\alpha$.

Let $V=[V_\alpha;F_\alpha;\mathfrak{F}_\alpha;T_{\beta\alpha}]$ be a $\mathfrak{p}$-variety and the x_α corresponding generic points of the V_α over k by the $T_{\beta\alpha}$; and let $(\xi_1,\cdots,\xi_h)$ be a specialization of $(x_1,\cdots,x_h)$ over $\mathfrak{p}$. By a full set of representatives attached to $\tilde{V}$, we understand the set $(\xi_{\alpha_1},\cdots,\xi_{\alpha_s})$ of all the ξ_α which are finite and not in $\mathfrak{F}_\alpha$. We say that V is $\mathfrak{p}$-*complete* if no full set of representatives attached to $\tilde{V}$ is empty. The following facts are easily proved: i) the underlying abstract variety of a $\mathfrak{p}$-complete $\mathfrak{p}$-variety is complete; ii) every subvariety of a $\mathfrak{p}$-complete $\mathfrak{p}$-variety is $\mathfrak{p}$-complete; iii) the product of $\mathfrak{p}$-complete $\mathfrak{p}$-varieties is $\mathfrak{p}$-complete; iv) every projective variety defined over k defines a $\mathfrak{p}$-complete $\mathfrak{p}$-variety.

V being as above, let $\mathfrak{W}=[\mathfrak{W}_\lambda;\mathfrak{G}_\lambda;\mathfrak{S}_{\mu\lambda}]$ be an abstract variety defined over an extension $\tilde{k}_1$ of $\tilde{k}$. We say that $\mathfrak{W}$ is a *variety in $\tilde{V}$*

if the following conditions are satisfied: i) there exists a full set of representatives $(\xi_{\alpha(1)},\cdots,\xi_{\alpha(s)})$ attached to $\tilde{V}$ such that, for every λ, $\mathfrak{W}_\lambda$ is the locus of $\xi_{\alpha(\lambda)}$ over $\tilde{k}_1$; ii) $\mathfrak{G}_\lambda = \mathfrak{W}_\lambda \cap \mathfrak{F}_{\alpha(\lambda)}$; iii) $\mathfrak{S}_{\mu\lambda}$ is the variety in $\tilde{T}_{\alpha(\mu)\alpha(\lambda)}$ with the projection $\mathfrak{W}_\lambda$ on $\tilde{V}_{\alpha(\lambda)}$ and $\mathfrak{W}_\mu$ on $\tilde{V}_{\alpha(\mu)}$. We call $\mathfrak{W}_\lambda$ the *representatives* of $\mathfrak{W}$ in $V_{\alpha(\lambda)}$. For every variety $\mathfrak{W}_\alpha$ in $\tilde{V}_\alpha$ which is not contained in $\mathfrak{F}_\alpha$, there exists one and only one variety $\mathfrak{W}$ in $\tilde{V}$ such that $\mathfrak{W}_\alpha$ is a representative of $\mathfrak{W}$ in V_α. By a *point* in $\tilde{V}$ we understand a 0-dimensional variety in $\tilde{V}$. It is obvious that all the representatives of a point in $\tilde{V}$ form a full set of representatives attached to $\tilde{V}$ and conversely. Let x be a point in V and ξ a point in $\tilde{V}$. We say that ξ is a *specialization of x over* $\mathfrak{p}$ if x and ξ have representatives x_α and ξ_α in some V_α such that ξ_α is a specialization of x_α over $\mathfrak{p}$; since $[x_\alpha \to \xi_\alpha; \mathfrak{p}]$ is independent of α, we denote it by $[x \to \xi; \mathfrak{p}]$. A variety $\mathfrak{W}$ in $\tilde{V}$ is called *simple* on V if a representative $\mathfrak{W}_\alpha$ of $\mathfrak{W}$ is simple on V_α.

Let $V = [V_\alpha; F_\alpha; \mathfrak{F}_\alpha; T_{\beta\alpha}]$ be a $\mathfrak{p}$-variety of dimension n. V is called $\mathfrak{p}$-*simple* if there exists one and only one variety $\mathfrak{V}$ of dimension n in $\tilde{V}$ and if every representative $\mathfrak{V}_\alpha$ of $\mathfrak{V}$ in V_α is of multiplicity 1 in the cycle $\mathfrak{p}(V_\alpha)$. If that is so, $\mathfrak{V}$ is an abstract variety defined over $\tilde{k}$. We call the abstract variety $\mathfrak{V}$ the *reduction of V modulo* $\mathfrak{p}$ and denote it by $\mathfrak{p}(V)$.

V and $\mathfrak{V}$ being as above, we see that every subvariety of $\mathfrak{V}$ is a variety in $\tilde{V}$ and conversely; and $\mathfrak{W}$ is simple on $\mathfrak{V}$ if and only if $\mathfrak{W}$ is simple on V. Let W be an algebraic subset of V, rational over k. We denote by $\mathfrak{p}(W)$ or $\tilde{W}$ the set of points of $\mathfrak{V}$ which are specializations of points in W. Then $\mathfrak{p}(W)$ is an algebraic subset of $\mathfrak{V}$, rational over $\tilde{k}$. Let $X = \sum_i m_i A_i$ be a cycle on V, rational over k, where the A_i are subvarieties of V. Let k' be a field of definition for the A_i containing k and $\mathfrak{p}'$ an extension of $\mathfrak{p}$ in k'. Take, for each i, a representative $A_{i\alpha}$ of A_i in V_α and put $\mathfrak{p}'(A_{i\alpha}) = \sum_j l_j \mathfrak{B}_{j\alpha}$, where the $\mathfrak{B}_{j\alpha}$ are varieties in $\tilde{V}_\alpha$. Put $\mathfrak{A}_i = \sum' l_j \mathfrak{B}_j$, where $\mathfrak{B}_j$ is the variety in $\mathfrak{V}$ having $\mathfrak{B}_{j\alpha}$ as the representative in V_α and the sum is taken over all $\mathfrak{B}_j$ which is simple on $\mathfrak{V}$. Then the cycle $\sum m_i \mathfrak{A}_i$ on $\mathfrak{V}$ is rational over $\tilde{k}$ and determined only by X and $\mathfrak{p}$. We denote it by

$\mathfrak{p}(X)$ or $\tilde{X}$. The reduction of cycles preserves the operation on cycles:

PROPOSITION 1. (1) *Let V be a $\mathfrak{p}$-simple $\mathfrak{p}$-variety; let X and Y be positive cycles on V, rational over k such that the intersection-products $X\cdot Y$ and $\mathfrak{p}(X)\cdot\mathfrak{p}(Y)$ are defined. Then we have*

$$\mathfrak{p}(X\cdot Y)=\mathfrak{p}(X)\cdot\mathfrak{p}(Y).$$

(2) *Let V and W be $\mathfrak{p}$-simple $\mathfrak{p}$-varieties, X a cycle on V and Y a cycle on W, both rational over k. Then $V\times W$ is $\mathfrak{p}$-simple and we have*

$$\mathfrak{p}(X\times Y)=\mathfrak{p}(X)\times\mathfrak{p}(Y).$$

(3) *Let V and W be $\mathfrak{p}$-simple $\mathfrak{p}$-varieties; denote by $\mathfrak{V}$ and $\mathfrak{W}$ the reduction of V and W modulo $\mathfrak{p}$, respectively. Suppose that W is $\mathfrak{p}$-complete and $\mathfrak{W}$ has no multiple point. If X is a cycle on $V\times W$, rational over k, then we have*

$$\mathfrak{p}(\mathrm{pr}_V(X))=\mathrm{pr}_{\mathfrak{V}}(\mathfrak{p}(X)).$$

10. REDUCTION OF RATIONAL MAPPINGS AND DIFFERENTIAL FORMS.

10.1. Reduction of rational mappings. Let V and W be two $\mathfrak{p}$-varieties and f a rational mapping of V into W defined over k. Let ξ be a point in $\tilde{V}$ and x a generic point of V over k; put $f(x)=y$. We say that f is *defined* at ξ if there exists a point η on $\tilde{W}$ such that

$$[y\rightarrow\eta;\mathfrak{p}]\subset[x\rightarrow\xi;\mathfrak{p}];$$

this definition is independent of the choice of x and any extension of $\mathfrak{p}$. It is easy to see that η is uniquely determined by f and ξ. We shall write $f(\xi)=\eta$.

V, W and f being as above, suppose that V and W are $\mathfrak{p}$-simple. Let T be the graph of f, $x\times y$ a generic point of T over k and ξ a generic point of $\tilde{V}$ over $\tilde{k}$. Since $[x\rightarrow\xi;\mathfrak{p}]$ is a valuation ring, f is defined at ξ whenever W is $\mathfrak{p}$-complete. Suppose that f is defined at some point in $\tilde{V}$; then f is defined at ξ; put $f(\xi)=\eta$. Define a rational mapping $\tilde{f}$ of $\tilde{V}$ into $\tilde{W}$ by $\tilde{f}(\xi)=\eta$ with respect to $\tilde{k}$. We call $\tilde{f}$ the *reduction of f modulo* $\mathfrak{p}$. We see easily that if f is defined at $\alpha \in \tilde{V}$, $\tilde{f}$ is also defined at α and $f(\alpha) = \tilde{f}(\alpha)$. Denote by $\mathfrak{T}$ the graph of $\tilde{f}$. Then we have clearly $\tilde{T} \supset \mathfrak{T}$; and $\mathfrak{T}$ is the only component of $\tilde{T}$ whose projection on $\tilde{V}$ is $\tilde{V}$.

PROPOSITION 2. *Let V and W be two $\mathfrak{p}$-simple $\mathfrak{p}$-varieties, f a rational mapping of V into W, defined over k. Suppose that f is everywhere defined on $\tilde{V}$. Let $\tilde{f}$ be the reduction of f modulo $\mathfrak{p}$; denote by T and $\mathfrak{T}$ the graphs of f and $\tilde{f}$, respectively. If $\mathfrak{T}$ is simple on $V \times W$, we have $\mathfrak{p}(T) = \mathfrak{T}$, where T and $\mathfrak{T}$ are considered as cycles.*

PROOF. The notations x, y, ξ, η being as above, let, $\alpha \times \beta$ a point of $\tilde{T}$. As f is defined at α, we have $\beta = f(\alpha) = \tilde{f}(\alpha)$, so that $\alpha \times \beta$ is a point of $\mathfrak{T}$. Hence $\mathfrak{T}$ is the only component of $\tilde{T}$. Put $\mathfrak{p}(T) = m\mathfrak{T}$, where m is a positive integer. If W is $\mathfrak{p}$-complete and $\mathfrak{p}(W)$ has no multiple point, we have $m = 1$ applying (3) of Proposition 1. We can prove $m = 1$, without such assumptions on W, applying Theorem 12 of [33] to a representative of T.

Let U, V and W be $\mathfrak{p}$-simple $\mathfrak{p}$-varieties; let f and g be rational mappings of U into V and of V into W, respectively. Suppose that f is defined at a point ξ on $\tilde{U}$ and g is defined at $f(\xi)$. Then it is easy to see that the rational mapping $g \circ f$ is defined at ξ and $g \circ f(\xi) = g(f(\xi))$. We see easily $g(f(\xi)) = g(\tilde{f}(\xi)) = \tilde{g}(\tilde{f}(\xi))$. This shows

$$\widetilde{g \circ f} = \tilde{g} \circ \tilde{f}.$$

10. 2. Reduction of functions. Let V be a $\mathfrak{p}$-simple variety and f a generalized function on V, defined over k, namely, a rational mapping of V into the projective space P^1 of dimension 1. Then $\tilde{f}$ gives a rational mapping of $\tilde{V}$ into P^1. We say that f is $\mathfrak{p}$-*finite* if $\tilde{f}$ is not the constant ∞.

PROPOSITION 3. *Let V be a $\mathfrak{p}$-simple $\mathfrak{p}$-variety, and f a function on V, defined over k. If f is $\mathfrak{p}$-finite and $\tilde{f}$ is not the constant* 0, *we have*

$$\mathfrak{p}((f)) = (\tilde{f}).$$

This is a restatement of Theorem 20 of [33].

Now denote by k^* the completion of k with respect to $\mathfrak{p}$ and by

$\mathfrak{o}^*$, $\mathfrak{p}^*$ the closure of $\mathfrak{o}$, $\mathfrak{p}$ in k^*; let μ denote the normalized exponential valuation of k^*; namely, μ is the mapping of k^* into $\boldsymbol{Z} \cup \{\infty\}$ such that

$$\mu(xy) = \mu(x)+\mu(y), \qquad \mu(x+y) \geqq \operatorname{Min}\{\mu(x), \mu(y)\},$$

$$\mathfrak{o}^* = \{a \mid a \in k^*, \mu(a) \geqq 0\},$$

and $\mu(a) = 1$ for every prime element a of $\mathfrak{o}^*$.

LEMMA 3. *Let $\mathcal{M}$ be a vector space over k^* of dimension n. Let λ be a mapping of $\mathcal{M}$ into $\boldsymbol{R} \cup \{\infty\}$ such that, for every $f, g \in \mathcal{M}$ and every $a \in k^*$,*

i) $\lambda(f) = \infty \Longleftrightarrow f = 0$,

ii) $\lambda(f+g) \geqq \operatorname{Min}\{\lambda(f), \lambda(g)\}$,

iii) $\lambda(af) = \mu(a)+\lambda(f)$.

Put $\mathcal{M}_0 = \{f \mid f \in \mathcal{M},\ \lambda(f) \geqq 0\}$, $\mathcal{N} = \{f \mid f \in \mathcal{M},\ \lambda(f) \geqq 1\}$. Then $\mathcal{M}_0$ is a free $\mathfrak{o}^*$-module of rank n; and $\mathcal{M}_0/\mathcal{N}$ is a vector space of dimension n over the residue field $\mathfrak{p}(k)$.

PROOF. It is easy to see that $\mathcal{M}_0$ forms an $\mathfrak{o}^*$-module, $\mathcal{M} = k^*\mathcal{M}_0$ and $\mathcal{M}_0/\mathcal{N}$ is considered as a vector space over $\tilde{k}$ of dimension $\leqq n$. Let $f_1, \cdots, f_m$ be elements of $\mathcal{M}_0$ giving a basis of $\mathcal{M}_0/\mathcal{N}$ over $\tilde{k}$; Now we shall show that $\mathcal{M}_0 = \mathfrak{o}^*f_1+\cdots+\mathfrak{o}^*f_m$. Take and fix a prime element π of $\mathfrak{o}^*$. Let g be an element of $\mathcal{M}_0$. Then there exist m elements a_{0i} of $\mathfrak{o}^*$ such that $g-\sum_i a_{0i}f_i \in \mathcal{N}$. Put $g = \sum_i a_{0i}f_i+\pi g_1$; then g_1 is contained in $\mathcal{M}_0$. Applying the same argument to g_1, we find m elements a_{1i} of $\mathfrak{o}^*$ and an element g_2 of $\mathcal{M}_0$ such that $g_1 = \sum_i a_{1i}f_i+\pi g_2$. Repeating this procedure, we obtain m sequences $\{a_{\nu i}\}$ of elements of $\mathfrak{o}^*$ and a sequence $\{g_\nu\}$ of elements of $\mathcal{M}_0$ such that $g_\nu = \sum_i a_{\nu i}f_i+\pi g_{\nu+1}$. Since k^* is complete, the series $\sum_{\nu=0}^{\infty} a_{\nu i}\pi^\nu$, for each i, has a meaning and defines an element b_i of $\mathfrak{o}^*$. Then, it can be easily verified that $g = \sum b_i f_i$. This proves that $\mathcal{M}_0 = \mathfrak{o}^*f_1+\cdots+\mathfrak{o}^*f_m$. As we have $\mathcal{M} = k^*\mathcal{M}_0$, we must have $m = n$; this proves our lemma.

Let V be a $\mathfrak{p}$-simple $\mathfrak{p}$-variety and X a divisor of V, rational over k. Consider the set $L(X; k)$ of the functions f on V, defined over k, such that $(f) > -X$. Denote by $L_0(X; k)$ the set of $\mathfrak{p}$-finite elements in $L(X; k)$. Suppose that $L(X; k)$ is of a finite dimension n over k. We shall now prove that $L_0(X; k)$ is a free $\mathfrak{o}$-module of rank n. The notations k^*, $\mathfrak{o}^*$ and $\mathfrak{p}^*$ being as above, we can choose our universal domain $\boldsymbol{K}$ so that it contains k^* as subfield. Let $k(V)$ and $k^*(V)$ denote the fields of functions on V defined over k and over k^*, respectively. Then, $k(V)$ and k^* is linearly disjoint over k; so we can define a tensor product $\mathcal{M}$ of $L(X; k)$ and k^* over k as a submodule of $k^*(V)$. Let x be a generic point of V over k^* and ξ a generic point of $\tilde{V}$ over $\mathfrak{p}^*(k^*)$. Then $[x \to \xi; \mathfrak{p}^*]$ is a discrete valuation ring and every prime element of $\mathfrak{o}$ gives a prime element of that valuation ring. Therefore, considering the isomorphism between $k^*(x)$ and $k^*(V)$, we obtain an exponential valuation λ of $k^*(V)$, which satisfies the conditions of Lemma 3. Hence, by that lemma, if we denote by $\mathcal{M}_0$ the set of $\mathfrak{p}^*$-finite elements in $\mathcal{M}$, $\mathcal{M}_0$ has a basis $\{g_1, \cdots, g_n\}$ over $\mathfrak{o}^*$. Let $\{h_1, \cdots, h_n\}$ be a basis of $L(X; k)$ over k; then the g_i are expressed in the form $g_i = \sum c_{ij} h_j$ with c_{ij} in k^*. As k is dense in k^*, there exist elements d_{ij} in k such that the matrix $(d_{ij})(c_{ij})^{-1}$ is congruent with the unit matrix modulo $\mathfrak{p}^*$. Put $f_i = \sum d_{ij} h_j$. Then we see that $\{f_1, \cdots, f_n\}$ gives a basis of $\mathcal{M}_0$ over $\mathfrak{o}^*$, and hence a basis of $L_0(X; k)$ over $\mathfrak{o}$. Thus we have proved that $L_0(X; k)$ is a free $\mathfrak{o}$-module of rank n. By Proposition 3, we have $(\tilde{f}_i) > -\mathfrak{p}(X)$. As the $\tilde{f}_i$ are linearly independent over $\tilde{k}$, we obtain the inequality

$$l(X) \leqq l(\mathfrak{p}(X)). \tag{1}$$

10. 3. Local parameters at a point of $\tilde{V}$. Let V be a $\mathfrak{p}$-simple $\mathfrak{p}$-variety of dimension r; let ξ be a simple point on $\tilde{V}$; then ξ is simple on V. We call a set of r functions $\varphi_1, \cdots, \varphi_r$ in $k(V)$ a *system of local parameters* for V at ξ, defined over k, if the following conditions are satisfied:

(L_0 1) *$k(V)$ is separably algebraic over $k(\varphi_1, \cdots, \varphi_r)$.*

(L_0 2) *The φ_i are all defined and finite at ξ.*

(L_0 3) *For every f in $k(V)$, defined and finite at ξ, $\partial f / \partial \varphi_i$ is defined and finite at ξ for every i.* (For the notation $\partial / \partial \varphi_i$, see § 2. 2.)

PROPOSITION 4. *V and ξ being as above, let x be a generic point of V over k and V_α, x_α, ξ_α be representatives of V, x, ξ; and let S^n be the ambient space for V_α. Then, r elements $\varphi_1, \cdots, \varphi_r$ in $k(V)$ form a system of local parameters at ξ if and only if the following conditions are satisfied.*

(L_0' 1) *The φ_i are defined and finite at ξ.*

(L_0' 2) *There exists a set of n polynomials $F_i(X_1, \cdots, X_n, T_1, \cdots, T_r)$ in $\mathfrak{o}[X_1, \cdots, X_n, T_1, \cdots, T_r]$ such that $F_i(x_\alpha, t) = 0$ for $1 \leqq i \leqq n$ and*

$$\det\left(\frac{\partial \tilde{F}_i}{\partial X_j}(\xi_\alpha, \tau)\right) \neq 0,$$

where $t_i = \varphi_i(x)$, $\tau_i = \varphi_i(\xi)$ for $1 \leqq i \leqq r$.

PROOF. We first prove the "if" part. Let $(x_{\alpha 1}, \cdots, x_{\alpha n})$ be the coordinates of x_α and f_i the function on V defined by $f_i(x) = x_{\alpha i}$, with respect to k. By Corollary of Theorem 1 of Weil [44] Chap. I, (L_0' 2) implies that $k(x)$ is separably algebraic over $k(t)$; so $k(V) = k(f_1, \cdots, f_n)$ is separably algebraic over $k(\varphi_1, \cdots, \varphi_r)$. Differentiating the equations $F_h(x_\alpha, t) = 0$, we have

$$(2)\quad \sum_{i=1}^{n} \frac{\partial F_h}{\partial X_i}(x_\alpha, t)\frac{\partial f_i}{\partial \varphi_j}(x) + \frac{\partial F_h}{\partial T_j}(x_\alpha, t) = 0 \qquad (1 \leqq h \leqq n,\ 1 \leqq j \leqq r).$$

As we have $\det(\partial \tilde{F}_h / \partial X_j(\xi_\alpha, \tau)) \neq 0$, we observe that the functions $\partial f_i / \partial \varphi_j$ are all defined and finite at ξ. If g is an element of $k(V)$ defined and finite at ξ, we get a representation $g(x) = G(x_\alpha)/H(x_\alpha)$, where $G(X)$ and $H(X)$ are polynomials in $\mathfrak{o}[X]$ such that $\tilde{H}(\xi_\alpha) \neq 0$. We have then

$$(3)\quad \frac{\partial g}{\partial \varphi_j}(x) = H(x_\alpha)^{-2}\left\{H(x_\alpha)\sum_{i=1}^{n}\frac{\partial G}{\partial X_i}(x_\alpha)\frac{\partial f_i}{\partial \varphi_j}(x) - G(x_\alpha)\sum_{i=1}^{n}\frac{\partial H}{\partial X_i}(x_\alpha)\frac{\partial f_i}{\partial \varphi_j}(x)\right\}$$

for $1 \leqq j \leqq n$. This shows that the functions $\partial g / \partial \varphi_j$ are all defined and finite at ξ. The "if" part is thereby proved. Conversely, suppose that the φ_i satisfy the conditions (L_0 1-3). As ξ_α is simple on V_α, there exist $n-r$ polynomials $A_\nu(X)$ in $\mathfrak{o}[X]$ such that $A_\nu(x_\alpha) = 0$ and

$$(4)\qquad \operatorname{rank}\left(\frac{\partial \tilde{A}_\nu}{\partial X_i}(\xi_\alpha)\right) = n-r.$$

From the relation $A_\nu(x_\alpha)=0$, it follows that

$$(5)\qquad \sum_{i=1}^{n}\frac{\partial \tilde{A}_\nu}{\partial X_i}(\xi_\alpha)\frac{\partial f_i}{\partial \varphi_j}(\xi)=0 \qquad (1\leqq \nu\leqq n-r,\ 1\leqq j\leqq r).$$

By (L_0 2), each φ_i has an expression $\varphi_i(x)=B_i(x_\alpha)/C_i(x_\alpha)$, where B_i and C_i are polynomials in $\mathfrak{o}[X]$ such that $\tilde{C}_i(\xi_\alpha)\neq 0$; then, differentiating $B_h(x_\alpha)-\varphi_h(x)C_h(x_\alpha)=0$ and substituting ξ for x, we have

$$(6)\qquad \sum_{i=1}^{n}\left[\frac{\partial \tilde{B}_h}{\partial X_i}(\xi_\alpha)-\varphi_h(\xi)\frac{\partial \tilde{C}_h}{\partial X_i}(\xi_\alpha)\right]\frac{\partial f_i}{\partial \varphi_j}(\xi)=\delta_{hj}\tilde{C}_h(\xi_\alpha),$$

where $\delta_{hj}=0$ or 1 according as $h\neq j$ or $h=j$. Put

$$F_h(X,T)=B_h(X)-T_hC_h(X) \qquad (1\leqq h\leqq r),$$

$$F_{r+\nu}(X,T)=A_\nu(X) \qquad (1\leqq \nu\leqq n-r).$$

We have then $F_i(x_\alpha,t)=0$ for $1\leqq i\leqq n$, and, by the relations (4), (5), (6),

$$\det\left(\frac{\partial \tilde{F}_i}{\partial X_j}(\xi_\alpha,\tau)\right)\neq 0.$$

This completes the proof.

We have to show the existence of a system of local parameters. Let the notations be the same as in Proposition 4. As ξ_α is simple on V_α, there exist $n-r$ polynomials $G_i(X)$ in $\mathfrak{o}[X]$ such that $G_i(x_\alpha)=0$ and

$$\operatorname{rank}\left(\frac{\partial \tilde{G}_i}{\partial X_j}(\xi_\alpha)\right)=n-r.$$

We can find r linear forms $H_i(X)=\sum_{j=1}^{n}c_{ij}X_j$ $(1\leqq i\leqq r)$ with c_{ij} in $\mathfrak{o}$, such that

$$\det\begin{bmatrix}\partial \tilde{G}_i/\partial X_j(\xi_\alpha)\\ \tilde{c}_{ij}\end{bmatrix}\neq 0.$$

Let φ_i, for each i, be the function on V defined by $\varphi_i(x)=\sum_{j=1}^{n}c_{ij}x_{\alpha j}$ with respect to k, where $(x_{\alpha 1},\cdots,x_{\alpha n})$ denotes the coordinates of x_α. Put

$$F_h(X, T) = T_h - \sum c_{hj}X_j \qquad (1 \leqq h \leqq r),$$
$$F_{r+i}(X, T) = G_i(X) \qquad (1 \leqq i \leqq n-r).$$

Then it can be easily verified that the set $\{\varphi_1, \cdots, \varphi_r\}$ satisfies the conditions (L_0' 1-2) of the above proposition for these F_i; so the φ_i are local parameters at ξ.

PROPOSITION 5. *Let V be a $\mathfrak{p}$-simple $\mathfrak{p}$-variety, ξ a simple point on $\tilde{V}$ and $\{\varphi_1, \cdots, \varphi_r\}$ a system of local parameters for V at ξ, defined over k. Then $\{\tilde{\varphi}_1, \cdots, \tilde{\varphi}_r\}$ is a system of local parameters for $\tilde{V}$ at ξ. Moreover, if f is an element of $k(V)$, defined and finite at ξ, then f and the $\partial f/\partial\varphi_i$ are all $\mathfrak{p}$-finite and we have, for every i,*

$$\widetilde{\frac{\partial f}{\partial \varphi_i}} = \frac{\partial \tilde{f}}{\partial \varphi_i}. \tag{7}$$

PROOF. The first assertion follows from Proposition 4. Let f be an element of $k(V)$, defined and finite at ξ. Then by (L_0 3), the $\partial f/\partial\varphi_j$ are defined and finite at ξ. It follows that f and the $\partial f/\partial\varphi_i$ are all defined and finite at a generic point η of $\tilde{V}$ over $\tilde{k}$; this implies that f and the $\partial f/\partial\varphi_i$ are all $\mathfrak{p}$-finite. Considering the equations (2) and (3) in the proof of Proposition 4 modulo the maximal ideal of the valuation ring $[x \to \eta; \mathfrak{p}]$, we obtain the equality (7).

10. 4. Reduction of differential forms. V being as in § 10.3, let ω be a differential form on V, defined over k. We say that ω is $\mathfrak{p}$-*finite* if it has an expression

$$\omega = \sum_{(i)} f_{(i)} dg_{i_1} \cdots dg_{i_s},$$

where the $f_{(i)}$ and the g_i are $\mathfrak{p}$-finite elements of $k(V)$. We say that ω is *finite* at a simple point ξ of $\tilde{V}$ if the $f_{(i)}$ and the g_i in the above expression can be taken in such a way that they are all defined and finite at ξ. ω is $\mathfrak{p}$-finite if and only if it is finite at a generic point on $\tilde{V}$ over $\tilde{k}$. Let $\{\varphi_1, \cdots, \varphi_r\}$ be a system of local parameters at ξ. We have then

$$\omega = \sum_{j_1 < \cdots < j_s} h_{j_1 \ldots j_s} d\varphi_{j_1} \cdots d\varphi_{j_s},$$

where

$$h_{j_1\cdots j_s}=\sum_{(i)}\sum_{(l)}\varepsilon\binom{l_1\cdots l_s}{j_1\cdots j_s}f_{(i)}\frac{\partial g_{i_1}}{\partial\varphi_{l_1}}\cdots\frac{\partial g_{i_s}}{\partial\varphi_{l_s}},$$

$\varepsilon\binom{l_1\cdots l_s}{j_1\cdots j_s}$ denoting the sign of the permutation $\binom{l_1\cdots l_s}{j_1\cdots j_s}$. By ($L_0$ 3), ω is finite at ξ if and only if the $h_{(j)}$ are defined and finite at ξ. Supposing that the $f_{(i)}$ and the g_i are $\mathfrak{p}$-finite, we have, by Proposition 5,

$$\tilde{h}_{j_1\cdots j_s}=\sum_{(i)}\sum_{(l)}\varepsilon\binom{l_1\cdots l_s}{j_1\cdots j_s}\tilde{f}_{(i)}\frac{\partial\tilde{g}_{i_1}}{\partial\tilde{\varphi}_{l_1}}\cdots\frac{\partial\tilde{g}_{i_s}}{\partial\tilde{\varphi}_{l_s}}.$$

so that

$$\tilde{f}_{(i)}d\tilde{g}_{i_1}\cdots d\tilde{g}_{i_s}=\sum_{j_1<\cdots<j_s}\tilde{h}_{(j)}d\tilde{\varphi}_{j_1}\cdots d\tilde{\varphi}_{j_s}. \tag{8}$$

As the $h_{(j)}$ are determined only by ω and $\varphi_1,\cdots,\varphi_r$, the relation (8) shows that the differential form $\sum_{(i)}\tilde{f}_{(i)}d\tilde{g}_{i_1}\cdots d\tilde{g}_{i_s}$ on $\tilde{V}$ is determined only by ω and is independent of the choice of the $f_{(i)}$ and the g_i. We denote the differential form by $\mathfrak{p}(\omega)$ or $\tilde{\omega}$ and call it the *reduction of ω modulo $\mathfrak{p}$*. We can easily verify the following facts.

i) *If ω and ω' are $\mathfrak{p}$-finite, then $\omega+\omega'$ and $\omega\cdot\omega'$ are $\mathfrak{p}$-finite and we have $\mathfrak{p}(\omega+\omega')=\mathfrak{p}(\omega)+\mathfrak{p}(\omega')$, $\mathfrak{p}(\omega\cdot\omega')=\mathfrak{p}(\omega)\cdot\mathfrak{p}(\omega')$.*

ii) *If ω is $\mathfrak{p}$-finite, then $d\omega$ is $\mathfrak{p}$-finite and we have*

$$d\mathfrak{p}(\omega)=\mathfrak{p}(d\omega).$$

iii) *If ω is a differential form other than 0, there exists an element a of k such that $a\omega$ is $\mathfrak{p}$-finite and $\mathfrak{p}(a\omega)\neq 0$.*

The last assertion is a special case of the following proposition.

PROPOSITION 6. *Let V be a $\mathfrak{p}$-simple $\mathfrak{p}$-variety; let $\mathcal{M}$ be a vector space over k of differential forms on V of degree s, defined over k, and $\mathcal{M}_0$ the set of $\mathfrak{p}$-finite elements in $\mathcal{M}$. If $\mathcal{M}$ is of a finite dimension m over k, then $\mathcal{M}_0$ is a free $\mathfrak{o}$-module of rank m, and the set $\{\mathfrak{p}(\omega)|\omega\in\mathcal{M}_0\}$ is a vector space of dimension m over $\tilde{k}$.*

PROOF. Let $\{\varphi_1,\cdots,\varphi_r\}$ be a system of local parameters for V at a generic point of $\tilde{V}$ over $\tilde{k}$. Denote by λ the exponential valuation of the field $k(V)$ introduced in § 10. 2. For every differential form

$$\omega = \sum_{i_1<\cdots<i_s} h_{(i)} d\varphi_{i_1}\cdots d\varphi_{i_s},$$

put

$$\lambda(\omega) = \operatorname*{Min}_{(i)} \{\lambda(h_{(i)})\}.$$

Then λ satisfies the conditions i-iii) of Lemma 3, and ω is $\mathfrak{p}$-finite if and only if $\lambda(\omega) \geqq 0$. So our proposition is proved by the same argument as in the last part of § 10. 2.

PROPOSITION 7. *Let V and W be $\mathfrak{p}$-simple $\mathfrak{p}$-varieties, T a rational mapping of V into W and ω a differential form on W, defined over k. Suppose that there exists a point ξ on $\tilde{V}$ such that T is defined at ξ and ω is finite at $T(\xi)$. Then $\omega\circ T$ is defined and finite at ξ; and we have*

$$\mathfrak{p}(\omega\circ T) = \mathfrak{p}(\omega)\circ\tilde{T}.$$

This follows easily from our definition.

PROPOSITION 8. *Let V be a $\mathfrak{p}$-simple $\mathfrak{p}$-variety of dimension r and ω a differential form on V defined over k. Suppose ω to be $\mathfrak{p}$-finite and $\mathfrak{p}(\omega) \neq 0$. Then we have*

$$\mathfrak{p}((\omega)) \prec (\mathfrak{p}(\omega)),$$

where (η) denotes the divisor of a differential form η. If ω is of degree r, then we have

$$\mathfrak{p}((\omega)) = (\mathfrak{p}(\omega)).$$

(For the definition of the divisor of a differential form, we refer to Nakai [28].)

PROOF. Let $\mathfrak{A}$ be a simple subvariety of $\tilde{V}$ of dimension $r-1$; let $\{\varphi_1,\cdots,\varphi_r\}$ be a system of local parameters on V at some point of $\mathfrak{A}$. Then, ω has an expression

$$\omega = \sum_{i_1<\cdots<i_s} f_{(i)} d\varphi_{i_1}\cdots d\varphi_{i_s},$$

where the $f_{(i)}$ are $\mathfrak{p}$-finite elements of $k(V)$; we have then

$$\mathfrak{p}(\omega) = \sum_{(i)} \tilde{f}_{(i)} d\tilde{\varphi}_{i_1}\cdots d\tilde{\varphi}_{i_s}.$$

Take an extension k' of k and an extension $\mathfrak{p}'$ of $\mathfrak{p}$ in k' such that the components of the divisors $(f_{(i)})$ are defined over k' and $\mathfrak{A}$ is defined over $\mathfrak{p}'(k')$. Let $A_1, \cdots, A_t$ be the components of $(f_{(i)})$ such that $\mathfrak{A}$ is a component of $\mathfrak{p}'(A_\nu)$. By Proposition 4, we see that the φ_i are local parameters for V along A_ν for every ν. Denote by $v_\nu(\alpha)$ the multiplicity of A_ν in the divisor (α) of a function or a differential form α, and similarly by $\tilde{v}$ the multiplicity of $\mathfrak{A}$; denote further by $\mu(A, \mathfrak{A})$ the multiplicity of $\mathfrak{A}$ in the cycle $\mathfrak{p}'(A)$. Then, by Proposition 3, we have, for every (i),

$$\tilde{v}(\tilde{f}_{(i)}) = \sum_{\nu=1}^{t} \mu(A_\nu, \mathfrak{A}) v_\nu(f_{(i)}) \geqq \sum_{\nu=1}^{t} \mu(A_\nu, \mathfrak{A}) v_\nu(\omega).$$

This proves $(\mathfrak{p}(\omega)) > \mathfrak{p}((\omega))$. If ω is of degree r, ω is written in the form $\omega = f d\varphi_1 \cdots d\varphi_r$, so that $\mathfrak{p}(\omega) = \tilde{f} d\tilde{\varphi}_1 \cdots d\tilde{\varphi}_r$. We have then

$$\tilde{v}(\tilde{f}) = \sum_{\nu} \mu(A_\nu, \mathfrak{A}) v_\nu(f) = \sum_{\nu} \mu(A_\nu, \mathfrak{A}) v_\nu(\omega);$$

this implies $(\mathfrak{p}(\omega)) = \mathfrak{p}((\omega))$.

PROPOSITION 9. *Let V be a $\mathfrak{p}$-simple $\mathfrak{p}$-variety; suppose that V is $\mathfrak{p}$-complete and $\tilde{V}$ has no multiple point. Let ω be a differential form on V of the first kind, defined over k. If ω is $\mathfrak{p}$-finite, then $\mathfrak{p}(\omega)$ is of the first kind.*

PROOF. We first note that V has no multiple point. Now by Proposition 5 of Koizumi [23], a differential form η on a complete non-singular variety is of the first kind if and only if $(\eta) > 0$. Our proposition follows from this and from Proposition 8.

U being a complete non-singular variety, denote by $h_s(U)$ the number of linearly independent differential forms on U of degree s, of the first kind. Then, by Propositions 6 and 9, we get:

PROPOSITION 10. *Let V be a $\mathfrak{p}$-simple $\mathfrak{p}$-variety. Suppose that V is $\mathfrak{p}$-complete and $\tilde{V}$ has no multiple point. Then we have, for every s,*

$$h_s(V) \leqq h_s(\tilde{V}).$$

We conclude this section by a simple application to curves:

PROPOSITION 11. *Let C be a $\mathfrak{p}$-simple curve. Suppose that C is $\mathfrak{p}$-*

complete and $\tilde{C}$ has no multiple point. Then C and $\tilde{C}$ have the same genus.

PROOF. Take a differential form ω on C such that ω is $\mathfrak{p}$-finite and $\mathfrak{p}(\omega) \neq 0$. This is possible by Proposition 6. Let g and $\tilde{g}$ be the genera of C and $\tilde{C}$, respectively. Then, by Proposition 8, we have

$$2g-2 = \deg(\omega) = \deg(\mathfrak{p}(\omega)) = 2\tilde{g}-2,$$

and hence $g = \tilde{g}$.

11. REDUCTION OF ABELIAN VARIETIES.

11. 1. Let A be an abelian variety defined over k. Denote by f the rational mapping of $A \times A$ into A defined by

$$f(x, y) = x+y.$$

and by g the rational mapping of A into itself defined by

$$g(x) = -x.$$

Suppose that a structure of $\mathfrak{p}$-variety is defined on A. We say that A has *no defect for* $\mathfrak{p}$ (with respect to this structure) if the following conditions (A1-3) are satisfied.

(A1) *A is $\mathfrak{p}$-simple and $\mathfrak{p}$-complete.*
(A2) *f is everywhere defined on $\tilde{A} \times \tilde{A}$.*
(A3) *g is everywhere defined on $\tilde{A}$.*

Under these conditions, $\tilde{A}$ becomes, in a natural way, an abelian variety defined over $\tilde{k}$. As is remarked in § 10.1, $\tilde{f}$ and $\tilde{g}$ are everywhere defined on $\tilde{A} \times \tilde{A}$ and on $\tilde{A}$, and we have $\tilde{f}(\xi, \eta) = f(\xi, \eta)$, $\tilde{g}(\xi) = g(\xi)$ for $\xi \in \tilde{A}$, $\eta \in \tilde{A}$. Put $\xi + \eta = \tilde{f}(\xi, \eta)$. Then it can be easily verified that $\tilde{A}$ is a group variety with respect to this law of composition, defined over $\tilde{k}$, and $\tilde{g}(\xi)$ gives $-\xi$. As A is $\mathfrak{p}$-complete, $\tilde{A}$ is a complete variety, so that $\tilde{A}$ is an abelian variety; if 0 denotes the origin of A, then $\mathfrak{p}(0)$ is the origin of $\tilde{A}$. We call the abelian variety $\tilde{A}$ the *reduction of* the abelian variety A *modulo* $\mathfrak{p}$.

PROPOSITION 12. *Let A and B be two abelian varieties having no* *defect for* $\mathfrak{p}$; *denote by* $\mathscr{H}(A, B; k)$ *the set of all homomorphisms of* A *into* B, *defined over* k, *and by* $\mathscr{H}(\tilde{A}, \tilde{B}; \tilde{k})$ *the set of all homomorphisms of* $\tilde{A}$ *into* $\tilde{B}$, *defined over* $\tilde{k}$. *Then, for every* $\lambda \in \mathscr{H}(A, B; k)$, *the reduction* $\tilde{\lambda}$ *of the rational mapping* λ *modulo* $\mathfrak{p}$ *is an element of* $\mathscr{H}(\tilde{A}, \tilde{B}; \tilde{k})$; *and the graph of* $\tilde{\lambda}$ *is the reduction of the graph of* λ *modulo* $\mathfrak{p}$, *in the sense of reduction of cycles. The correspondence* $\lambda \to \tilde{\lambda}$ *defines an isomorphism of the additive group* $\mathscr{H}(A, B; k)$ *into* $\mathscr{H}(\tilde{A}, \tilde{B}; \tilde{k})$. *If* $A = B$, *this isomorphism is a ring-isomorphism. If* A *and* B *have the same dimension, we have* $\nu(\lambda) = \nu(\tilde{\lambda})$ *for every* $\lambda \in \mathscr{H}(A, B; k)$.

PROOF. We shall first show that every $\lambda \in \mathscr{H}(A, B; k)$ is everywhere defined on $\tilde{A}$. Let ξ be a point of $\tilde{A}$ and η a generic point of $\tilde{A}$ over $\tilde{k}(\xi)$. Then, $\xi + \eta$ is generic on $\tilde{A}$ over $\tilde{k}$, so that λ is defined at η and $\xi + \eta$. Take two independent generic points x, y of A over k and define a rational mapping h of $A \times A$ into B by

$$h(x, y) = \lambda(x+y) - \lambda(y);$$

then h is defined at $\xi \times \eta$ since λ is defined at η and at $\xi + \eta$. Put $\zeta = h(\xi, \eta)$. We have clearly $h(x, y) = \lambda(x)$. Hence we have

$$[\lambda(x) \to \zeta; \mathfrak{p}] \subset [x \times y \to \xi \times \eta; \mathfrak{p}].$$

Since the ring in the left hand side is containd in $k(x)$, we have

$$[\lambda(x) \to \zeta; \mathfrak{p}] \subset [x \to \xi; \mathfrak{p}]$$

by virtue of Proposition 7 of [33]; this shows that λ is defined at ξ. Thus λ is everywhere defined on $\tilde{A}$. Then, by Proposition 2, the graph $\Gamma_{\tilde{\lambda}}$ of $\tilde{\lambda}$ is the reduction of the graph Γ_λ of λ modulo $\mathfrak{p}$, both considered as cycles. It is easy to see that $\tilde{\lambda}$ is a homomorphism of $\tilde{A}$ into $\tilde{B}$ and $\lambda \to \tilde{\lambda}$ gives an additive mapping of $\mathscr{H}(A, B; k)$ into $\mathscr{H}(\tilde{A}, \tilde{B}; \tilde{k})$. If λ is not 0, we have $\dim_k(\lambda x) \geqq 1$ for a generic point x of A over k. Let D be the locus of $\lambda(x)$ over k. As B is $\mathfrak{p}$-complete, $\mathfrak{p}(D)$ is not empty, so that there exists a specialization η of $\lambda(x)$ over $\mathfrak{p}$ such that $\dim_{\tilde{k}}(\eta) \geqq 1$. As A is $\mathfrak{p}$-complete, there exists a point ξ such that $x \times \lambda(x) \to \xi \times \eta$ ref. $\mathfrak{p}$; we have then $\tilde{\lambda}(\xi) = \eta$; this shows that $\tilde{\lambda}$ is not 0. It follows that $\lambda \to \tilde{\lambda}$ is an isomorphism. Now assume that A and B have the same dimension. By the definition of $\nu(\lambda)$, we have $\mathrm{pr}_B(\Gamma_\lambda) = \nu(\lambda)B$, $\mathrm{pr}_{\tilde{B}}(\Gamma_{\tilde{\lambda}}) = \nu(\tilde{\lambda})\tilde{B}$. As we have $\mathfrak{p}(B) = \tilde{B}$, $\mathfrak{p}(\Gamma_\lambda) = \Gamma_{\tilde{\lambda}}$, we get, by (3) of Proposition 1, $\nu(\tilde{\lambda}) = \nu(\lambda)$. It is clear that, when $A = B$, $\lambda \to \tilde{\lambda}$ gives a ring-isomorphism.

PROPOSITION 13. *Notations being as in Proposition* 12, *let* λ *be an element of* $\mathscr{H}(A, B; k)$. *Suppose that* λ *is an isogeny of* A *onto* B *and every element of the kernel* $\mathfrak{g}(\lambda)$ *of* λ *is rational over* k. *Then the reduction of points modulo* $\mathfrak{p}$ *defines a homomorphism of* $\mathfrak{g}(\lambda)$ *onto the kernel* $\mathfrak{g}(\tilde{\lambda})$ *of* $\tilde{\lambda}$. *If* $\nu_i(\tilde{\lambda}) = 1$, *this homomorphisms is an isomorphism.*

PROOF. Denote by Γ_λ and $\Gamma_{\tilde{\lambda}}$ the graphs of λ and $\tilde{\lambda}$, respectively. We have then

$$\mathrm{pr}_A[\Gamma_\lambda \cdot (A \times 0)] = \sum \alpha_t t, \qquad \mathrm{pr}_{\tilde{A}}[\Gamma_{\tilde{\lambda}} \cdot (\tilde{A} \times \tilde{0})] = \sum \alpha_\tau \tau,$$

where the sums are taken over all elements $t \in \mathfrak{g}(\lambda)$, $\tau \in \mathfrak{g}(\tilde{\lambda})$ with certain multiplicities α_t, α_τ, respectively. By the relation $\mathfrak{p}(\Gamma_\lambda) = \Gamma_{\tilde{\lambda}}$ and by Proposition 1, we obtain

$$\mathfrak{p}\{\mathrm{pr}_A[\Gamma_\lambda \cdot (A \times 0)]\} = \mathrm{pr}_{\tilde{A}}[\Gamma_{\tilde{\lambda}} \cdot (\tilde{A} \times \tilde{0})].$$

This shows that the reduction modulo $\mathfrak{p}$ gives a surjective mapping of $\mathfrak{g}(\lambda)$ onto $\mathfrak{g}(\tilde{\lambda})$. It is clear that this mapping is a homomorphism. Hence the order of $\mathfrak{g}(\lambda)$ is not less than the order of $\mathfrak{g}(\tilde{\lambda})$, so that $\nu_s(\lambda) \geqq \nu_s(\tilde{\lambda})$. If $\nu_i(\tilde{\lambda}) = 1$, we get, by the relation $\nu(\lambda) = \nu(\tilde{\lambda})$, the equality $\nu_s(\lambda) = \nu_s(\tilde{\lambda})$. This proves the last assertion.

PROPOSITION 14. *Notations being as in Proposition* 12, *let* l *be a prime other than the characteristic of* $\tilde{k}$. *Then, we can choose* l*-adic coordinate-systems of* $\mathfrak{g}_l(A)$, $\mathfrak{g}_l(B)$, $\mathfrak{g}_l(\tilde{A})$, $\mathfrak{g}_l(\tilde{B})$ *in such a way that:*

i) *for every* $\lambda \in \mathscr{H}(A, B; k)$, *we have* $M_l(\lambda) = M_l(\tilde{\lambda})$;

ii) *for every divisor* X *on* A, *rational over* k, *we have* $E_l(X) = E_l(\tilde{X})$.

PROOF. Let k' be an extension of k over which every point of $\mathfrak{g}_l(A)$ and $\mathfrak{g}_l(B)$ are rational. Take an extension $\mathfrak{p}'$ of $\mathfrak{p}$ in k'; $\mathfrak{p}'$ may not be discrete. We will now consider the reduction of the points in $\mathfrak{g}_l(A)$ and $\mathfrak{g}_l(B)$ modulo $\mathfrak{p}'$. Since every point of $\mathfrak{g}_l(A)$ and $\mathfrak{g}_l(B)$ is rational over a finite extension of k, the reduction modulo $\mathfrak{p}'$ of a point of $\mathfrak{g}_l(A)$ and $\mathfrak{g}_l(B)$ is in substance the same as the reduction modulo a discrete place. Then, we see by Proposition 13 that the reduction modulo $\mathfrak{p}'$ gives an isomorphism of $\mathfrak{g}_l(A)$ onto $\mathfrak{g}_l(\tilde{A})$ and an isomorphism of $\mathfrak{g}_l(B)$ onto $\mathfrak{g}_l(\tilde{B})$. Hence we can choose l-adic coordinate-systems of $\mathfrak{g}_l(A)$, $\mathfrak{g}_l(\tilde{A})$, $\mathfrak{g}_l(B)$, $\mathfrak{g}_l(\tilde{B})$ in such a way that a point x in $\mathfrak{g}_l(A)$, or $\mathfrak{g}_l(B)$, has the same l-adic coordinates as $\mathfrak{p}'(x)$. Then, we get obviously, with respect to these systems, $M_l(\lambda) = M_l(\tilde{\lambda})$ for every $\lambda \in \mathscr{H}(A, B; k)$. Let k'' be the algebraic closure of k' and U_l the set of roots of unity in k'' whose orders are powers of l. Take an extension $\mathfrak{p}''$ of $\mathfrak{p}'$ in k''; then $\mathfrak{p}''(U_l)$ is the set of roots of unity in $\mathfrak{p}''(k'')$ whose orders are powers of l. Choose isomorphisms of U_l and $\mathfrak{p}''(U_l)$ onto $\boldsymbol{Q}_l/\boldsymbol{Z}_l$ in such a way that for every $\zeta \in U_l$, ζ and $\mathfrak{p}''(\zeta)$ have the same image in $\boldsymbol{Q}_l/\boldsymbol{Z}_l$. Then we can easily verify, following step by step the definition of the matrix $E_l(X)$, the relation $E_l(X) = E_l(\tilde{X})$ for every divisor X on A, rational over k.

11.2. k and $\mathfrak{p}$ being as before, let F be an algebraic number field; and let (A, ι) be an abelian variety of type (F), defined over k. Put $\mathfrak{r} = \iota^{-1}[\mathscr{A}(A) \cap \iota(F)]$. If A has no defect for $\mathfrak{p}$, then, for every $\lambda \in \iota(\mathfrak{r})$, we obtain, by reduction modulo $\mathfrak{p}$, an element $\tilde{\lambda}$ of $\mathscr{A}(\tilde{A})$. Put $\tilde{\iota}(\mu) = \widetilde{\iota(\mu)}$ for every $\mu \in \mathfrak{r}$. Then $\tilde{\iota}$ is an isomorphism of $\mathfrak{r}$ into $\mathscr{A}(\tilde{A})$ such that $\tilde{\iota}(1) = 1_{\tilde{A}}$; we can extend this isomorphism to an isomorphism of F into $\mathscr{A}_0(\tilde{A})$, which we denote again by $\tilde{\iota}$. Thus we obtain an abelian variety $(\tilde{A}, \tilde{\iota})$ of type (F), defined over $\tilde{k}$. We call $(\tilde{A}, \tilde{\iota})$ the reduction of (A, ι) modulo $\mathfrak{p}$. $(\tilde{A}, \tilde{\iota})$ is clearly of the same index as (A, ι). If (A, ι) is principal, so is $(\tilde{A}, \tilde{\iota})$.

PROPOSITION 15. *Let (A, ι) be an abelian variety of type (F), defined over k, which is principal. Let $\mathfrak{a}$ be an integral ideal of F and $(A_1, \iota_1; \lambda)$ an $\mathfrak{a}$-transform of (A, ι), defined over k. Suppose that A and A_1 have no defect for $\mathfrak{p}$. Then, $(\tilde{A}_1, \tilde{\iota}_1; \tilde{\lambda})$ is an $\mathfrak{a}$-transform of $(\tilde{A}, \tilde{\iota})$.*

PROOF. It is clear that $\tilde{\lambda}$ commutes with the operation of F. Let x be a generic point of A over k and ξ a generic point of $\tilde{A}$ over $\tilde{k}$. For every $\alpha \in \mathfrak{a}$, we have $k(\iota(\alpha)x) \subset k(\lambda x)$, so that we obtain a rational mapping μ of A_1 into A, defined over k, such that $\mu(\lambda x) = \iota(\alpha)x$; μ is clearly a homomorphism. We have then $\tilde{\mu}\tilde{\lambda}\xi = \tilde{\iota}(\alpha)\xi$, and hence $\tilde{k}(\tilde{\iota}(\alpha)\xi) \subset \tilde{k}(\tilde{\lambda}\xi)$. Therefore, if $\tilde{\lambda}_1$ is an $\mathfrak{a}$-multiplication of $\tilde{A}$, defined over $\tilde{k}$, we have $\tilde{k}(\tilde{\lambda}\xi) \supset \tilde{k}(\tilde{\lambda}_1\xi)$. On the other hand, by Proposition 10 of § 7.2 and Proposition 12 of § 11.1, we have

$$[\tilde{k}(\xi):\tilde{k}(\tilde{\lambda}\xi)] = \nu(\tilde{\lambda}) = \nu(\lambda) = N(\mathfrak{a})^m = \nu(\tilde{\lambda}_1) = [\tilde{k}(\xi):\tilde{k}(\tilde{\lambda}_1\xi)],$$

where m denotes the index of (A, ι). Hence $\tilde{k}(\tilde{\lambda}\xi) = \tilde{k}(\tilde{\lambda}_1\xi)$. This shows that $\tilde{\lambda}$ is an $\mathfrak{a}$-multiplication.

PROPOSITION 16. *(A, ι) being as in Proposition 15, let $\mathfrak{a}$ be an integral ideal of F. Suppose that A has no defect for $\mathfrak{p}$ and every point of $\mathfrak{g}(\mathfrak{a}, A)$ is rational over k. Then, the reduction modulo $\mathfrak{p}$ defines a homomorphism of $\mathfrak{g}(\mathfrak{a}, A)$ onto $\mathfrak{g}(\mathfrak{a}, \tilde{A})$. Moreover, if $\mathfrak{a}$ is prime to the characteristic of $\tilde{k}$, this homomorphism is an isomorphism.*

PROOF. We can find an integral ideal $\mathfrak{b}$, prime to $\mathfrak{a}$ and the characteristic p of $\tilde{k}$, such that $\mathfrak{a}\mathfrak{b}$ is a principal ideal (γ). By Proposition 18 of § 7.5, we have

$$\mathfrak{g}((\gamma), A) = \mathfrak{g}(\mathfrak{a}, A)+\mathfrak{g}(\mathfrak{b}, A), \qquad \mathfrak{g}((\gamma), \tilde{A}) = \mathfrak{g}(\mathfrak{a}, \tilde{A})+\mathfrak{g}(\mathfrak{b}, \tilde{A}).$$

Take an extension k' of k such that every point of $\mathfrak{g}((\gamma), A)$ is rational over k', and an extension $\mathfrak{p}'$ of $\mathfrak{p}$ in k'. Then, the reduction modulo $\mathfrak{p}'$ gives homomorphisms of $\mathfrak{g}((\gamma), A)$, $\mathfrak{g}(\mathfrak{a}, A)$, $\mathfrak{g}(\mathfrak{b}, A)$ respectively into $\mathfrak{g}((\gamma), \tilde{A})$, $\mathfrak{g}(\mathfrak{a}, \tilde{A})$, $\mathfrak{g}(\mathfrak{b}, \tilde{A})$. By Proposition 13, $\mathfrak{g}((\gamma), A)$ is mapped *onto* $\mathfrak{g}((\gamma), \tilde{A})$; so $\mathfrak{g}(\mathfrak{a}, A)$ must be mapped onto $\mathfrak{g}(\mathfrak{a}, \tilde{A})$. If $\mathfrak{a}$ is prime to p, $\mathfrak{g}(\mathfrak{a}, A)$ and $\mathfrak{g}(\mathfrak{a}, \tilde{A})$ are of the same order $N(\mathfrak{a})^m$, where m is the index of (A, ι); hence the reduction modulo $\mathfrak{p}$ gives an isomorphism of $\mathfrak{g}(\mathfrak{a}, A)$ onto $\mathfrak{g}(\mathfrak{a}, \tilde{A})$.

11. 3. Consider now the case where both k and $\tilde{k}$ are of characteristic 0. Let k be a subfield of $\boldsymbol{C}$ and $\mathfrak{p}$ a place of k taking values in $\boldsymbol{C}$. Let $(F; \{\varphi_i\})$ be a CM-type and (A, ι) an abelian variety of type $(F; \{\varphi_i\})$, defined over k. Suppose that A has no defect for $\mathfrak{p}$, k contains $\bigcup F^{\varphi_i}$ and for every $\xi \in \bigcup F^{\varphi_i}$, $\mathfrak{p}(\xi) = \xi$. Under these assumptions, we shall prove that the reduction $(\tilde{A}, \tilde{\iota})$ of (A, ι) modulo $\mathfrak{p}$ is of type $(F; \{\varphi_i\})$. By the definition of CM-type, there exist invariant differential forms $\omega_1, \cdots, \omega_n$ on A such that

$$\delta(\iota(\alpha))\omega_i = \alpha^{\varphi_i}\omega_i \qquad (1 \leqq i \leqq n)$$

for every $\alpha \in \mathfrak{r}$, where n is the dimension of A and $\mathfrak{r}$ is the order of (A, ι). On account of the results of § 2, we may assume that the ω_i

are defined over a finite algebraic extension k' of k. Take an extension $\mathfrak{p}'$ of $\mathfrak{p}$ in k' and consider the reduction modulo $\mathfrak{p}'$. By the assertion iii) of § 10.4, which is a particular case of Proposition 6, we may assume that the ω_i are $\mathfrak{p}'$-finite and $\mathfrak{p}'(\omega_i) \neq 0$ for every i. Then we get, by Proposition 7,

$$\delta(\tilde{\iota}(\alpha))\mathfrak{p}'(\omega_i) = \mathfrak{p}'(\alpha^{\varphi_i})\mathfrak{p}'(\omega_i) \qquad (1 \leqq i \leqq n). \tag{1}$$

By our assumption, we have $\mathfrak{p}'(\alpha^{\varphi_i}) = \alpha^{\varphi_i}$; so the relation (1) shows that $(\tilde{A}, \tilde{\iota})$ is of type $(F; \{\varphi_i\})$.

12. THE THEORY "FOR ALMOST ALL $\mathfrak{p}$".

12.1. Preliminary lemmas. The notations k, $\mathfrak{o}$, $\mathfrak{p}$ being as before, let V be a variety of dimension r in the affine space S^n, defined over k. Let (x) be a generic point of V over k and the t_{ij}, for $0 \leqq i \leqq r$, $1 \leqq j \leqq n$, be $(r+1)n$ independent variables over $k(x)$. Put $y_i = \sum_{j=1}^{n} t_{ij}x_j$ for $0 \leqq i \leqq r$. Then we have $k(t, x) = k(t, y)$. As $(y_0, \cdots, y_r)$ is of dimension r over $k(t)$, there exists an irreducible polynomial $F(T, Y)$ in $k[T, Y]$ such that $F(t, y) = 0$. Substituting $\sum_{j=1}^{n} T_{ij}X_j$ for Y_i, we obtain from $F(T, Y)$ a polynomial $G(T, X)$ in (T_{ij}) and (X_j). We write $G(T, X)$ as a polynomial in (T_{ij}) with coefficients in $k[X]$ and denote by the $H_\alpha(X)$ for $1 \leqq \alpha \leqq s$ those coefficients. We call the set $\{H_\alpha(X)\}$ a *k-basic system* for V. We can take F in such a way that all its coefficients are contained in $\mathfrak{o}$ and some coefficient is a $\mathfrak{p}$-unit. F being taken as this, we call $\{H_\alpha(X)\}$ a *$\mathfrak{p}$-basic system* for V.

LEMMA 4. *Let V be a variety of dimension r in S^n, defined over k, and $\{H_\alpha(X) \mid 1 \leqq \alpha \leqq s\}$ a $\mathfrak{p}$-basic system for V. Then a point (ξ) of $\tilde{S}^n$ is contained in $\tilde{V}$ if and only if $\tilde{H}_\alpha(\xi) = 0$ for $1 \leqq \alpha \leqq s$.*

PROOF. Let (x), (t), (y), F, G be as above; and let (ξ) be a specialization of (x) over $\mathfrak{p}$. As we have $F(t_{ij}, \sum_{j=1}^{n} t_{ij}x_j) = 0$ and the t_{ij} are independent over $k(x)$, we have $H_\alpha(x) = 0$ for $1 \leqq \alpha \leqq s$, so that $\tilde{H}_\alpha(\xi) = 0$ for $1 \leqq \alpha \leqq s$. This proves the "only if" part. Conversely, let (ξ) be a point of $\tilde{S}^n$ such that $\tilde{H}_\alpha(\xi)=0$ for $1 \leqq \alpha \leqq s$. Let the τ_{ij} for $0 \leqq i \leqq r$, $1 \leqq j \leqq n$ be $(r+1)n$ independent variables over $\tilde{k}(\xi)$. Put $\eta_i = \sum_{j=1}^n \tau_{ij}\xi_j$ for $0 \leqq i \leqq r$. We have then

$$\tilde{F}(\tau_{ij}, \eta_i) = \tilde{F}(\tau_{ij}, \sum_{j=1}^n \tau_{ij}\xi_j) = 0.$$

Let W be the locus of (y) over $k(t)$ in S^{r+1}. The specialization $(t) \to (\tau)$ ref. $\mathfrak{p}$ gives an extension $\mathfrak{p}'$ of $\mathfrak{p}$ in $k(t)$. By Theorem 21 of [33], we have

$$\mathfrak{p}'(W) = \{(\zeta) \mid (\zeta) \in \tilde{S}^{r+1}, \tilde{F}(\tau_{ij}, \zeta_j) = 0\}.$$

Hence (η) is contained in $\mathfrak{p}'(W)$; so (η) is a specialization of (y) over $\mathfrak{p}'$. Let (ξ') be a specialization of (x) such that

$$(x, y) \to (\xi', \eta) \text{ ref. } \mathfrak{p}'.$$

By Proposition 16 of [33], (ξ') is finite, so that it is a point of $\tilde{S}^n$; and we have $\sum_{j=1}^n \tau_{ij}\xi'_j = \eta_i = \sum_{j=1}^n \tau_{ij}\xi_j$ for $0 \leqq i \leqq r$. Assume that $\xi_j \neq \xi_j'$ for one of the j, say 1; we have then

$$\tau_{i1} = -\sum_{j=2}^n \tau_{ij}\left(\frac{\xi_j - \xi'_j}{\xi_1 - \xi'_1}\right) \qquad (0 \leqq i \leqq r).$$

As (ξ') is a specialization of (x) over $\mathfrak{p}$, we have $\dim_{\tilde{k}}(\xi') \leqq r$. Hence we have

$$\dim_{\tilde{k}(\xi)}(\tau) \leqq \dim_{\tilde{k}(\xi)}(\xi', \tau_{ij}\ (j>1)) \leqq r+(r+1)(n-1) < (r+1)n.$$

This contradicts the assumption that the τ_{ij} are $(r+1)n$ independent variables over $\tilde{k}(\xi)$. Therefore we have $(\xi) = (\xi')$. Hence (ξ) is a point of $\tilde{V}$; this completes the proof.

We will now study the reduction of algebraic varieties modulo infinitely many $\mathfrak{p}$. Let k be a field and $\sum$ a set of discrete places of k. In the rest of this section, we use k and $\sum$ always in this sense. We call a subset σ of $\sum$ an *open set* of $\sum$ if there exist a finite number of elements $a_1, \cdots, a_r$, other than 0, in k such that

$$\sigma = \{\mathfrak{p} \mid \mathfrak{p} \in \textstyle\sum, \mathfrak{p}(a_1) \neq 0, \cdots, \mathfrak{p}(a_r) \neq 0\}.$$

For any set of elements $\{a_1, \cdots, a_r\}$ in k, none of which is 0, the set of $\mathfrak{p}$ in Σ such that the a_i are $\mathfrak{p}$-units, is an open set. In fact, we have

$$\sigma = \{\mathfrak{p} \mid \mathfrak{p} \in \Sigma, \mathfrak{p}(a_1) \neq 0, \mathfrak{p}(a_1^{-1}) \neq 0, \cdots, \mathfrak{p}(a_r) \neq 0, \mathfrak{p}(a_r^{-1}) \neq 0\}.$$

We say that a proposition $P(\mathfrak{p})$ concerned with $\mathfrak{p}$ in Σ holds for *almost all* $\mathfrak{p}$ if $P(\mathfrak{p})$ holds for all $\mathfrak{p}$ in an open set of Σ.

LEMMA 5. *k and Σ being as above, let k' be a finitely generated extension of k, of dimension s over k. Let Σ' be a set of discrete places of k' satisfying the following conditions:*

i) *there exists a set of elements $(t_1, \cdots, t_s)$ in k' such that we have $\dim_{\mathfrak{p}'(k)}(\mathfrak{p}'(t_1), \cdots, \mathfrak{p}'(t_s)) = s$ for every $\mathfrak{p}'$ in Σ';*

ii) *for every $\mathfrak{p}$ in Σ, there exists an extension of $\mathfrak{p}$ in Σ'.*

Let σ' be an open set of Σ' and σ the subset of Σ consisting of all $\mathfrak{p}$ in Σ such that $\mathfrak{p}$ has at least one extension $\mathfrak{p}'$ in Σ'. Then σ contains an open set of Σ.

PROOF. By our definition, there exists a set of elements $(y_1, \cdots, y_r)$ in k' such that $y_i \neq 0$, and if $\mathfrak{p}'(y_1) \neq 0, \cdots, \mathfrak{p}'(y_r) \neq 0$ and if $\mathfrak{p}' \in \Sigma'$, then $\mathfrak{p}' \in \sigma'$. By our assumption, $t_1, \cdots, t_s$ are independent variables over k, and k' is algebraic over $k(t)$. Let $\sum_{\nu} b_{i\nu} Y^{\nu} = 0$ be an irreducible equation for y_i^{-1} over $k(t)$, for each i. We may assume that the $b_{i\nu}$ are polynomials in $k[t_1, \cdots, t_s]$. Let σ_0 be the set of all $\mathfrak{p}$ in Σ such that all non-zero coefficients of the polynomials $b_{i\nu}$ are $\mathfrak{p}$-units. Then σ_0 is an open set of Σ. Let $\mathfrak{p}$ be a place in σ_0; by our assumption, there exists in Σ' an extension $\mathfrak{p}'$ of $\mathfrak{p}$, and $\mathfrak{p}'(t_1), \cdots, \mathfrak{p}'(t_s)$ are independent variables over $\mathfrak{p}(k)$, so that the $b_{i\nu}$ are all $\mathfrak{p}'$-integral; moreover, any one of the $b_{i\nu}$, other than 0, is a $\mathfrak{p}'$-unit. It follows that the y_i^{-1} are all $\mathfrak{p}'$-integral, so that $\mathfrak{p}'(y_i) \neq 0$ for every i; namely, $\mathfrak{p}'$ is contained in σ'. Hence σ_0 is contained in σ; this proves our lemma.

12.2. Now, it is easy to verify that the results of [33] § 6 are extended to the present case. Namely, Proposition 29, Lemma 3, Proposition 30, Theorem 26 in that section are all true when we use the terms "for almost all $\mathfrak{p}$" in the sense explained above. In particular, we have

PROPOSITION 17. *Let V be a variety in S^n defined over k. Then, for almost all $\mathfrak{p}$, $\mathfrak{p}(V)$ is not empty and V is $\mathfrak{p}$-simple.*

We have to show that $\mathfrak{p}(V)$ is not empty for almost all $\mathfrak{p}$, as it was not explicitly proved in [33]. Take a point $(a_1,\cdots,a_n)$ in V such that the a_i are contained in a finite algebraic extension k' of k. Let $\sum'$ be the set of all extensions in k' of all $\mathfrak{p}$ in $\sum$ and σ' be the set of $\mathfrak{p}'$ in $\sum'$ such that the a_i are $\mathfrak{p}'$-integral. Let σ be the set of all $\mathfrak{p}$ in $\sum$ having an extension $\mathfrak{p}'$ in σ'. Then by Lemma 5, σ is an open set of $\sum$. It is easy to see that $\mathfrak{p}(V)$ is not empty for every $\mathfrak{p}$ in σ.

12. 3. We shall now give several properties preserved for almost all $\mathfrak{p}$ in the process of reduction modulo $\mathfrak{p}$.

PROPOSITION 18. *Let $F_1(X),\cdots,F_r(X)$ be r polynomials in $k[X_1,\cdots,X_n]$ and U the algebraic set in S^n given by*

$$U=\{(x)\mid F_i(x)=0\ (1\leqq i\leqq r)\}.$$

Then, we have

$$\mathfrak{p}(U)=\{(\xi)\mid F_{i\mathfrak{p}}(\xi)=0\ (l\leqq i\leqq r)\}$$

for almost all $\mathfrak{p}$.

PROOF. We may consider only those $\mathfrak{p}$ for which the coefficients of the F_i are all $\mathfrak{p}$-integral. It is easy to see

$$\mathfrak{p}(U)\subset\{(\xi)\mid F_{i\mathfrak{p}}(\xi)=0\ (1\leqq i\leqq r)\};$$

so we will now prove that the inverse inclusion holds for almost all $\mathfrak{p}$. Suppose that U is not empty. Let $U_1,\cdots,U_s$ be the components of U and k' be a finite algebraic extension of k such that the U_i are all defined over k'. Let $\sum'$ be the set of all extensions in k' of all $\mathfrak{p}$ in $\sum$. Let $\{H^{(i)}{}_\alpha(X);\ 1\leqq\alpha\leqq t_i\}$ be a k'-basic system for U_i, for each i. Then, by the definition of basic system, $\{H^{(i)}{}_\alpha\}$ is a $\mathfrak{p}'$-basic system for U_i for almost all $\mathfrak{p}'$ in $\sum'$. Put

$$H_{\alpha_1\cdots\alpha_s}(X)=H^{(1)}{}_{\alpha_1}(X)\cdots H^{(s)}{}_{\alpha_s}(X);$$

put $H_1(X)=1$, if U is empty. Then, by Lemma 4, we see easily

$$\mathfrak{p}'(U)=\{(\xi)\mid H_{\alpha_1\cdots\alpha_s\mathfrak{p}'}(\xi)=0\ \text{for every}\ (\alpha)\}$$

for almost all $\mathfrak{p}'$ in Σ'. By Hilbert's theorem, there exists a positive integer ρ such that $H_{\alpha_1\cdots\alpha_s}(X)^\rho = \sum Q_{(\alpha)i}(X)F_i(X)$, where the $Q_{(\alpha)i}$ are polynomials in $k'[X]$. The coefficients of $Q_{(\alpha)i}$ are all $\mathfrak{p}'$-integral for almost all $\mathfrak{p}'$ in Σ'. For those $\mathfrak{p}'$, we have

$$H_{(\alpha)\mathfrak{p}'}{}^{\rho} = \sum Q_{(\alpha)i\mathfrak{p}'}F_{i\mathfrak{p}'},$$

and hence

$$\mathfrak{p}'(U) \supset \{(\xi) \mid F_{i\mathfrak{p}'}(\xi) = 0\,(1 \leqq i \leqq r)\}.$$

By virtue of Lemma 5, this proves our proposition.

PROPOSITION 19. *Let U and V be two algebraic sets in S^n, defined over k. Then, we have $\mathfrak{p}(U \cap V) = \mathfrak{p}(U) \cap \mathfrak{p}(V)$ for almost all $\mathfrak{p}$.*

PROOF. Let $\mathfrak{a}$ and $\mathfrak{b}$ be the ideals of $k[X_1,\cdots, X_n]$ given by

$$\mathfrak{a} = \{F(X) \mid F(x) = 0 \text{ for every } (x) \in U\},$$

$$\mathfrak{b} = \{G(X) \mid G(x) = 0 \text{ for every } (x) \in V\}.$$

Let $\{F_1(X),\cdots, F_r(X)\}$ and $\{G_1(X),\cdots, G_s(X)\}$ be bases for $\mathfrak{a}$ and $\mathfrak{b}$, respectively. Then we have

$$U = \{(x)|F_i(x) = 0 \ (1 \leqq i \leqq r)\}, \qquad V = \{(x)|G_j(x) = 0 \ (1 \leqq j \leqq s)\},$$
$$U \cap V = \{(x)|F_i(x) = 0, G_j(x) = 0\,(1 \leqq i \leqq r,\ 1 \leqq j \leqq s)\}.$$

Therefore, our proposition is an immediate consequence of Proposition 18.

PROPOSITION 20. *Let U be an algebraic set, defined over k, in $S^{n+m} = S^n \times S^m$ and V the projection of U on the first factor S^n. Then, $\mathfrak{p}(V)$ is the projection of $\mathfrak{p}(U)$ on the first factor of $\mathfrak{p}(S^{n+m}) = \mathfrak{p}(S^n) \times \mathfrak{p}(S^m)$, for almost all $\mathfrak{p}$.*

PROOF. It is sufficient to prove our proposition in case where U is a variety defined over k, since the general case is easily reduced to this particular case by means of Lemma 5. Assuming U to be a variety defined over k, let (x, y) be a generic point of U over k with the projection (x) on S^n and (y) on S^m; and let s be the dimension of $(y) = (y_1,\cdots, y_m)$ over $k(x)$. If s is not 0, we may assume that $y_1,\cdots, y_s$ are independent variables over $k(x)$ and (y) is algebraic over $k(x, y_1,\cdots, y_s)$.

The locus of $(x, y_1, \cdots, y_s)$ over k is the variety $V \times S^s$. As we have $\mathfrak{p}(V \times S^s) = \mathfrak{p}(V) \times \mathfrak{p}(S^s)$, the projection of $\mathfrak{p}(V \times S^s)$ on the first factor of $\mathfrak{p}(S^n) \times \mathfrak{p}(S^s)$ is $\mathfrak{p}(V)$. Therefore, our proposition is proved if we show that the projection of $\mathfrak{p}(U)$ on the factor $\mathfrak{p}(S^n) \times \mathfrak{p}(S^s)$ of $\mathfrak{p}(S^n) \times \mathfrak{p}(S^s) \times \mathfrak{p}(S^{m-s})$ is $\mathfrak{p}(V \times S^s)$ for almost all $\mathfrak{p}$. Hence it is sufficient to prove our proposition in case where (y) is algebraic over $k(x)$. Suppose that this is so; let t_{ij}, for $1 \leqq i \leqq r$, $1 \leqq j \leqq n$, be rn independent variables over $k(x)$, where r is the dimension of $(x) = (x_1, \cdots, x_n)$ over k. Put $z_i = \sum_{j=1}^{n} t_{ij} x_j$ for $1 \leqq i \leqq r$; then (t, z) is $r(n+1)$ independent variables over k and (x) is algebraic over $k(t, z)$. By Proposition 17, $\mathfrak{p}(V)$ is a variety defined over $\mathfrak{p}(k)$ for every $\mathfrak{p}$ in an open set σ of $\sum$. Let $\tau_{ij\mathfrak{p}}$ and $\zeta_{i\mathfrak{p}}$, for $1 \leqq i \leqq r$, $1 \leqq j \leqq n$, be $r(n+1)$ independent variables over $\mathfrak{p}(k)$. Take and fix, for each $\mathfrak{p}$ in σ, a point $\xi_{\mathfrak{p}}$ in the intersection of $\mathfrak{p}(V)$ and the generic linear variety defined by

$$\sum_{j=1}^{n} \tau_{ij\mathfrak{p}} X_j - \zeta_{i\mathfrak{p}} = 0 \qquad (1 \leqq i \leqq r).$$

Then, $\xi_{\mathfrak{p}}$ is a generic point of $\mathfrak{p}(V)$ over $\mathfrak{p}(k)$. We see that $(\xi_{\mathfrak{p}}, \tau_{\mathfrak{p}}, \zeta_{\mathfrak{p}})$ is a specialization of (x, t, z) over $\mathfrak{p}$. Let $\sum'$ be the set of all extensions $\mathfrak{p}'$ of $\mathfrak{p}$ in $k(x, t, z, y)$ such that

$$(x, t, z) \rightarrow (\xi_{\mathfrak{p}}, \tau_{\mathfrak{p}}, \zeta_{\mathfrak{p}}) \text{ ref. } \mathfrak{p}'.$$

Let σ' be the set of all $\mathfrak{p}'$ in $\sum'$ such that the y_i are all $\mathfrak{p}'$-integral, and let σ_0 be the set of all $\mathfrak{p}$ in σ such that $\mathfrak{p}$ has at least one extension $\mathfrak{p}'$ in σ'. Then, by Lemma 5, σ_0 contains an open set of $\sum$. Let $\mathfrak{V}_{\mathfrak{p}}$ denote the projection of $\mathfrak{p}(U)$ on the first factor $\mathfrak{p}(S^n)$ of $\mathfrak{p}(S^n) \times \mathfrak{p}(S^m)$. For every $\mathfrak{p}$ in σ_0, we can find a point $\eta_{\mathfrak{p}}$ in $\mathfrak{p}(S^m)$ such that $(x, y) \rightarrow (\xi_{\mathfrak{p}}, \eta_{\mathfrak{p}})$ ref. $\mathfrak{p}$. Hence $\mathfrak{V}_{\mathfrak{p}}$ contains $\xi_{\mathfrak{p}}$; this implies $\mathfrak{V}_{\mathfrak{p}} \supset \mathfrak{p}(V)$. On the other hand, if $\alpha_{\mathfrak{p}}$ is a generic point of a component of $\mathfrak{V}_{\mathfrak{p}}$ over the algebraic closure of $\mathfrak{p}(k)$, there exists a point $(\alpha_{\mathfrak{p}}, \beta_{\mathfrak{p}})$ in $\mathfrak{p}(U)$. As $(\alpha_{\mathfrak{p}}, \beta_{\mathfrak{p}})$ is a specialization of (x, y) over $\mathfrak{p}$, the point $\alpha_{\mathfrak{p}}$ is contained in $\mathfrak{p}(V)$; so we have $\mathfrak{V}_{\mathfrak{p}} \subset \mathfrak{p}(V)$. Thus we have proved $\mathfrak{V}_{\mathfrak{p}} = \mathfrak{p}(V)$ for every $\mathfrak{p}$ in σ_0. This proves our proposition.

PROPOSITION 21. *Let V be a variety in S^n, defined over k, and f a rational mapping of V into S^m, defined over k. Let F be an algebraic* *set contained in V, defined over k, different from V. Suppose that f is defined at every point in $V-F$. Then, for almost all $\mathfrak{p}$, f is defined at every point in $\mathfrak{p}(V)-\mathfrak{p}(F)$.*

PROOF. It is sufficient to prove the proposition in case where $m=1$. Let x be a generic point of V; then we have an expression $f(x)=Q(x)/P(x)$, where P and Q are polynomials in $k[X_1,\cdots,X_n]$. Let the $W_{1\beta}$ denote the components of the algebraic set $\{a|a\in V, P(a)=0\}$ which are not contained in F. Then, r being the dimension of V, we have $\dim W_{1\beta}\leqq r-1$. Denote by k_1 the algebraic closure of k; and let $x_{1\beta}$ be a generic point of $W_{1\beta}$ over k_1. As $x_{1\beta}$ is not contained in F, we have expressions $f(x)=Q_{1\beta}(x)/P_{1\beta}(x)$ where $Q_{1\beta}$ and $P_{1\beta}$ are polynomials in $k[X]$ such that $P_{1\beta}(x_{1\beta})\neq 0$. Let the $W_{2\gamma}$ be the components of the algebraic set

$$\{a\mid a\in V, P(a)=0, P_{1\beta}(a)=0 \text{ for every } \beta\},$$

which are not contained in F. We have then $\dim W_{2\gamma}\leqq r-2$. After repeating (at most r times) this procedure, we obtain a set of polynomials $P_{ij}(X)$ in $k[X]$ such that

$$F\supset V\cap\{a\mid P_{ij}(a)=0 \text{ for every } i \text{ and } j\};$$

and for each (i, j), we have $f(x)=Q_{ij}(x)/P_{ij}(x)$, where Q_{ij} is a polynomial in $k[X]$. By Propositions 18 and 19, we have

$$\mathfrak{p}(F)\supset\mathfrak{p}(V)\cap\{\xi\mid P_{ij\mathfrak{p}}(\xi)=0 \text{ for every } i \text{ and } j\}$$

for every $\mathfrak{p}$ in an open set σ. If $\mathfrak{p}$ is in σ, we see that, for every point η in $\mathfrak{p}(V)-\mathfrak{p}(F)$, there exists a polynomial P_{ij} such that $P_{ij\mathfrak{p}}(\eta)\neq 0$, namely, f is defined at η. Our proposition is thereby proved.

PROPOSITION 22. *Let V be a variety in S^n, defined over k, and F an algebraic set contained in V, defined over k. Suppose that every point in $V-F$ is simple on V. Then, for almost all $\mathfrak{p}$, every point in $\mathfrak{p}(V)-\mathfrak{p}(F)$ is simple on V.*

PROOF. Let $\{G_1(X),\cdots,G_s(X)\}$ be a basis for the ideal $\mathfrak{a}$ of $k[X]$ given by

$$\mathfrak{a}=\{G(X)\mid G(x)=0 \text{ for every } x\in V\}.$$

Let the $H_\nu(X)$ denote the determinants of degree $n-r$ belonging to the matrix $(\partial G_i/\partial X_j)$, where r is the dimension of V. Our assumption implies

$$F \supset \{x \mid G_i(x) = 0,\ H_\nu(x) = 0 \text{ for every } i \text{ and every } \nu\}.$$

By Proposition 18, we have, for almost all $\mathfrak{p}$,

$$\mathfrak{p}(F) \supset \{\xi \mid G_{i\mathfrak{p}}(\xi) = 0,\ H_{\nu\mathfrak{p}}(\xi) = 0 \text{ for every } i \text{ and every } \nu\}.$$

Hence, if η is a point in $\mathfrak{p}(V)-\mathfrak{p}(F)$, there exists a polynomial H_ν such that $H_{\nu\mathfrak{p}}(\eta) \neq 0$, namely, we have $\mathrm{rank}(\partial G_{i\mathfrak{p}}/\partial X_j(\eta)) \geqq n-r$. This proves our proposition.

PROPOSITION 23. *Let $V = [V_\alpha;\ F_\alpha;\ T_{\beta\alpha}]$ be an abstract variety defined over k. Then, for almost all $\mathfrak{p}$, the system $[V_\alpha;\ F_\alpha;\ \mathfrak{p}(F_\alpha);\ T_{\beta\alpha}]$ defines a $\mathfrak{p}$-variety. If V is complete, the $\mathfrak{p}$-variety is $\mathfrak{p}$-complete for almost all $\mathfrak{p}$. Moreover, let H be an algebraic set in V such that every point in $V-H$ is simple on V. Then, for almost all $\mathfrak{p}$, every point in $\mathfrak{p}(V)-\mathfrak{p}(H)$ is simple on V.*

PROOF. Let $B_{\beta\alpha}$ be the set of points in V_α such that the projection from $T_{\beta\alpha}$ to V_α is regular at x if and only if x is not contained in $B_{\beta\alpha}$. Then, $B_{\beta\alpha}$ is an algebraic set in V_α defined over k. This fact is well-known and is proved by the same argument as in the proof of Proposition 21. By Proposition 21, for almost all $\mathfrak{p}$, $T_{\beta\alpha}$ is regular at every point in $\mathfrak{p}(V_\alpha)-\mathfrak{p}(B_{\beta\alpha})$ for every (α, β). By the definition of abstract variety, we have

$$T_{\beta\alpha} \cap [(B_{\beta\alpha}\times V_\beta) \cup (V_\alpha\times B_{\alpha\beta})] \subset T_{\beta\alpha} \cap [(F_\alpha\times V_\beta) \cup (V_\alpha\times F_\beta)].$$

By Proposition 19, for almost all $\mathfrak{p}$,

$$\begin{aligned}\mathfrak{p}(T_{\beta\alpha}) &\cap [(\mathfrak{p}(B_{\beta\alpha})\times\mathfrak{p}(V_\beta)) \cup (\mathfrak{p}(V_\alpha)\times\mathfrak{p}(B_{\alpha\beta}))]\\ &\subset \mathfrak{p}(T_{\beta\alpha}) \cap [(\mathfrak{p}(F_\alpha)\times\mathfrak{p}(V_\beta)) \cup (\mathfrak{p}(V_\alpha)\times\mathfrak{p}(F_\beta))].\end{aligned}$$

This shows that the system $[V_\alpha;\ F_\alpha;\ \mathfrak{p}(F_\alpha);\ T_{\beta\alpha}]$ is a $\mathfrak{p}$-variety for almost all $\mathfrak{p}$. Let the $(x_{\alpha 1},\cdots, x_{\alpha n_\alpha})$, for $1 \leqq \alpha \leqq h$, be corresponding generic points of the V_α by $T_{\beta\alpha}$. Let $\{\varepsilon(\alpha i)\}$ be a set of integers which are equal to 1 or -1. Let W_ε denote the locus of

$$(x_{11}{}^{\varepsilon(11)},\cdots, x_{1n_1}{}^{\varepsilon(1n_1)},\cdots, x_{h1}{}^{\varepsilon(h1)},\cdots, x_{hn_h}{}^{\varepsilon(hn_h)})$$

over k, where we omit $x_{\alpha i}$ which are equal to 0. Let $\{G_{\alpha\nu}(X)\}$ be a basis of the ideal

$$\{G(X) \mid G(X) \in k[X],\ G(x) = 0 \text{ for every } x \in F_\alpha\},$$

for each α. Then, we have, for almost all $\mathfrak{p}$,

$$\mathfrak{p}(F_\alpha) = \{\xi \mid G_{\alpha\nu\mathfrak{p}}(\xi) = 0 \text{ for every } \nu\},$$

for every α. Suppose that V is complete. Then, we have, for every ε,

$$\phi = W_\varepsilon \cap \left\{(u_{1i})\times\cdots\times(u_{hi}) \,\middle|\, \frac{1-\varepsilon(\alpha i)}{2}u_{\alpha i} = 0 \text{ for every } \alpha, i,\right.$$

$$\left. \text{and } G_{\alpha\nu}(u_{\alpha i})\prod_i \frac{1+\varepsilon(\alpha i)}{2} = 0 \text{ for every } \alpha, \nu\right\}.$$

By Propositions 18 and 19, we have, for almost all $\mathfrak{p}$,

$$\phi = \mathfrak{p}(W_\varepsilon) \cap \left\{(\xi_{1i})\times\cdots\times(\xi_{hi}) \,\middle|\, \frac{1-\varepsilon(\alpha i)}{2}\xi_{\alpha i} = 0 \text{ for every } \alpha, i,\right.$$

$$\left. \text{and } G_{\alpha\nu\mathfrak{p}}(\xi_{\alpha i})\prod_i \frac{1+\varepsilon(\alpha i)}{2} = 0 \text{ for every } \alpha, \nu\right\}$$

for every ε. This shows that V is $\mathfrak{p}$-complete for almost all $\mathfrak{p}$. The algebraic set H has an expression $H = \cup H^{(\alpha)}$, where, for each α, $H^{(\alpha)}$ is the join of the components of H having representatives in V_α. Let H_α be the join of the representatives in V_α for the components of $H^{(\alpha)}$. Then, H_α is an algebraic set defined over k. By our assumption, every point in $V_\alpha-(H_\alpha \cup F_\alpha)$ is simple on V_α. Then, by Proposition 22, every point in $\mathfrak{p}(V_\alpha)-(\mathfrak{p}(H_\alpha) \cup \mathfrak{p}(F_\alpha))$ is simple on V_α for almost all $\mathfrak{p}$. This proves the last assertion of our proposition.

Let $V=[V_\alpha;\ F_\alpha;\ T_{\beta\alpha}]$ be an abstract variety defined over k. Then, by Proposition 23, the system $[V_\alpha;\ F_\alpha;\ \mathfrak{p}(F_\alpha);\ T_{\beta\alpha}]$ defines a $\mathfrak{p}$-variety for almost all $\mathfrak{p}$; and, by Proposition 17, the $\mathfrak{p}$-variety is $\mathfrak{p}$-simple for almost all $\mathfrak{p}$. Thus we obtain, for almost all $\mathfrak{p}$, an abstract variety $\mathfrak{p}(V)=[\mathfrak{p}(V_\alpha):\ \mathfrak{p}(F_\alpha);\ \mathfrak{p}(T_{\beta\alpha})]$, defined over $\mathfrak{p}(k)$. Proposition 23 shows that, if V is complete, then, for almost all $\mathfrak{p}$, $\mathfrak{p}(V)$ is complete, and, if V has no multiple point, then, for almost all $\mathfrak{p}$, $\mathfrak{p}(V)$ has no multiple point.

PROPOSITION 24. *Let* $V=[V_\alpha;\ F_\alpha;\ T_{\beta\alpha}]$ *and* $W=[W_\lambda;\ G_\lambda;\ S_{\mu\lambda}]$ *be two abstract varieties defined over* k*; and let* f *be a rational mapping* *of V into W and H an algebraic set in V, defined over k, such that f is defined at every point in $V-H$. Then, for almost all $\mathfrak{p}$, f is defined at every point in $\mathfrak{p}(V)-\mathfrak{p}(H)$.*

PROOF. We may consider only those $\mathfrak{p}$ for which $[V_\alpha; F_\alpha; \mathfrak{p}(F_\alpha); T_{\beta\alpha}]$ and $[W_\lambda; G_\lambda; \mathfrak{p}(G_\lambda); S_{\mu\lambda}]$ define $\mathfrak{p}$-varieties. Let H_α be an algebraic set in V_α defined for H in the same manner as in the last part of the proof of Proposition 23. Let Z be the graph of f and $Z_{\alpha\lambda}$ the representative of Z in $V_\alpha \times W_\lambda$; in the following we shall consider only those pairs (α, λ) for which Z has the representative in $V_\alpha \times W_\lambda$. Let $B_{\alpha\lambda}$ be the algebraic set in V_α such that the projection from $Z_{\alpha\lambda}$ to V_α is regular at a if and only if a is not contained in $B_{\alpha\lambda}$. Let $C_{\alpha\lambda}$ be the projection of $Z_{\alpha\lambda} \cap (V_\alpha \times G_\lambda)$ on V_α. We will now prove

$$\bigcap_\lambda (B_{\alpha\lambda} \cup C_{\alpha\lambda}) \subset H_\alpha \cup F_\alpha. \tag{1}$$

If a point x_α in V_α is not contained in $H_\alpha \cup F_\alpha$, f is defined at the point x having x_α as its representative in V_α, so that there exists a suffix λ such that $Z_{\alpha\lambda}$ contains a point $x_\alpha \times y_\lambda$ with the projection x_α on V_α, y_λ on $W_\lambda - G_\lambda$ and $Z_{\alpha\lambda}$ is regular at x_α. Suppose that x_α is contained in $B_{\alpha\lambda} \cup C_{\alpha\lambda}$; then, by the definition of $B_{\alpha\lambda}$, we have $x_\alpha \in C_{\alpha\lambda}$. This implies that there exists a point $x'_\alpha \times y'_\lambda$ in $Z_{\alpha\lambda} \cap (V_\alpha \times G_\lambda)$ such that $x'_\alpha \to x_\alpha$ ref. k. As $Z_{\alpha\lambda}$ is regular at x_α, we must have $x'_\alpha \times y'_\lambda \to x_\alpha \times y_\lambda$ ref. k, so that we have $y_\lambda \in G_\lambda$; this is a contradiction; so x_α is not contained in $B_{\alpha\lambda} \cup C_{\alpha\lambda}$. We have thus proved the above inclusion (1). By Propositions 19, 20, 21, there exists an open set σ of $\sum$ such that, if $\mathfrak{p} \in \sigma$, then we have

$$\bigcap_\lambda (\mathfrak{p}(B_{\alpha\lambda}) \cup \mathfrak{p}(C_{\alpha\lambda})) \subset \mathfrak{p}(H_\alpha) \cup \mathfrak{p}(F_\alpha) \tag{2}$$

for every α, $Z_{\alpha\lambda}$ is regular at every point in $\mathfrak{p}(V_\alpha) - \mathfrak{p}(B_{\alpha\lambda})$ and $\mathfrak{p}(C_{\alpha\lambda})$ is the projection of $\mathfrak{p}(Z_{\alpha\lambda}) \cap (\mathfrak{p}(V_\alpha) \times \mathfrak{p}(G_\lambda))$ on $\mathfrak{p}(V_\alpha)$. Now $\mathfrak{p}$ being in σ, let ξ be a point in $\mathfrak{p}(V) - \mathfrak{p}(H)$. Then there exists a representative ξ_α of ξ in $\mathfrak{p}(V_\alpha)$ such that $\xi_\alpha \notin \mathfrak{p}(H_\alpha) \cup \mathfrak{p}(F_\alpha)$. By (2), ξ_α is not contained in $\mathfrak{p}(B_{\alpha\lambda}) \cup \mathfrak{p}(C_{\alpha\lambda})$ for some λ. For such a λ, $\mathfrak{p}(Z_{\alpha\lambda})$ contains a point $\xi_\alpha \times \eta_\lambda$ and $Z_{\alpha\lambda}$ is regular at ξ_α. As ξ_α is not contained in $\mathfrak{p}(C_{\alpha\lambda})$, η_λ is not contained in $\mathfrak{p}(G_\lambda)$; so there exists a point η in $\mathfrak{p}(W)$ having

η_λ as its representative in W_λ. This shows that f is defined at ξ and $f(\xi)=\eta$. Thus we have proved that, for every $\mathfrak{p}$ in σ, f is defined at every point in $\mathfrak{p}(V)-\mathfrak{p}(H)$.

PROPOSITION 25. *Let A be an abelian variety defined over k. Then, A has no defect for almost all $\mathfrak{p}$.*

This is an immediate consequence of Propositions 17, 23, 24.

12.4. We shall now consider the case where k and $\sum$ are given as follows. Given a field k_0, we take as k a finitely generated extension of k_0 and as $\sum$ the set of discrete places $\mathfrak{p}$ of k, taking values in the universal domain over k, such that $\mathfrak{p}(a)=a$ for every $a \in k_0$. Let A be an abelian variety defined over k. By Proposition 25, there exists a set of non-zero elements $\{x_1,\cdots,x_r\}$ in k such that, if $\mathfrak{p}\in\sum$ and $\mathfrak{p}(x_i)\neq 0$ for every i, then A has no defect for $\mathfrak{p}$. Take elements $x_{r+1},\cdots,x_s$ so that $k=k_0(x_1,\cdots,x_r,\ x_{r+1},\cdots,x_s)$ and denote by V the locus of $(x_1,\cdots,x_s)$ over k_0. V may not be absolutely irreducible. As we have $x_i\neq 0$ for $1\leqq i\leqq r$, V carries a point $(a_1,\cdots,a_s)$ such that $a_i\neq 0$ for $1\leqq i\leqq r$ and all the a_i are algebraic over k_0. (Cf. [44] Chap. IV, Proposition 3). By Lemma 2, we can find a place $\mathfrak{p}$ in $\sum$ such that $\mathfrak{p}(x_i)=a_i$ for every i. Then, A has no defect for $\mathfrak{p}$; and $\mathfrak{p}(A)$ is defined over $\mathfrak{p}(k)$. Suppose that $\dim_{k_0}k>0$. Then, one of the x_i is not algebraic over k_0. Since the a_i are algebraic over k_0, we see that $\dim_{k_0}\mathfrak{p}(k)<\dim_{k_0}k$. We shall use this result in the proof of the following proposition.

PROPOSITION 26. *Let $(F;\{\varphi_i\})$ be a CM-type and (A,ι) an abelian variety of type $(F;\{\varphi_i\})$. Then, there exists an abelian variety of type $(F;\{\varphi_i\})$, isomorphic to (A,ι), defined over an algebraic number field of finite degree.*

PROOF. Take an abelian variety (A_1,ι_1) of type $(F;\{\varphi_i\})$ and a field k of definition for (A_1,ι_1). Let k_0 be the composite of the fields F^{φ_i}. We may assume that k is a finitely generated extension of $\mathbf{Q}$ and k contains k_0. If $\dim_{k_0}k>0$, we obtain, by means of the above argument, an abelian variety (A_2,ι_2) of type (F), defined over an extension k_1 of k_0 such that $\dim_{k_0} k_1 < \dim_{k_0} k$. By the result of § 11. 3, (A_2, ι_2) is of type $(F; \{\varphi_i\})$. Repeating this procedure, we get an abelian variety (A_0, ι_0) of type $(F; \{\varphi_i\})$, defined over an algebraic number field. Now let (A, ι) be an arbitrary abelian variety of type $(F; \{\varphi_i\})$. Then, by Corollary of Theorem 2 of § 6 and Remark below it, there exists a homomorphism λ of (A_0, ι_0) onto (A, ι). We can find a finite algebraic extension k_0' of k_0, over which (A_0, ι_0) is defined and every point of $\mathfrak{g}(\lambda)$ is rational. Taking k_0' in place of k_0, apply the above argument to (A, ι). Then we obtain from (A, ι), after several times of reduction, an abelian variety (A', ι') of type $(F; \{\varphi_i\})$, defined over a finite algebraic extension of k_0'; moreover we obtain, at the same time, a homomorphism λ' of (A_0, ι_0) onto (A', ι') as the result of reduction of the homomorphism λ. We observe that A_0 and $\mathfrak{g}(\lambda)$ never change in the reduction process; so the kernel of λ' coincides with $\mathfrak{g}(\lambda)$. It follows that (A, ι) is isomorphic to (A', ι'). This proves our proposition.

13. PRIME IDEAL DECOMPOSITION OF $N(\mathfrak{p})$-TH POWER HOMOMORPHISMS.

We shall now prove a fundamental relation for an abelian variety with complex multiplication, which is a generalization of Kronecker's congruence formula for elliptic functions with singular moduli. The relation is described as follows in terms of the reduction modulo $\mathfrak{p}$ of an abelian variety belonging to a given CM-type.

Let $(F; \{\varphi_i\})$ be a CM-type and $(K^*; \{\psi_\alpha\})$ the dual of $(F; \{\varphi_i\})$. Let (A, ι) be an abelian variety of type $(F; \{\varphi_i\})$, defined over an algebraic number field k of finite degree. We assume that (A, ι) *is principal*. By Proposition 30 of § 8. 5, we know that k contains K^*. We extend the ψ_α to isomorphisms of k which we denote again by ψ_α. Let $\mathfrak{p}$ be a prime ideal of K^*, $\mathfrak{P}$ a prime ideal of k dividing $\mathfrak{p}$, and p the rational prime divisible by $\mathfrak{p}$. Suppose that *A has no defect for $\mathfrak{P}$ and p is unramified in F.* Denote by $(\tilde{A}, \tilde{\iota})$ the reduction of (A, ι) modulo $\mathfrak{P}$.

THEOREM 1. *Notations and assumptions being as above, let $\pi_\mathfrak{p}$ denote* *the* $N(\mathfrak{p})$*-th power homomorphism of* $\tilde{A}$ *onto* $\tilde{A}^{N(\mathfrak{p})}$ *and* π *the* $N(\mathfrak{P})$*-th power endomorphism of* $\tilde{A}$. *Then:*

(π1) $\prod_\alpha \mathfrak{p}^{\psi_\alpha}$ *is an ideal of* F, *and* $(\tilde{A}^{N(\mathfrak{p})}, \tilde{\iota}^{N(\mathfrak{p})}; \pi_{\mathfrak{p}})$ *is a* $\prod_\alpha \mathfrak{p}^{\psi_\alpha}$*-transform of* $(\tilde{A}, \tilde{\iota})$;

(π2) *there exists an element* π_0 *in* F *such that* $\tilde{\iota}(\pi_0) = \pi$; *and we have*

$$(\pi_0) = \prod_\alpha N_{k/K^*}(\mathfrak{P})^{\psi_\alpha}.$$

PROOF. Let n be the dimension of A and $\mathfrak{o}$ the ring of integers in F. By the definition of CM-type, there exist n invariant differential forms ω_i on A such that

$$\delta\iota(\mu)\omega_i = \mu^{\varphi_i}\omega_i \qquad (1 \leqq i \leqq n) \tag{0}$$

for every $\mu \in \mathfrak{o}$. In view of the results of § 2, we may assume that the ω_i are defined over a finite algebraic extension of k. Let k_1 be a Galois extension of $\boldsymbol{Q}$, containing k and F, over which the ω_i are defined. Let $\mathfrak{P}_1$ be a prime ideal of k_1 dividing $\mathfrak{P}$. We indicate by tilde the reduction modulo $\mathfrak{P}_1$. By the property iii) (or Proposition 6) of § 10.4, taking a suitable multiple of each ω_i in place of ω_i, if necessary, we may assume that ω_i is $\mathfrak{P}_1$-finite and $\tilde{\omega}_i \neq 0$ for every i. We shall show that the $\tilde{\omega}_i$ are linearly independent over $\mathfrak{P}_1(k_1)$. Let $\{\beta_1, \cdots, \beta_{2n}\}$ be a basis of $\mathfrak{o}$ over $\boldsymbol{Z}$. Then, denoting by θ_i the complex conjugate of the isomorphism φ_i for each i, the determinant of the matrix

$$\begin{pmatrix} \beta_1^{\varphi_1} & \cdots & \beta_1^{\varphi_n} & \beta_1^{\theta_1} & \cdots & \beta_1^{\theta_n} \\ \beta_2^{\varphi_1} & \cdots & \beta_2^{\varphi_n} & \beta_2^{\theta_1} & \cdots & \beta_2^{\theta_n} \\ & \cdots & & & \cdots & \\ \beta_{2n}^{\varphi_1} & \cdots & \beta_{2n}^{\varphi_n} & \beta_{2n}^{\theta_1} & \cdots & \beta_{2n}^{\theta_n} \end{pmatrix} \tag{1}$$

is not divisible by $\mathfrak{P}_1$, because p is not ramified in F. Hence, the matrix composed of the first n columns of (1) has rank n, modulo $\mathfrak{P}_1$; so suitable n rows of the matrix are linearly independent modulo $\mathfrak{P}_1$. It follows from this that there exist n elements $\mu_1, \cdots, \mu_n$ in $\mathfrak{o}$ such that

$$\det(\mu_j^{\varphi_i}) \not\equiv 0 \qquad \text{mod } \mathfrak{P}_1. \tag{2}$$

Suppose that $\sum_{i=1}^{n} \xi_i\tilde{\omega}_i = 0$ for some ξ_i in the residue field $\mathfrak{P}_1(k_1)$. Multiplying by $\delta\iota(\mu_j)$ this relation, we get, by means of (0) and (2), $\xi_i\tilde{\omega}_i = 0$ for every i. Since we have $\tilde{\omega}_i \neq 0$, the coefficients ξ_i must be all 0. This proves that the $\tilde{\omega}_i$ are linearly independent over $\mathfrak{P}_1(k_1)$, so that they form a basis for the linear space of invariant differential forms on $\tilde{A}$. Now, as is seen in § 11. 2, $(\tilde{A}, \tilde{\iota})$ is an abelian variety of type (F), defined over the finite field with $N(\mathfrak{P})$ elements. Hence, there exists an element π_0 of $\mathfrak{o}$ such that $\tilde{\iota}(\pi_0) = \pi$ (cf. § 7. 6). We have obviously $N(\pi_0) = \nu(\pi) = N(\mathfrak{P})^n$. Let

$$(\pi_0) = \mathfrak{p}_1^{e_1} \cdots \mathfrak{p}_s^{e_s}$$

be the decomposition of the principal ideal (π_0) in prime ideals $\mathfrak{p}_t$ of F. Extend φ_i^{-1} to an automorphism of k_1, for each i, and denote it by σ_i. Let d_t be the number of i such that $\mathfrak{P}_1^{\sigma_i}$ divides $\mathfrak{p}_t$. If we denote by h the class number of F, $\mathfrak{p}_t^{he_t}$ is a principal ideal; put $\mathfrak{p}_t^{he_t} = (\gamma_t)$ for each t. Then, it is easy to see that d_t is the number of i such that $\gamma_t^{\varphi_i} \in \mathfrak{P}_1$. Considering modulo $\mathfrak{P}_1$, we have

$$\delta\tilde{\iota}(\gamma_t)\tilde{\omega}_i = \widetilde{\gamma_t^{\varphi_i}}\tilde{\omega}_i \qquad (1 \leq i \leq n).$$

Since the $\tilde{\omega}_i$ form a basis for the vector space $\mathfrak{D}_0(\tilde{A})$ of invariant differential forms on $\tilde{A}$, we see that the linear mapping $\delta\tilde{\iota}(\gamma_t)$ of $\mathfrak{D}_0(\tilde{A})$ into itself is of rank $n-d_t$. Furthermore, if $\tilde{x}$ is a generic point of $\tilde{A}$ over $\tilde{k}$, we have

$$\tilde{k}(\tilde{\iota}(\gamma_t)\tilde{x}) \supset \tilde{k}(\pi^h\tilde{x}) = \tilde{k}(\tilde{x}^{N(\mathfrak{P})^h}),$$

since $\pi_0^h \in \mathfrak{p}_t^{he_t} = (\gamma_t)$. By Theorem 1 of § 2. 8, we have

$$N(\mathfrak{p}_t^{he_t}) = N(\gamma_t) = \nu(\tilde{\iota}(\gamma_t)) \leq N(\mathfrak{P})^{hd_t},$$

so that

$$N(\mathfrak{p}_t)^{e_t} \leq N(\mathfrak{P})^{d_t}. \tag{3}$$

Put $N_{k_1/k}(\mathfrak{P}_1) = \mathfrak{P}^r$; we have then

$$N(\mathfrak{p}_t)^{e_t r} \leq N(\mathfrak{P})^{d_t r} = \Pi' N(\mathfrak{P}_1^{\sigma_i}), \tag{4}$$

where the product is taken over all i such that $\mathfrak{P}_1^{\sigma_i}$ divides $\mathfrak{p}_t$. This shows in particular that d_t is not 0, so that every $\mathfrak{p}_t$ is divisible by at least one of the $\mathfrak{P}_1^{\sigma_i}$. Each $\mathfrak{P}_1^{\sigma_i}$ divides at most one of the $\mathfrak{p}_t$. Hence, from the relations (4) and $(\pi_0) = \mathfrak{p}_1^{e_1} \cdots \mathfrak{p}_s^{e_s}$ follows

$$N(\pi_0)^r \leqq \prod_{i=1}^{n} N(\mathfrak{P}_1^{\sigma_i}).$$

We note that both sides are equal to $N(\mathfrak{P})^{nr}$. Therefore, (3) and (4) must be equalities; and every $\mathfrak{P}_1^{\sigma_i}$ must divide exactly one of the $\mathfrak{p}_t$. Put $N_{k_1/F}(\mathfrak{P}_1^{\sigma_i}) = \mathfrak{p}_t^{u_t}$ for every $\mathfrak{p}_t$ divisible by $\mathfrak{P}_1^{\sigma_i}$; as k_1 is a Galois extension of F, u_t does not depend on the choice of i. We have then $N(\mathfrak{P}_1^{\sigma_i}) = N(\mathfrak{p}_t)^{u_t}$, and, by the equality (4), $N(\mathfrak{p}_t)^{re_t} = N(\mathfrak{p}_t)^{u_t d_t}$. Hence we get $re_t = u_t d_t$, so that

$$\mathfrak{p}_t^{e_t r} = (\mathfrak{p}_t^{u_t})^{d_t} = \Pi' N_{k_1/F}(\mathfrak{P}_1^{\sigma_i}),$$

where the product is taken over all i such that $\mathfrak{P}_1^{\sigma_i} \mid \mathfrak{p}_t$. We obtain therefore,

$$(\pi_0)^r = \mathfrak{p}_1^{re_1} \cdots \mathfrak{p}_s^{re_s} = N_{k_1/F}(\prod_{i=1}^{n} \mathfrak{P}_1^{\sigma_i}). \tag{5}$$

Now take a Frobenius substitution σ for $\mathfrak{P}_1$ over K^*; σ is an automorphism of k_1 over K^* such that $\mathfrak{P}_1^\sigma = \mathfrak{P}_1$ and $z^\sigma \equiv z^{N(\mathfrak{p})} \bmod \mathfrak{P}_1$. Put $N(\mathfrak{p}) = q$. As $\mathfrak{P}_1^\sigma = \mathfrak{P}_1$, A^σ has no defect for $\mathfrak{P}_1$ and the reduction modulo $\mathfrak{P}_1$ of (A^σ, ι^σ) is identified with $(\tilde{A}^q, \tilde{\iota}^q)$. By Proposition 31 of § 8. 5 and Proposition 16 (or Proposition 23) of § 7, (A^σ, ι^σ) is a c-transform of (A, ι) for an ideal-class c of F; so by Proposition 15 of § 11. 2, $(\tilde{A}^q, \tilde{\iota}^q)$ is a c-transform of $(\tilde{A}, \tilde{\iota})$. By the result of § 7. 6, $\pi_\mathfrak{p}$ is a homomorphism of $(\tilde{A}, \tilde{\iota})$ onto $(\tilde{A}^q, \tilde{\iota}^q)$; so by Proposition 13 of § 7. 2, $\pi_\mathfrak{p}$ is an $\mathfrak{a}$-multiplication for an ideal $\mathfrak{a}$ of $\mathfrak{o}$. Put $N_{k/K^*}(\mathfrak{P}) = \mathfrak{p}^v$; then, $N(\mathfrak{P}) = q^v$. Now let π_a denote the q-th power homomorphism of $\tilde{A}^{q^{a-1}}$ onto $\tilde{A}^{q^a}$ for each positive integer a. Then, as $(\tilde{A}^{q^{a-1}}, \tilde{A}^{q^a}, \pi_a)$ is an isomorphic image of $(\tilde{A}, \tilde{A}^q, \pi_\mathfrak{p})$, we observe that $(\tilde{A}^{q^a}, \tilde{\iota}^{q^a}; \pi_a)$ is an $\mathfrak{a}$-transform of $(\tilde{A}^{q^{a-1}}, \tilde{\iota}^{q^{a-1}})$. Hence $\pi_v \cdots \pi_2 \pi_1$ is an $\mathfrak{a}^v$-multiplication of $\tilde{A}$ onto $\tilde{A}^{N(\mathfrak{P})} = \tilde{A}$. On the other hand, we have

$$(\pi_v \cdots \pi_1)\tilde{x} = \tilde{x}^{q^v} = \tilde{x}^{N(\mathfrak{P})} = \pi x,$$

so that $\pi = \pi_v \cdots \pi_1$. Since π is a (π_0)-multiplication, we have $(\pi_0) = \mathfrak{a}^v$; therefore, by the relation (5), we obtain

$$\mathfrak{a}^{vr} = (\pi_0)^r = N_{k_1/F}(\prod_{i=1}^{n} \mathfrak{P}_1^{\sigma_i}). \tag{6}$$

Let G denote the Galois group of k_1 over $\boldsymbol{Q}$; let H and H^* be the subgroup of G corresponding to F and K^*, respectively. Then, by the definition of dual of CM-type, denoting by S^* the set of elements of G which induce some ψ_α on K^*, we have

$$S^* = \bigcup_i \sigma_i H = \bigcup_\alpha H^* \psi_\alpha.$$

It follows from this and (6) that

$$(7) \qquad \mathfrak{a}^{vr} = \prod_{\tau \in S^*} \mathfrak{P}_1^{\tau} = \prod_\alpha (\prod_{\rho \in H^*} \mathfrak{P}_1^{\rho})^{\psi_\alpha} = \prod_\alpha (N_{k_1/K^*} \mathfrak{P}_1)^{\psi_\alpha} = \prod_\alpha (\mathfrak{p}^{rv})^{\psi_\alpha}.$$

Hence we have $\mathfrak{a} = \prod \mathfrak{p}^{\psi_\alpha}$; this proves the assertion ($\pi 1$) of our theorem. As we have $(\pi_0) = \mathfrak{a}^v$ and $\mathfrak{p}^v = N_{k/K^*}(\mathfrak{P})$, we obtain ($\pi 2$); so our theorem is completely proved.

THEOREM 2. *Notations and assumptions being as in Theorem* 1, *suppose that A is simple. Then, if $\mathfrak{p}$ is of absolute degree* 1 *and the rational prime p divisible by $\mathfrak{p}$ is unramified in F and in K^*, $\tilde{A}$ is simple.*

PROOF. We use the same notations as in the proof of Theorem 1. We observe that, for a sufficiently large positive integer g, every element of $\mathscr{A}(\tilde{A})$ is defined over a finite field with $N(\mathfrak{P})^g$ elements. g being taken as this, π^g is contained in the center of $\mathscr{A}_0(\tilde{A})$; by Proposition 3 of § 5. 1, we can find an element ξ of F such that $\pi^g = \tilde{\iota}(\xi)$. Let σ be an element of G. If $\xi^\sigma = \xi$, we have $\mathfrak{a}^{vr} = (\mathfrak{a}^{vr})^\sigma$, and hence, by virtue of (7),

$$(8) \qquad \prod_{\tau \in S^*} \mathfrak{P}_1^{\tau} = \prod_{\tau \in S^*} \mathfrak{P}_1^{\tau\sigma}.$$

Denote by Z the subgroup of G consisting of the elements τ such that $\mathfrak{P}_1^\tau = \mathfrak{P}_1$; then, by the assumption of our theorem, Z is contained in H^*. The relation (8) implies $S^*\sigma \subset ZS^* \subset H^*S^* = S^*$; so we have $S^*\sigma = S^*$. As $(F; \{\varphi_i\})$ is primitive, we must have, by Proposition 26 of § 8. 2, $\sigma \in H$. We have thus proved that $\xi^\sigma = \xi$ implies $\sigma \in H$; this shows $F = \boldsymbol{Q}(\xi)$. Therefore, every element of $\mathscr{A}_0(\tilde{A})$ commutes with the elements of $\tilde{\iota}(F)$. By Proposition 3 of § 5. 1, the commutor of $\tilde{\iota}(F)$ in $\mathscr{A}_0(\tilde{A})$ coincides with $\tilde{\iota}(F)$ itself; hence we have $\mathscr{A}_0(\tilde{A}) = \tilde{\iota}(F)$. This proves that $\tilde{A}$ is simple; in fact, if $\tilde{A}$ is not simple, $\mathscr{A}_0(\tilde{A})$ can not be a field; so our theorem is proved.

CHAPTER IV. CONSTRUCTION OF CLASS-FIELDS.

Throughout this chapter, we shall denote by $\bar{\alpha}$ the complex conjugate of a complex number α; $\mathfrak{a}$ being an ideal of an algebraic number field, $\bar{\mathfrak{a}}$ will denote the ideal consisting of the elements $\bar{\alpha}$ for $\alpha \in \mathfrak{a}$.

14. POLARIZED ABELIAN VARIETIES OF TYPE $(K; \{\varphi_i\})$.

14. 1. Let $(K; \{\varphi_i\})$ be a primitive CM-type, $(K^*; \{\psi_\alpha\})$ the dual of $(K; \{\varphi_i\})$. As is seen in § 8. 2, K must be a totally imaginary quadratic extension of a totally real field K_0; put $n = [K_0 : \boldsymbol{Q}]$. The automorphism of K over K_0 other than the identity is given by $\alpha \rightarrow \bar{\alpha}$. Let $\mathfrak{o}$ denote the ring of integers in K. In §§ 14-17, the notations $(K; \{\varphi_i\})$, $(K^*; \{\psi_\alpha\})$, K_0 and n will be always used in this sense.

Let (A, ι) be an abelian variety of type $(K; \{\varphi_i\})$. Then, by Proposition 6 of § 5. 1, $\mathscr{A}_0(A) = \iota(K)$.

PROPOSITION 1. *$(K; \{\varphi_i\})$ being a primitive CM-type, let (A, ι) and (A', ι') be abelian varieties of type $(K; \{\varphi_i\})$. Then, every homomorphism of A into A' is a homomorphism of (A, ι) into (A', ι').*

PROOF. By Corollary of Theorem 2 of § 6. 1 and by Remark below it, there exists a homomorphism λ of (A', ι') onto (A, ι). Let μ be a homomorphism of A into A'. Then $\lambda\mu$ is an element of $\mathscr{A}_0(A)$. As we have $\mathscr{A}_0(A) = \iota(K)$, there exists an element ξ of K such that $\lambda\mu = \iota(\xi)$; so we have $\mu = \lambda^{-1}\iota(\xi)$. Hence μ commutes with the operation of K; this proves our proposition.

14. 2. We shall now consider polarizations. β being an element of K, we denote by $v(\beta)$ the vector of $\boldsymbol{C}^n$ with the components $\beta^{\varphi_1}, \cdots, \beta^{\varphi_n}$ and by $T(\beta)$ the diagonal matrix with the diagonal elements $\beta^{\varphi_1}, \cdots, \beta^{\varphi_n}$. If $\mathfrak{m}$ is a free $\boldsymbol{Z}$-submodule of K of rank $2n$, we denote by $D(\mathfrak{m})$ the set of all vectors $v(\beta)$ for $\beta \in \mathfrak{m}$. Let (A, ι) be an abelian variety of type $(K;\ \{\varphi_i\})$. By Theorem 2 of § 6. 1, $(A,\ \iota)$ is represented by a complex torus $\boldsymbol{C}^n/D(\mathfrak{m})$ for a suitable $\mathfrak{m}$. Let $E(u, v)$ be a non-degenerate Riemann form on $\boldsymbol{C}^n/D(\mathfrak{m})$. By Theorem 4 of § 6. 2, there exists an element ζ of K such that

$$(1) \qquad E(v(\xi), v(\eta)) = \mathrm{Tr}_{K/Q}(\zeta\xi\bar{\eta})$$

for every $\xi \in K,\ \eta \in K$; the element ζ satisfies

$$(2) \qquad \bar{\zeta} = -\zeta, \qquad \mathrm{Im}(\zeta^{\varphi_i}) > 0 \qquad (1 \leqq i \leqq n).$$

Conversely, any such element ζ of K determines a non-degenerate Riemann form on $\boldsymbol{C}^n/D(\mathfrak{m})$ by the relation (1).

Let A^* be a Picard variety of A; put, for every $\alpha \in K$,

$$\iota^*(\alpha) = {}^t\iota(\bar{\alpha}).$$

Then, we have seen in § 6. 3 that $(A^*,\ \iota^*)$ is of type $(K;\ \{\varphi_i\})$; and $(A^*,\ \iota^*)$ is analytically represented by the complex torus $\boldsymbol{C}^n/D(\mathfrak{m}^*)$, where $\mathfrak{m}^*$ is given by

$$(3) \qquad \mathfrak{m}^* = \{\beta \mid \beta \in K, \mathrm{Tr}_{K/Q}(\beta\bar{\mathfrak{m}}) \subset \boldsymbol{Z}\}.$$

Furthermore, if X is a divisor on A corresponding to the Riemann form defined by (1), then the homomorphism φ_X of A onto A^* is represented by the matrix $T(\zeta)$. The following proposition is an easy consequence of this fact and the relation (2).

Proposition 2. *$(A,\ \iota)$ and $\boldsymbol{C}^n/D(\mathfrak{m})$ being as above, let X and Y be two non-degenerate divisors on A; and let E_1, E_2 be the Riemann forms on $\boldsymbol{C}^n/D(\mathfrak{m})$ defined by X, Y, respectively. Let ζ_i, for $i = 1, 2$, be the elements of K determined by the relation*

$$E_i(v(\xi), v(\eta)) = \mathrm{Tr}_{K/Q}(\zeta_i\xi\bar{\eta}).$$

Then, $\zeta_1^{-1}\zeta_2$ is a totally positive element of K_0 and we have

$$\varphi_X^{-1}\varphi_Y = \iota(\zeta_1^{-1}\zeta_2).$$

Now put

$$\mathfrak{r} = \iota^{-1}(\mathscr{A}(A));$$

then $\mathfrak{r}$ is an order in K.

Proposition 3. *Notations being as in Proposition 2, the polarized abelian varieties* $(A, \mathscr{C}(X))$ *and* $(A, \mathscr{C}(Y))$ *are isomorphic if and only if there exist a unit* ε *of* $\mathfrak{r}$ *and a positive rational number* s *such that* $\zeta_1^{-1}\zeta_2 = s\varepsilon\bar{\varepsilon}$.

PROOF. As we have $\mathscr{A}(A) = \iota(\mathfrak{r})$, every automorphism of A is given by $\iota(\varepsilon)$ for a unit ε of $\mathfrak{r}$. Suppose that $\iota(\varepsilon)^{-1}$ maps $\mathscr{C}(X)$ onto $\mathscr{C}(Y)$. Then, by the definition of $\mathscr{C}(X)$, there exist two positive integers m and m' such that $m\iota(\varepsilon)^{-1}(X)$ is algebraically equivalent to $m'Y$. Consider the homomorphisms φ_X and φ_Y of A onto the Picard variety A^* of A; we have then by (7) of § 1. 3, $m^t\iota(\varepsilon)\varphi_X\iota(\varepsilon) = m'\varphi_Y$. Put $s = m/m'$. By the relations (5) and (6) of § 6. 3, and by Proposition 2, we have $s\iota(\varepsilon\bar{\varepsilon}) = \varphi_X^{-1}\varphi_Y = \iota(\zeta_1^{-1}\zeta_2)$. This proves the "only if" part. The "if" part is proved by following up the above argument in the opposite direction.

COROLLARY. *(A, ι) and $\mathfrak{r}$ being as above, let $\mathscr{C}$ be a polarization of A. Then, for every root of unity ε contained in $\mathfrak{r}$, $\iota(\varepsilon)$ gives an automorphism of $(A, \mathscr{C})$. Conversely, every automorphism of $(A, \mathscr{C})$ is given by $\iota(\varepsilon)$ for a root of unity ε contained in $\mathfrak{r}$.*

PROOF. Put $\mathscr{C} = \mathscr{C}(X) = \mathscr{C}(Y)$ and $\zeta_1 = \zeta_2$ in the above proposition. We see then that if ε is a unit of $\mathfrak{r}$, $\iota(\varepsilon)$ gives an automorphism of $(A, \mathscr{C})$ if and only if $\varepsilon\bar{\varepsilon} = 1$. Since $(\bar{\varepsilon})^{\varphi_i}$ is the complex conjugate of ε^{φ_i} (cf. Lemma 2 of § 5. 1), the condition $\varepsilon\bar{\varepsilon} = 1$ is equivalent to that the ε^{φ_i} are all of absolute value 1. It is well-known that an algebraic integer α is a root of unity if and only if every conjugate of α over $\boldsymbol{Q}$ is of absolute value 1. This proves the assertion of our corollary.

14. 3. $(K; \{\varphi_i\})$ being as before, by a *polarized abelian variety of type* $(K; \{\varphi_i\})$, we shall understand a triplet $\mathscr{P} = (A, \iota, \mathscr{C})$ formed by an abelian variety (A, ι) of type $(K; \{\varphi_i\})$ and a polarization $\mathscr{C}$ of A; $\mathscr{P} = (A, \iota, \mathscr{C})$ and $\mathscr{P}_1 = (A_1, \iota_1, \mathscr{C}_1)$ are said to be *isomorphic* if there exists an isomorphism of (A, ι) onto (A_1, ι_1) which sends $\mathscr{C}$ onto $\mathscr{C}_1$. As we have restricted ourselves to primitive CM-type, every isomorphism of $(A, \mathscr{C})$ onto $(A_1, \mathscr{C}_1)$ gives an isomorphism of $\mathscr{P}$ onto $\mathscr{P}_1$ on account of Proposition 1.

Now we impose one more condition on our abelian varieties

(A, ι). From now on, until the end of § 16, *by an abelian variety* (A, ι) *of type* $(K; \{\varphi_i\})$, *we shall understand a principal one;* namely, we assume

$$\iota(\mathfrak{o}) = \mathscr{A}(A),$$

where $\mathfrak{o}$ is the ring of integers in K.

Let (A, ι) be an abelian variety of type $(K; \{\varphi_i\})$. (A^*, ι^*), $\boldsymbol{C}^n/D(\mathfrak{m})$ and $\boldsymbol{C}^n/D(\mathfrak{m}^*)$ being determined as above, we observe that (A^*, ι^*) is also principal and $\mathfrak{m}$, $\mathfrak{m}^*$ are ideals of K. Moreover, if we denote by $\mathfrak{d}$ the different of K with respect to $\boldsymbol{Q}$, the relation (3) of § 14. 2 shows that

$$\mathfrak{m}^* = (\mathfrak{d}\bar{\mathfrak{m}})^{-1}.$$

Let X be a non-degenerate divisor of A, corresponding to the Riemann form given by (1) of § 14. 2. The homomorphism φ_X of A onto A^* is represented by the matrix $T(\zeta)$. Hence, by Proposition 15 of § 7. 4, φ_X is a $(\zeta\mathfrak{d}\mathfrak{m}\bar{\mathfrak{m}})$-multiplication of (A, ι) onto (A^*, ι^*). Put

$$\mathfrak{f} = \zeta\mathfrak{d}\mathfrak{m}\bar{\mathfrak{m}}.$$

We shall now prove that $\mathfrak{f}$ is an "ideal of K_0", namely, there exists an ideal $\mathfrak{f}_0$ of K_0 such that $\mathfrak{f} = \mathfrak{o}\mathfrak{f}_0$. Let $\mathfrak{d}_0$ be the different of K_0 with respect to $\boldsymbol{Q}$ and $\mathfrak{d}_1$ the different of K with respect to K_0; we have then $\mathfrak{d} = \mathfrak{d}_0\mathfrak{d}_1$. The ideal $\mathfrak{d}_1$ is generated by the elements $\theta - \bar{\theta}$ for $\theta \in \mathfrak{o}$. By the property (2) of the element ζ, we see that $\zeta(\theta - \bar{\theta})$ is contained in K_0 for every $\theta \in \mathfrak{o}$, so that $\zeta\mathfrak{d}_1$ is an ideal of K_0. It is obvious that $\mathfrak{d}_0\mathfrak{m}\bar{\mathfrak{m}}$ is an ideal of K_0. Hence $\mathfrak{f} = (\zeta\mathfrak{d}_1)(\mathfrak{d}_0\mathfrak{m}\bar{\mathfrak{m}})$ is an ideal of K_0.

Let $\mathscr{C}$ be a polarization of A. Take a basic polar divisor Y of $(A, \mathscr{C})$ (cf. § 4. 2). Then, the above argument shows that there exists an ideal $\mathfrak{f}_0$ of K_0 such that φ_Y is an $(\mathfrak{o}\mathfrak{f}_0)$-multiplication of (A, ι) onto (A^*, ι^*). We observe that the ideal $\mathfrak{f}_0$ is determined by $\mathscr{P} = (A, \iota, \mathscr{C})$ and does not depend on the choice of the basic polar divisor Y; so we say that the polarized abelian variety $\mathscr{P}$ is of type $(K; \{\varphi_i\}; \mathfrak{f}_0)$.

PROPOSITION 4. *Let* $\mathfrak{f}_0$ *be an ideal of* K_0. *Then, there exists a polarized abelian variety of type* $(K; \{\varphi_i\}; s\mathfrak{f}_0)$ *for some rational number* s *if and only if there exists an ideal* $\mathfrak{m}$ *of* K *and an element* ζ *of* K *such that*

$$\mathfrak{o}\mathfrak{f}_0 = \zeta\mathfrak{d}\mathfrak{m}\bar{\mathfrak{m}},$$

$$(2) \qquad \bar{\zeta} = -\zeta, \qquad \operatorname{Im}(\zeta^{\varphi_i}) > 0 \qquad (1 \leqq i \leqq n),$$

where $\mathfrak{d}$ *denotes the different of* K *with respect to* $\boldsymbol{Q}$.

PROOF. We have already proved the "only if" part; so we shall now prove the "if" part. We may assume that $\mathfrak{f}_0$ is an integral ideal. If $\mathfrak{m}$ and ζ are given as above, we obtain an abelian variety (A, ι) of type $(K;\ \{\varphi_i\})$ by means of the complex torus $\boldsymbol{C}^n/D(\mathfrak{m})$; and ζ defines a bilinear form $E(u, v)$ by the relation (1) of § 14.2. As $\zeta\mathfrak{d}\mathfrak{m}\bar{\mathfrak{m}} = \mathfrak{o}\mathfrak{f}_0$ is integral, the values of E on $D(\mathfrak{m})\times D(\mathfrak{m})$ are rational integers; hence by Theorem 4 of § 6.2, E is a non-degenerate Riemann form on $\boldsymbol{C}^n/D(\mathfrak{m})$. If X is a divisor on A corresponding to the form E, φ_X is an $(\mathfrak{o}\mathfrak{f}_0)$-multiplication; so $(A, \iota, \mathscr{C}(X))$ is of type $(K;\ \{\varphi_i\};\ s\mathfrak{f}_0)$ for a suitable rational number s; this completes the proof.

(A, ι) being as above, let $\mathscr{C}_1$ and $\mathscr{C}_2$ be two polarizations of A; suppose that $(A, \iota, \mathscr{C}_1)$ and $(A, \iota, \mathscr{C}_2)$ are of the same type $(K;\ \{\varphi_i\};\ \mathfrak{f}_0)$. Then $\mathscr{C}_i$ contains a divisor Y_i such that φ_{Y_i} is an $(\mathfrak{o}\mathfrak{f}_0)$-multiplication, for each i. Let ζ_i be the element of K for which the bilinear form $\operatorname{Tr}_{K/Q}(\zeta_i\xi\bar{\eta})$ defines the Riemann form defined by Y_i. Then, by Proposition 2, we have $(\varphi_{Y_1})^{-1}\varphi_{Y_2} = \iota(\zeta_1^{-1}\zeta_2)$; and $\zeta_1^{-1}\zeta_2$ is a totally positive element of K_0. Since both the φ_{Y_i} are $(\mathfrak{o}\mathfrak{f}_0)$-multiplications, $\zeta_1^{-1}\zeta_2$ is a unit of K_0. Conversely, take a totally positive unit ε of K_0 and put $\zeta = \varepsilon\zeta_1$. Then ζ satisfies the relation (2); and hence there exists a divisor X on A corresponding to the form $\operatorname{Tr}(\zeta\xi\bar{\eta})$. Then, we see easily that $(A, \iota, \mathscr{C}(X))$ is of type $(K;\ \{\varphi_i\};\ \mathfrak{f}_0)$. By Proposition 3, $(A, \iota, \mathscr{C}_1)$ is isomorphic to $(A, \iota, \mathscr{C}_2)$ if and only if $\zeta_1^{-1}\zeta_2$ is of the form $\alpha\bar{\alpha}$ for a unit α of K. The following proposition is a consequence of these considerations.

PROPOSITION 5. *Let* U *be the group of totally positive units of* K_0 *and* U_1 *the subgroup of* U *consisting of the elements* $N_{K/K_0}(\varepsilon)$ *for units* ε *of* K. *Then, there exist exactly* $[U : U_1]$ *polarized abelian varieties* $(A, \iota, \mathscr{C})$ *of the same type* $(K;\ \{\varphi_i\};\ \mathfrak{f}_0)$ *with the same underlying abelian variety* (A, ι) *of type* $(K;\ \{\varphi_i\})$, *of which no two are isomorphic.*

We note that the index $[U: U_1]$ is finite.

14. 4. Let $(A, \iota, \mathscr{C})$ and $(A_1, \iota_1, \mathscr{C}_1)$ be two polarized abelian varieties of the same type $(K; \{\varphi_i\}; \mathfrak{f}_0)$. Put $\mathfrak{f} = \mathfrak{o}\mathfrak{f}_0$. Let X and Y be respectively a basic polar divisor in $\mathscr{C}$ and a basic polar divisor in $\mathscr{C}_1$; then both φ_X and φ_Y are $\mathfrak{f}$-multiplications. Let λ be a homomorphism of (A, ι) onto (A_1, ι_1). By Proposition 23 of §7. 5, λ is an $\mathfrak{a}$-multiplication of (A, ι) onto (A_1, ι_1) for an ideal $\mathfrak{a}$ of $\mathfrak{o}$. Put $Z = \lambda^{-1}(Y)$. Then $\varphi_X{}^{-1}\varphi_Z$ is an element of $\mathscr{A}_0(A)$; so there exists an element α of K such that $\iota(\alpha) = \varphi_X{}^{-1}\varphi_Z$. We observe that α is determined only by λ and does not depend on the choice of X and Y; we write

$$\alpha = f(\lambda).$$

Let (A^*, ι^*) and $(A_1{}^*, \iota_1{}^*)$ be respectively duals of (A, ι) and (A_1, ι_1). Now we need the following fact.

PROPOSITION 6. *Notations being as above, if λ is an $\mathfrak{a}$-multiplication of (A, ι) onto (A_1, ι_1) then ${}^t\lambda$ is an $\bar{\mathfrak{a}}$-multiplication of $(A_1{}^*, \iota_1{}^*)$ onto (A^*, ι^*).*

PROOF. By Proposition 1, ${}^t\lambda$ is a homomorphism of $(A_1{}^*, \iota_1{}^*)$ onto (A^*, ι^*). By Proposition 13 of §7. 2, and by Proposition 1, we have $\mathscr{H}(A, A_1) = \lambda\iota(\mathfrak{a}^{-1})$. Now consider the mapping $\mu \rightarrow {}^t\mu$ which gives an isomorphism of $\mathscr{H}(A, A_1)$ onto $\mathscr{H}(A_1{}^*, A^*)$. As we have ${}^t(\lambda\iota(\xi)) = {}^t(\iota_1(\xi)\lambda) = {}^t\lambda{}^t\iota_1(\xi) = {}^t\lambda\iota_1{}^*(\bar{\xi})$, we obtain $\mathscr{H}(A_1{}^*, A^*) = {}^t\lambda\iota_1{}^*((\bar{\mathfrak{a}})^{-1})$. This proves our proposition. We can also prove the proposition by means of Proposition 15 of §7. 4.

Now, since $Z = \lambda^{-1}(Y)$, we have $\varphi_Z = {}^t\lambda\varphi_Y\lambda$, and hence

$$\iota(f(\lambda)) = \varphi_Y{}^{-1}\cdot{}^t\lambda\varphi_Y\lambda.$$

As both φ_X and φ_Y are $\mathfrak{f}$-multiplications, we see, by the above proposition, that $\iota(f(\lambda))$ is an $\mathfrak{a}\bar{\mathfrak{a}}$-multiplication. On the other hand, by Proposition 2, $f(\lambda)$ is a totally positive element of K_0. We have thus proved that $f(\lambda)$ is a totally positive element of K_0 such that

$$\mathfrak{a}\bar{\mathfrak{a}} = (f(\lambda)).$$

Conversely, let $\mathfrak{b}$ be an ideal of $\mathfrak{o}$ such that there exists a totally positive element β of K_0 for which we have $\mathfrak{b}\bar{\mathfrak{b}} = (\beta)$. Let $(A_2, \iota_2; \mu)$ be a $\mathfrak{b}$-transform of $(A,\ \iota)$. By the results of § 7.4, we can take complex tori $\boldsymbol{C}^n/D(\mathfrak{m})$ and $\boldsymbol{C}^n/D(\mathfrak{b}^{-1}\mathfrak{m})$ as analytic representations of $(A,\ \iota)$ and $(A_2,\ \iota_2)$. Let ζ be the element of K corresponding to the basic polar divisor X. We have then

$$\mathfrak{f} = \zeta\mathfrak{d}\mathfrak{m}\bar{\mathfrak{m}} = (\beta\zeta)\mathfrak{d}(\mathfrak{b}^{-1}\mathfrak{m})(\overline{\mathfrak{b}^{-1}\mathfrak{m}})\,; \tag{4}$$

and we see that $\beta\zeta$ satisfies the condition (2) of Proposition 4. Then, it can be easily verified, by means of the same argument as in the proof of that proposition, that A_2 has a polarization $\mathscr{C}_2$ for which $(A_2,\ \iota_2,\ \mathscr{C}_2)$ is of type $(K;\ \{\varphi_i\}\,;\ \mathfrak{f}_0)$. Thus we have proved:

PROPOSITION 7. *Let* $(A,\ \iota,\ \mathscr{C})$ *be a polarized abelian variety of type* $(K;\ \{\varphi_i\}\,;\ \mathfrak{f}_0)$; *let* $\mathfrak{a}$ *be an ideal of* $\mathfrak{o}$ *and* $(A_1,\ \iota_1)$ *be an* $\mathfrak{a}$-*transform of* $(A,\ \iota)$. *Then,* A_1 *has a polarization* $\mathscr{C}_1$ *such that* $(A_1,\ \iota_1,\ \mathscr{C}_1)$ *is of type* $(K;\ \{\varphi_i\}\,;\ \mathfrak{f}_0)$ *if and only if there exists a totally positive element* α *of* K_0 *such that* $\mathfrak{a}\bar{\mathfrak{a}} = (\alpha)$.

λ being as above, we have $\mathscr{H}(A,\ A_1) = \lambda\iota(\mathfrak{a}^{-1})$ by virtue of Proposition 13 of § 7.2; we shall now prove that for every $\xi \in \mathfrak{a}^{-1}$,

$$f(\lambda\iota(\xi)) = f(\lambda)\xi\bar{\xi}. \tag{5}$$

Put $\mu = \lambda\iota(\xi)$. We have then $\iota(f(\mu)) = \varphi_X{}^{-1}\cdot{}^t\mu\varphi_Y\mu = \varphi_X{}^{-1}\cdot{}^t\iota(\xi){}^t\lambda\varphi_Y\lambda\iota(\xi) = \iota(\bar{\xi})\varphi_X{}^{-1}\cdot{}^t\lambda\varphi_Y\lambda\iota(\xi) = \iota(\bar{\xi})\iota(f(\lambda))\iota(\xi) = \iota(f(\lambda)\xi\bar{\xi})$. This proves the relation (5). Therefore, f is considered as a Hermitian form defined on the module $\mathfrak{a}^{-1}$.

14.5 Class of Hermitian forms. Before proceeding further, we give a definition concerning a certain class of Hermitian forms on K. Let $\mathfrak{a}$ be an ideal of K such that there exists a totally positive element ρ of K_0 for which we have $\mathfrak{a}\bar{\mathfrak{a}} = (\rho)$. Then the form $\rho\xi\bar{\xi}$ for $\xi \in K$ is a positive Hermitian form on K taking algebraic integral values on $\mathfrak{a}^{-1}$. Now let $\{\mathfrak{a}_1,\ \rho_1\}$ be another pair such that $\mathfrak{a}_1\bar{\mathfrak{a}}_1 = (\rho_1)$ and ρ_1 is totally positive. We say that $\{\mathfrak{a}_1,\ \rho_1\}$ and $\{\mathfrak{a},\ \rho\}$ are *equivalent* if there exists an element $\mu \in K$ for which we have $\mu\mathfrak{a} = \mathfrak{a}_1$ and $\rho_1 = \rho\mu\bar{\mu}$, in other words, if the module $\mathfrak{a}^{-1}$ with the form $\rho\xi\bar{\xi}$ is isomorphic to $\mathfrak{a}_1{}^{-1}$ with $\rho_1\xi\bar{\xi}$ by the mapping $\xi \to \mu^{-1}\xi$. The class determined by this equivalence relation will be denoted by $(\mathfrak{a},\ \rho)$; we call it a *class of* *positive Hermitian forms in K.* Define the multiplication of two classes $(\mathfrak{a}, \rho)$ and $(\mathfrak{a}_1, \rho_1)$ by

$$(\mathfrak{a}, \rho)(\mathfrak{a}_1, \rho_1) = (\mathfrak{a}\mathfrak{a}_1, \rho\rho_1).$$

Then the set of classes becomes a group; and the identity element is given by $(\mathfrak{o}, 1)$. We denote this group by $\mathfrak{C}(K)$.

14. 6. Let $\mathcal{P} = (A, \iota, \mathcal{C})$ and $\mathcal{P}_1 = (A_1, \iota_1, \mathcal{C}_1)$ be two polarized abelian varieties of the same type $(K; \{\varphi_i\}; \mathfrak{f}_0)$. Take a homomorphism λ of (A, ι) onto (A_1, ι_1); there exists an ideal $\mathfrak{a}$ of $\mathfrak{o}$ such that λ is an $\mathfrak{a}$-multiplication. We have shown that $f(\lambda)$ is totally positive and $\mathfrak{a}\bar{\mathfrak{a}} = (f(\lambda))$; so we obtain an element $(\mathfrak{a}, f(\lambda))$ of $\mathfrak{C}(K)$. By means of the relation (5), we see that the class $(\mathfrak{a}, f(\lambda))$ does not depend on the choice of λ. We write

$$\{\mathcal{P}_1 : \mathcal{P}\} = (\mathfrak{a}, f(\lambda)).$$

PROPOSITION 8. *If $\mathcal{P}$, $\mathcal{P}_1$, $\mathcal{P}_2$ are three polarized abelian varieties of the same type $(K; \{\varphi_i\}; \mathfrak{f}_0)$, we have*

$$\{\mathcal{P}_2 : \mathcal{P}_1\}\{\mathcal{P}_1 : \mathcal{P}\} = \{\mathcal{P}_2 : \mathcal{P}\}.$$

PROOF. By our definition, there exist ideals $\mathfrak{a}$, $\mathfrak{b}$ of $\mathfrak{o}$ and an $\mathfrak{a}$-multiplication λ of $\mathcal{P}$ onto $\mathcal{P}_1$ and a $\mathfrak{b}$-multiplication μ of $\mathcal{P}_1$ onto $\mathcal{P}_2$ such that

$$\{\mathcal{P}_1 : \mathcal{P}\} = (\mathfrak{a}, f(\lambda)), \qquad \{\mathcal{P}_2 : \mathcal{P}_1\} = (\mathfrak{b}, f(\mu)).$$

Then $\mu\lambda$ is an $\mathfrak{a}\mathfrak{b}$-multiplication of $\mathcal{P}$ onto $\mathcal{P}_2$. Let X, Y, Z be respectively basic polar divisors of $\mathcal{P}$, $\mathcal{P}_1$, $\mathcal{P}_2$. We have then

$$\begin{aligned}\varphi_X{}^{-1}\cdot{}^t(\mu\lambda)\varphi_Z(\mu\lambda) &= \varphi_X{}^{-1}\cdot{}^t\lambda{}^t\mu\varphi_Z\mu\lambda = \varphi_X{}^{-1}\cdot{}^t\lambda\varphi_Y(\varphi_Y{}^{-1}\cdot{}^t\mu\varphi_Z\mu)\lambda \\ &= \varphi_X{}^{-1}\cdot{}^t\lambda\varphi_Y\iota_1(f(\mu))\lambda = \varphi_X{}^{-1}\cdot{}^t\lambda\varphi_Y\lambda\iota(f(\mu)) = \iota(f(\lambda))\iota(f(\mu)) = \iota(f(\lambda)f(\mu)).\end{aligned}$$

Hence we have $\{\mathcal{P}_2 : \mathcal{P}\} = (\mathfrak{a}\mathfrak{b}, f(\lambda)f(\mu))$; this proves the proposition.

PROPOSITION 9. *Let $\mathcal{P} = (A, \iota, \mathcal{C})$ and $\mathcal{P}_1 = (A_1, \iota_1, \mathcal{C}_1)$ be two polarized abelian varieties of the same type $(K; \{\varphi_i\}; \mathfrak{f}_0)$; and let η be an isomorphism of A onto A_1. Then, η is an isomorphism of $\mathcal{P}$ onto $\mathcal{P}_1$ if and only if $f(\eta) = 1$.*

PROOF. Let X and Y be basic polar divisors of $\mathcal{C}$ and $\mathcal{C}_1$, respectively. Put $Z = \eta^{-1}(Y)$. If η is an isomorphism of $\mathcal{P}$ onto $\mathcal{P}_1$, there exist two positive integers m and m' such that mZ is algebraically equivalent to $m'X$, namely, $m\varphi_Z = m'\varphi_X$; we have then $f(\eta) = m'/m$. Since η is an $\mathfrak{o}$-multiplication, we have $\mathfrak{o} = (f(\eta))$. It follows that $f(\eta) = 1$; this proves the "only if" part. Conversely, if $f(\eta) = 1$, we get $\varphi_X^{-1}\varphi_Z = 1_A$ and hence $\varphi_X = \varphi_Z$, so that $\eta^{-1}(Y) = Z$ is algebraically equivalent to X; hence η is an isomorphism of $\mathcal{P}$ onto $\mathcal{P}_1$. This completes the proof.

PROPOSITION 10. *Let $\mathcal{P}$ and $\mathcal{P}_1$ be two polarized abelian varieties of the same type. Then, $\mathcal{P}$ and $\mathcal{P}_1$ are isomorphic if and only if we have $\{\mathcal{P}_1 : \mathcal{P}\} = (\mathfrak{o}, 1)$.*

PROOF. The "only if" part follows directly from Proposition 9; so we prove the "if" part. If $\{\mathcal{P}_1 : \mathcal{P}\} = (\mathfrak{o}, 1)$, there exist an ideal $\mathfrak{a}$ of $\mathfrak{o}$ and an $\mathfrak{a}$-multiplication λ of A onto A_1 such that $(\mathfrak{o}, 1) = (\mathfrak{a}, f(\lambda))$. By our definition, we can find an element γ of K such that $\mathfrak{a} = (\gamma)$ and $f(\lambda) = \gamma\bar{\gamma}$. Then, as $\iota(\lambda)$ is an $\mathfrak{a}$-multiplication of A onto itself, there exists an isomorphism η of (A, ι) onto (A_1, ι_1) such that $\eta\iota(\gamma) = \lambda$. By the relation (5) of § 14.4, we have $f(\eta) = 1$, so that by Proposition 9, $\mathcal{P}$ is isomorphic to $\mathcal{P}_1$. This completes the proof.

COROLLARY. *Let $\mathcal{P}$, $\mathcal{P}_1$, $\mathcal{P}_2$ be three polarized abelian varieties of the same type. Then, $\mathcal{P}_1$ and $\mathcal{P}_2$ are isomorphic if and only if we have $\{\mathcal{P}_1 : \mathcal{P}\} = \{\mathcal{P}_2 : \mathcal{P}\}$.*

This is an immediate consequence of Propositions 8 and 10.

14.7. Let $\mathcal{P} = (A, \iota, \mathscr{C})$ be a polarized abelian variety of type $(K; \{\varphi_i\}; \mathfrak{f}_0)$. We say that $\mathcal{P}$ is defined over k if (A, ι) is defined over k and $\mathscr{C}$ is defined over k. If that is so, by Proposition 30 of § 8.5, k must contain the field K^*. Let τ be an isomorphism of k onto a field k', which leaves invariant the elements of K^*. Then we obtain naturally a system $\mathcal{P}^\tau = (A^\tau, \iota^\tau, \mathscr{C}^\tau)$. By Proposition 31 of § 8.5, (A^τ, ι^τ) is of type $(K; \{\varphi_i\})$. Let (A^*, ι^*) be a dual of (A, ι) and k_1 a field of definition for (A^*, ι^*) containing k. We extend τ to an isomorphism of k_1, which we denote again by τ. It is easy to see that $(A^{*\tau}, \iota^{*\tau})$ gives a dual of (A^τ, ι^τ). Let X be a basic polar divisor in $\mathscr{C}$; we take k_1 so large that X is rational over k_1; φ_X is an $\mathfrak{f}$-multiplication. As is seen in § 7. 6, $\varphi_{(X^\tau)} = (\varphi_X)^\tau$ is an $\mathfrak{f}$-multiplication. Therefore, $\mathscr{P}^\tau = (A^\tau, \iota^\tau, \mathscr{C}^\tau)$ is of the same type as $\mathscr{P}$.

Let $\mathscr{P}_1 = (A_1, \iota_1, \mathscr{C}_1)$ be another abelian variety of the same type as $\mathscr{P}$ and λ a homomorphism of (A, ι) onto (A_1, ι_1); let Y be a basic polar divisor in $\mathscr{C}_1$. We may assume that (A_1, ι_1) and λ is defined over k_1 and Y is rational over k_1; if this is not so, we take a suitable extension of k_1 instead of k_1. Now λ being an $\mathfrak{a}$-multiplication, we have $\mathfrak{a}\bar{\mathfrak{a}} = (f(\lambda))$ and $\iota(f(\lambda)) = \varphi_X{}^{-1} \cdot {}^t\lambda\varphi_Y\lambda$. We see easily that $\iota^\tau(f(\lambda)) = \varphi_{(X^\tau)}{}^{-1} \cdot {}^t(\lambda^\tau)\varphi_{(Y^\tau)}\lambda^\tau$ and λ^τ is an $\mathfrak{a}$-multiplication. We have thus proved the following proposition.

Proposition 11. *Let $\mathscr{P}$ and $\mathscr{P}_1$ be two polarized abelian varieties of the same type $(K; \{\varphi_i\}; \mathfrak{f}_0)$, defined over k; let τ be an isomorphism of k onto a field k', which leaves invariant the elements of K^*. Then, $\mathscr{P}^\tau$ and $\mathscr{P}_1{}^\tau$ are of the same type $(K; \{\varphi_i\}; \mathfrak{f}_0)$ as $\mathscr{P}$ and $\mathscr{P}_1$; and we have*

$$\{\mathscr{P}_1{}^\tau : \mathscr{P}^\tau\} = \{\mathscr{P}_1 : \mathscr{P}\}.$$

15. UNRAMIFIED CLASS-FIELD OBTAINED FROM THE FIELD OF MODULI.

15. 1. We shall now proceed in the theory of construction of class-fields. First we introduce some notations concerning ideal-groups. Let k be an algebraic number field of finite degree; let $\mathfrak{m}$ be an integral ideal of k. We denote by $I_k(\mathfrak{m})$ the group of ideals of k which are prime to $\mathfrak{m}$, and by $P_k(\mathfrak{m})$ the subgroup of $I_k(\mathfrak{m})$ consisting of all principal ideals (α) such that $\alpha \in k$, $\alpha \equiv 1 \bmod \mathfrak{m}$. The factor group $I_k(\mathfrak{m})/P_k(\mathfrak{m})$ is then the group of ideal-classes modulo $\mathfrak{m}$. For our purpose in this section, it is not necessary to consider infinite primes. If k' is a Galois extension of k, we denote by $G(k'/k)$ the Galois group of k' over k.

As before, let $(K; \{\varphi_i\})$ be a primitive CM-type, $[K : Q] = 2n$, $(K^*; \{\psi_\alpha\})$ the dual of $(K; \{\varphi_i\})$, K_0 the totally real subfield of K of degree n, and $\mathfrak{o}$ the ring of integers in K. Let (A, ι) be an abelian variety of type $(K; \{\varphi_i\})$ which is principal. We assume in the sequel that (A, ι) is defined over an algebraic number field. Let $\mathscr{C}$ be a polarization of A and Y a basic polar divisor in $\mathscr{C}$. We may assume that Y is algebraic over $\boldsymbol{Q}$; in fact, if Y is not algebraic over $\boldsymbol{Q}$, we can find a specialization Y' of Y algebraic over $\boldsymbol{Q}$; we see easily that Y' is also a basic polar divisor in $\mathscr{C}$. By the result of § 14, there exists an integral ideal $\mathfrak{f}_0$ of K_0 such that φ_Y is an $(\mathfrak{o}\mathfrak{f}_0)$-multiplication of (A, ι) onto its dual. Put $\mathscr{P} = (A, \iota, \mathscr{C})$ and $\mathfrak{f} = \mathfrak{o}\mathfrak{f}_0$. Let k be an algebraic number field of finite degree satisfying the following conditions:

i) *k is normal over K^*;*

ii) *A is defined over k;*

iii) *for every $\sigma \in G(k/K^*)$, all the elements of $\mathscr{H}(A, A^\sigma)$ are defined over k;*

iv) *Y is rational over k.*

Such a field k really exists, since there are only finitely many transforms A^σ of A over K^*. As $(K; \{\varphi_i\})$ is the dual of $(K^*; \{\psi_\alpha\})$, k contains K. By Proposition 30 of § 8.5, every element of $\mathscr{A}(A^\sigma)$ is defined over k. Let k_0 be the field of moduli of $(A, \mathscr{C})$. Then, k_0 is contained in k. Put $k_0^* = k_0K^*$. These notations and assumptions will be never changed until the end of § 16.

15.2. Our purpose is to describe the extension k_0^* of K^* in terms of class-field theory. Let σ be an element of $G(k/K^*)$. By Proposition 11, $\mathscr{P}^\sigma$ is of the same type as $\mathscr{P}$; so $\{\mathscr{P}^\sigma : \mathscr{P}\}$ has a meaning. Put

$$[\sigma] = \{\mathscr{P}^\sigma : \mathscr{P}\}.$$

By Propositions 8 and 11, we have, for every $\sigma, \tau \in G(k/K^*)$,

$$\begin{aligned}[\sigma\tau] = \{\mathscr{P}^{\sigma\tau} : \mathscr{P}\} &= \{\mathscr{P}^{\sigma\tau} : \mathscr{P}^\tau\}\{\mathscr{P}^\tau : \mathscr{P}\} \\ &= \{\mathscr{P}^\sigma : \mathscr{P}\}\{\mathscr{P}^\tau : \mathscr{P}\} = [\sigma][\tau];\end{aligned}$$

namely, $\sigma \to [\sigma]$ gives a homomorphism of $G(k/K^*)$ into the group $\mathfrak{C}(K)$. Let H be the kernel of this homomorphism. By Proposition 10, we have $\sigma \in H$ if and only if $\mathscr{P}^\sigma$ is isomorphic to $\mathscr{P}$. On the other hand, by Proposition 1 and by the definition of field of moduli, $\mathscr{P}^\sigma$

is isomorphic to $\mathscr{P}$ if and only if σ leaves invariant the elements of the field of moduli k_0. Therefore, H is the set of elements of $G(k/K^*)$ which leave invariant the elements of k_0^*. If follows that $\sigma \to [\sigma]$ induces an isomorphism of $G(k_0^*/K^*)$ into $\mathfrak{C}(K)$. As $\mathfrak{C}(K)$ is an abelian group, k_0^* must be an abelian extension of K^*.

15. 3. Now we consider reduction of (A, ι) modulo prime ideals of k. By Proposition 25 of § 12. 3, A has no defect for almost all prime ideals of k. Here and in the following, the terms "almost all" mean "all except a finite number of". Let $\mathfrak{m}$ be the product of prime ideals $\mathfrak{p}$ of K^* satisfying at least one of the following conditions.

i) There exists a prime ideal of k dividing $\mathfrak{p}$, for which A has defect.

ii) The rational prime divisible by $\mathfrak{p}$ is ramified in k.

Let $\mathfrak{p}$ be a prime ideal of K^* which does not divide $\mathfrak{m}$, and $\mathfrak{P}$ a prime ideal of k dividing $\mathfrak{p}$; then, by our definition of $\mathfrak{m}$, for every $\sigma \in G(k/K^*)$, A^σ has no defect for $\mathfrak{P}$. In the following treatment, we denote by tilde the reduction modulo $\mathfrak{P}$. Put $N(\mathfrak{p}) = q$. Let σ be a Frobenius automorphism of k for $\mathfrak{P}/\mathfrak{p}$. We can identify $(\tilde{A}^q, \tilde{\iota}^q)$ with the reduction of (A^σ, ι^σ) modulo $\mathfrak{P}$. Let π be the q-th power homomorphism of $\tilde{A}$ onto $\tilde{A}^q$. Put

$$\mathfrak{q} = \prod_\alpha \mathfrak{p}^{\phi_\alpha};$$

then, by Theorem 1 of § 13, π is a $\mathfrak{q}$-multiplication of $(\tilde{A}, \tilde{\iota})$ onto $(\tilde{A}^q, \tilde{\iota}^q)$. If c denotes the ideal-class of $\mathfrak{q}$, $(\tilde{A}^q, \tilde{\iota}^q)$ is a c-transform of $(\tilde{A}, \tilde{\iota})$, so that, by Proposition 15 of § 11. 2, (A^σ, ι^σ) is a c-transform of (A, ι). Hence there exists a $\mathfrak{q}$-multiplication μ of (A, ι) onto (A^σ, ι^σ). Then $\tilde{\mu}$ is a $\mathfrak{q}$-multiplication of $(\tilde{A}, \tilde{\iota})$ onto $(\tilde{A}^q, \tilde{\iota}^q)$; so by Proposition 7 of § 7. 1, there exists an automorphism η of $(\tilde{A}^q, \tilde{\iota}^q)$ such that $\pi = \eta\tilde{\mu}$. By Proposition 3 of § 5. 1, η must be of the form $\tilde{\iota}^q(\varepsilon)$ for $\varepsilon \in \mathfrak{o}$. Put $\lambda = \mu \cdot \iota(\varepsilon)$. We have then $\tilde{\lambda} = \pi$; and as ε is a unit of $\mathfrak{o}$, λ is a $\mathfrak{q}$-multiplication. We have thus proved the existence of a $\mathfrak{q}$-multiplication λ of (A, ι) onto (A^σ, ι^σ) whose reduction modulo $\mathfrak{P}$ is π.

Put $Z = \lambda^{-1}(Y^\sigma)$; we have then $\tilde{Z} = \pi^{-1}(\tilde{Y}^q)$, and hence $\tilde{Z} = q\tilde{Y}$. Take a prime l which is not divisible by $\mathfrak{p}$ and consider l-adic representations of the divisors Y, Z, $\tilde{Y}$, $\tilde{Z}$. By Proposition 14 of § 11. 1, with respect to suitable l-adic coordinate-systems, we obtain $E_l(Z) = E_l(\tilde{Z})$; and $E_l(Y) = E_l(\tilde{Y})$, so that $E_l(Z) = qE_l(Y)$; this implies that Z is algebraically equivalent to qY. Hence we have $\varphi_Y^{-1}\varphi_Z = q\cdot 1_A$ so that

$$f(\lambda) = q,$$

f being determined as in § 14. 4. We have thus arrived at an important conclusion

$$(1) \qquad [\sigma] = (\prod_\alpha \mathfrak{p}^{\psi_\alpha}, N(\mathfrak{p})).$$

We have seen above that $\sigma \to [\sigma]$ induces an isomorphism of $G(k_0^*/K^*)$ into $\mathfrak{C}(K)$; we denote this isomorphism also by $[\sigma]$. Now, $\mathfrak{p}$ being a prime ideal of K^* which is prime to $\mathfrak{m}$, let $\sigma(\mathfrak{p})$ denote a Frobenius automorphism of k_0^*/K^* for $\mathfrak{p}$; we note that, since k_0^* is abelian over K^*, $\sigma(\mathfrak{p})$ is uniquely determined by $\mathfrak{p}$. For every ideal $\mathfrak{a} \in I_{K^*}(\mathfrak{m})$, consider the prime ideal decomposition $\mathfrak{a} = \prod \mathfrak{p}^{e(\mathfrak{p})}$ and put

$$\sigma(\mathfrak{a}) = \prod_{\mathfrak{p}} \sigma(\mathfrak{p})^{e(\mathfrak{p})}.$$

Then, by means of the relation (1), we obtain, for every $\mathfrak{a} \in I_{K^*}(\mathfrak{m})$,

$$[\sigma(\mathfrak{a})] = (\prod_\alpha \mathfrak{a}^{\psi_\alpha}, N(\mathfrak{a})).$$

Let H_1 denote the kernel of the homomorphism $\mathfrak{a} \to \sigma(\mathfrak{a})$ of $I_{K^*}(\mathfrak{m})$ into $G(k_0^*/K^*)$. Since $\sigma \to [\sigma]$ is an isomorphism of $G(k_0^*/K^*)$ into $\mathfrak{C}(K)$, H_1 is the set of ideals $\mathfrak{a}$ of ideals of $I_{K^*}(\mathfrak{m})$ such that

$$(\prod_\alpha \mathfrak{a}^{\psi_\alpha}, N(\mathfrak{a})) = (\mathfrak{o}, 1).$$

Let H_0 be the subgroup of $I_{K^*}((1))$ consisting of ideals $\mathfrak{a}$ such that there exists an element $\mu \in K$ for which we have $\prod_\alpha \mathfrak{a}^{\psi_\alpha} = (\mu)$ and $N(\mathfrak{a}) = \mu\bar{\mu}$. Then, we see easily that $H_0 \cap I_{K^*}(\mathfrak{m}) = H_1$. Let $\mathfrak{b} = (\beta)$ be a principal ideal in K^*. Put $\gamma = \prod_\alpha \beta^{\psi_\alpha}$; then, by Proposition 29 of § 8. 3, γ is contained in K and $\gamma\bar{\gamma} = N(\beta)$. As $\gamma\bar{\gamma} > 0$, we get $\gamma\bar{\gamma} = N(\mathfrak{b})$. This shows that H_0 contains $P_{K^*}((1))$. Therefore, according to the results of class-field theory, k_0^* is the unramified class-field over K^* corresponding to the ideal-group H_0. We have thus established our first main theorem.

MAIN THEOREM 1. *Let* $(K^*; \{\psi_\alpha\})$ *be a primitive CM-type and* $(K; \{\varphi_i\})$ *the dual of* $(K^*; \{\psi_\alpha\})$. *Let* H_0 *be the group of all ideals* $\mathfrak{a}$ *of* K^* *such that there exists an element* $\mu \in K$ *for which we have*

$$\prod_\alpha \mathfrak{a}^{\psi_\alpha} = (\mu), \qquad N(\mathfrak{a}) = \mu\bar{\mu},$$

where $\bar{\mu}$ *denotes the complex conjugate of* μ. *Let* (A, ι) *be an abelian variety of type* $(K; \{\varphi_i\})$ *and* $\mathscr{C}$ *a polarization of* A. *Let* k_0 *be the field of moduli of* $(A, \mathscr{C})$. *Then,* H_0 *is an ideal-group of* K^*, *defined modulo* (1); *and the composite* $k_0{}^*$ *of the fields* k_0 *and* K^* *is the unramified class-field over* K^* *corresponding to the ideal-group* H_0.

NOTE 1. We have to explain why we may drop the condition that (A, ι) is defined over an algebraic number field. Let (A, ι) be an abelian variety of type $(K; \{\varphi_i\})$ and $\mathscr{C}$ a polarization of A. By Proposition 26 of § 12. 4, there can be found an abelian variety (A_1, ι_1), defined over an algebraic number field, which is isomorphic to (A, ι). If we denote by $\mathscr{C}_1$ the image of $\mathscr{C}$ by an isomorphism of (A, ι) onto (A_1, ι_1), the fields of moduli of $(A, \mathscr{C})$ and of $(A_1, \mathscr{C}_1)$ are the same. Therefore we obtain the results of our theorem, applying the above discussion to (A_1, ι_1).

NOTE 2. The field $k_0{}^* = k_0K^*$ depends only upon $(K^*; \{\psi_\alpha\})$ and is independent of the choice of (A, ι) and $\mathscr{C}$. A similar fact holds for another type of abelian varieties, which is related to automorphic functions (cf. [36] *n*° 23).

NOTE 3. In the classical case where the dimension of A is equal to 1, every abelian variety of the same type as A is isomorphic to some conjugate A^σ of A over K^*; this implies the so-called " irreducibility of the class-equation ". We shall now consider this problem in a general case. $(A, \iota, \mathscr{C})$ being as above, let (A_1, ι_1) be another abelian variety of type $(K; \{\varphi_i\})$. By Proposition 16 of § 7. 4, there exists an ideal $\mathfrak{b}$ of K such that (A_1, ι_1) is a $\mathfrak{b}$-multiplication of (A, ι). By Proposition 7, A_1 has a polarization $\mathscr{C}_1$ such that $(A_1, \iota_1, \mathscr{C}_1)$ is of the same type as $(A, \iota, \mathscr{C})$ if and only if there exists a totally positive element ρ of K_0 such that $\mathfrak{b}\bar{\mathfrak{b}} = (\rho)$. Let h' be the number of ideal-classes of K whose members $\mathfrak{b}$ have this property. Then there exist exactly h'

distinct abelian varieties (A_1, ι_1) of type $(K; \{\varphi_i\})$ on which we can find a polarization $\mathscr{C}_1$ such that $(A_1, \iota_1, \mathscr{C}_1)$ is of the given type $(K; \{\varphi_i\}; \mathfrak{f}_0)$. On the other hand, by Proposition 5, there exist $[U: U_1]$ polarized abelian varieties, of which no two are isomorphic, having the same (A_1, ι_1) as the underlying abelian variety, U and U_1 being as in that proposition. Put $[U: U_1] = d$. Thus we observe that there exist exactly dh' polarized abelian varieties of type $(K; \{\varphi_i\}; \mathfrak{f}_0)$, not isomorphic to each other. We have shown that for every $\mathfrak{a} \in I_{K^*}(\mathfrak{m})$, $(A^{\sigma(\mathfrak{a})}, \iota^{\sigma(\mathfrak{a})})$ is a $(\prod \mathfrak{a}^{\psi_\alpha})$-transform of (A, ι). Let h_0' be the number of ideal-classes of K containing ideals of the form $\prod_\alpha \mathfrak{a}^{\psi_\alpha}$ for ideals $\mathfrak{a}$ of K^*. Then, we see that there exist exactly h_0' conjugates A^σ of A over K^*, of which no two are isomorphic; h_0' is clearly a divisor of h'. If $A^{\sigma(\mathfrak{a})}$ is isomorphic to A, $\prod \mathfrak{a}^{\psi_\alpha}$ is a principal ideal (μ) of K; then $N(\mathfrak{a})(\mu\bar{\mu})^{-1}$ is a totally positive unit of K_0. Let U_0 be the group of units ε in K_0 of the form $\varepsilon = N(\mathfrak{a})(\mu\bar{\mu})^{-1}$, where $\mathfrak{a}$ is an ideal of K^* such that $\prod \mathfrak{a}^{\psi_\alpha}$ is a principal ideal (μ) of K. Then we have $U \supset U_0 \supset U_1$; put $d_0 = [U_0: U_1]$. We see that there exist exactly $d_0 h_0'$ conjugates $\mathscr{P}^\sigma$ of $\mathscr{P} = (A, \iota, \mathscr{C})$ over K^*, of which no two are isomorphic; and the number $d_0 h_0'$ is a divisor of dh'. If we have $d_0 h_0' = dh'$, the analogy of the irreducibility of class-equation holds for $(A, \iota, \mathscr{C})$. It is not easy, however, to see in which case the equality $d_0 h_0' = dh'$ holds.

15.4. Examples. 1) We shall first consider the "classical case" where $n = 1$. In this case, K is an imaginary quadratic field and $(K; \varphi) = (K^*; \psi)$. The ideal-group H_0 coincides with $P_K((1))$. Hence $k_0 K$ is the absolute class-field over K. As A is of dimension 1, A has only one polarization $\mathscr{C}$. It is easy to see that k_0 is generated over Q by the value of the classical modular function $j(\tau)$ (cf. [35] n° 7).

2) Let l be an odd prime and C the plane algebraic curve defined by the equation $y^2 = 1 - x^l$. Then the genus g of C is equal to $(l-1)/2$; and $\omega_\nu = x^\nu dx/y$ for $\nu = 0, 1, \cdots, g-1$ give a basis for the differential forms of the first kind. If ζ denotes a primitive l-th root of unity, then $(x, y) \to (\zeta x, y)$ gives a birational correspondence of C onto itself, which is represented with respect to the basis $\{\omega_\nu\}$ by the diagonal matrix having $\zeta, \zeta^2, \cdots, \zeta^g$ as the diagonal elements. Let C_0 be a com-

plete non-singular curve, defined over $\boldsymbol{Q}$, birationally equivalent to C over $\boldsymbol{Q}$; we can find a Jacobian variety J of C_0, defined over $\boldsymbol{Q}$ (cf. Chow [5], Weil [51], [52]). Now denote by $\iota(\zeta)$ the endomorphism of J corresponding to the above birational correspondence $(x, y) \to (\zeta x, y)$ of C. Then we can easily verify that $\zeta \to \iota(\zeta)$ is extended to an isomorphism ι of $\boldsymbol{Q}(\zeta)$ into $\mathscr{A}_0(J)$. Let φ_ν denote the automorphism $\zeta \to \zeta^\nu$ of $\boldsymbol{Q}(\zeta)$ for $\nu = 1, 2, \cdots, g$. Then (J, ι) is of type $(\boldsymbol{Q}(\zeta); \{\varphi_\nu\})$. As is seen in § 8. 4, $(\boldsymbol{Q}(\zeta); \{\varphi_\nu\})$ is a primitive CM-type and its dual is given by $(\boldsymbol{Q}(\zeta); \{\varphi_\nu^{-1}\})$. Therefore, the abelian variety J must be simple; and we have $\mathscr{A}_0(J) = \boldsymbol{Q}(\zeta)$. Since $\boldsymbol{Z}[\zeta]$ is the ring of integers in $\boldsymbol{Q}(\zeta)$ and $\iota(\zeta) \in \mathscr{A}(J)$, we have $\mathscr{A}(J) = \iota(\boldsymbol{Z}[\zeta])$, so that (J, ι) is principal. Hence we can apply our theorem to this case; so, for every polarization $\mathscr{C}$ of J, the field of moduli k_0 of $(J, \mathscr{C})$ generates a class-field $k_0(\zeta)$ over $\boldsymbol{Q}(\zeta)$, which corresponds to the ideal-group H_0. Since J is defined over $\boldsymbol{Q}$, we can find a polarization $\mathscr{C}$ of J, defined over $\boldsymbol{Q}$; then k_0 must coincide with $\boldsymbol{Q}$. Therefore in this case, the class-field k_0K^* is not a proper extension of K^*. We can conclude from this the following interesting fact. By class-field theory, H_0 must coincide with the whole ideal-group $I_K((1))$. Hence, putting $\psi_\nu = \varphi_\nu^{-1}$, we see that, for every ideal $\mathfrak{a}$ of $\boldsymbol{Q}(\zeta)$, there exists an element μ of K such that $\prod \mathfrak{a}^{\psi_\nu} = (\mu)$ and $N(\mathfrak{a}) = \mu\bar{\mu}$. This is a particular case of "Stickelberger's relation" (cf. [39], [6]); our result gives a proof of this relation. Finally, we note that this example shows the invalidity of "irreducibility of class-equation" in a general case.

3) Let us consider the example (2. c) of § 8. 4. Notations being as there, put $\psi = \sigma\tau$. We have then $\prod \mathfrak{a}^{\psi_\alpha} = \mathfrak{a}\mathfrak{a}^{\psi} = N_{L/K}(\mathfrak{a})$ for every ideal $\mathfrak{a}$ of K^*. Now assume that the class-number h of K is an odd number. Let H denote the subgroup of $I_K((1))/P_K((1))$ consisting of the classes which contain $N_{L/K}(\mathfrak{A})$ for an ideal $\mathfrak{A}$ of L. Then H is of index $\leqq [L:K] = 2$; as h is odd, the index must be 1. Hence, every ideal-class of K contains an ideal of the form $N_{L/K}(\mathfrak{A})$ for some ideal $\mathfrak{A}$ of L. Let H' be the subgroup of $I_K((1))/P_K((1))$ consisting of the classes whose members $\mathfrak{b}$ have the property $\mathfrak{b}\bar{\mathfrak{b}} = (\xi)$ for a totally positive element ξ of K_0. As the order h' of H' is odd, for every $c \in H'$, there exists an element c' of H' such that $c = c'^2$. Take an

ideal $\mathfrak{A}$ of L such that $N_{L/K}(\mathfrak{A}) \in c'$. Put $\mathfrak{b} = \mathfrak{A}\mathfrak{A}^{\tau}\mathfrak{A}^{\phi}\mathfrak{A}^{\phi\tau}$; then $\mathfrak{b}$ is an ideal of K^*. Since $N_{L/K}(\mathfrak{A})$ is contained in c', by the definition of H', there exists a totally positive element ξ of K_0 such that we have $(\xi) = N_{L/K}(\mathfrak{A})\ \overline{N_{L/K}(\mathfrak{A})}$. We can easily verify that

$$N_{L/K}(\mathfrak{b}) = N_{L/K}(\mathfrak{A})^2(\xi^{\tau}).$$

This shows that the class c contains $N_{L/K}(\mathfrak{b})$. It follows from this that $h' = h_0'$. Since K_0 is a real quadratic field, the group of units in K_0 is the direct product of $\{1, -1\}$ and the free cyclic group $\{\varepsilon^n | n \in \boldsymbol{Z}\}$ generated by a unit ε, which we call a fundamental unit of K_0. Assume that $N_{K_0/Q}(\varepsilon) = -1$. Then the group of totally positive units in K_0 is the free cyclic group generated by ε^2; and, since $N_{K/K_0}(\varepsilon) = \varepsilon^2$, we have $d = d_0 = 1$. Therefore, if the class-number h of K is odd and if the norm $N_{K_0/Q}(\varepsilon)$ of a fundamental unit ε of K_0 is -1, we have $dh' = d_0 h_0'$, so that the analogy of the irreducibility of class-equation holds in this case. This result is due to Hecke [20].

16. THE CLASS-FIELDS GENERATED BY IDEAL-SECTION POINTS.

16. 1. Notations and assumptions being as in the preceding section, let (V, F) be a normalized Kummer variety of $(A, \mathscr{C})$ (cf § 4. 4). Let $\mathfrak{b}$ be an integral ideal of K and t a proper $\mathfrak{b}$-section point of A; then we say that a system $(\mathscr{P}, t) = (A, \iota, \mathscr{C}, t)$ is of type $(K; \{\varphi_i\}; \mathfrak{f}_0; \mathfrak{b})$. We shall denote $(K; \{\varphi_i\}; \mathfrak{f}_0; \mathfrak{b})$ briefly by $\mathfrak{K}(\mathfrak{b})$. Our purpose is to show that the field $k_0^*(F(t))$ is a class-field over K^* and to determine the corresponding ideal-group of K^*.

Let $(\mathscr{P}_1, t_1) = (A_1, \iota_1, \mathscr{C}_1, t_1)$ be another system of type $\mathfrak{K}(\mathfrak{b})$. By Proposition 24 of § 7. 5, there exists a homomorphism λ of A onto A_1 such that $\lambda t = t_1$; and λ is an $\mathfrak{a}$-multiplication for an ideal $\mathfrak{a}$ of K which is prime to $\mathfrak{b}$. Now consider the function $f(\lambda)$ defined in § 14. 4; $f(\lambda)$ is a totally positive element of K_0, and $f(\lambda\iota(\xi)) = f(\lambda)\xi\bar{\xi}$ for every $\xi \in \mathfrak{a}^{-1}$. Let λ_0 be another homomorphism of A onto A_1 such that $\lambda_0 t = t_1$. As we have $\mathscr{H}(A, A_1) = \lambda\iota(\mathfrak{a}^{-1})$, there exists an element $\mu \in \mathfrak{a}^{-1}$ such that $\lambda_0 = \lambda\iota(\mu)$. Then, λ_0 is a $(\mu\mathfrak{a})$-multiplication and

$f(\lambda_0) = f(\lambda)\mu\bar{\mu}$. Moreover, we see that $\lambda - \lambda_0 = \lambda\iota(1-\mu)$ is a $(1-\mu)\mathfrak{a}$-multiplication. Hence, as $(\lambda-\lambda_0)\,t = 0$, we have $(1-\mu)\mathfrak{a} \subset \mathfrak{b}$, by virtue of Proposition 24 of § 7. 5. Since $\mathfrak{a}$ is prime to $\mathfrak{b}$, we get $\mu \equiv 1 \bmod \mathfrak{b}$. Thus we are led to the following definition.

$\mathfrak{b}$ being as above an integral ideal of K, consider a pair $\{\mathfrak{a}, \rho\}$ formed by an ideal $\mathfrak{a}$ of K which is *prime to* $\mathfrak{b}$ and a totally positive element ρ of K_0 such that

$$\mathfrak{a}\bar{\mathfrak{a}} = (\rho).$$

$\{\mathfrak{a}_1, \rho_1\}$ being another pair satisfying these conditions, we say that $\{\mathfrak{a}, \rho\}$ and $\{\mathfrak{a}_1, \rho_1\}$ are *equivalent modulo* $\mathfrak{b}$, if there exists an element $\mu \in K$ for which we have

$$\mathfrak{a}_1 = \mu\mathfrak{a}, \qquad \rho_1 = \rho\mu\bar{\mu}, \qquad \mu \equiv 1 \bmod \mathfrak{b}.$$

The class determined by this equivalence relation will be denoted by $(\mathfrak{a}, \rho)_{\mathfrak{b}}$. Define the multiplication of two classes $(\mathfrak{a}, \rho)_{\mathfrak{b}}$ and $(\mathfrak{a}_1, \rho_1)_{\mathfrak{b}}$ by

$$(\mathfrak{a}, \rho)_{\mathfrak{b}}(\mathfrak{a}_1, \rho_1)_{\mathfrak{b}} = (\mathfrak{a}\mathfrak{a}_1, \rho\rho_1)_{\mathfrak{b}}.$$

Then, it can be easily verified that the classes $(\mathfrak{a}, \rho)_{\mathfrak{b}}$ form a group by this law of multiplication; we denote this group by $\mathfrak{C}(K; \mathfrak{b})$; the identity element of $\mathfrak{C}(K; \mathfrak{b})$ is given by $(\mathfrak{o}, 1)_{\mathfrak{b}}$.

Now consider the pair $\{\mathfrak{a}, f(\lambda)\}$ determined by $(\mathscr{P}, t)$ and $(\mathscr{P}_1, t_1)$; by the above considerations, the class $(\mathfrak{a}, f(\lambda))_{\mathfrak{b}}$ does not depend on the choice of λ; so we write

$$\{(\mathscr{P}_1, t_1) : (\mathscr{P}, t)\} = (\mathfrak{a}, \rho)_{\mathfrak{b}}.$$

If furthermore $(\mathscr{P}_2, t_2)$ is of type $\mathfrak{K}(\mathfrak{b})$, we have

$$\{(\mathscr{P}_2, t_2) : (\mathscr{P}_1, t_1)\}\,\{(\mathscr{P}_1, t_1) : (\mathscr{P}, t)\} = \{(\mathscr{P}_2, t_2) : (\mathscr{P}, t)\}.$$

This is proved in a straightforward way, using the proof of Proposition 8.

An isomorphism η of $\mathscr{P}$ onto $\mathscr{P}_1$ is called an isomorphism of $(\mathscr{P}, t)$ onto $(\mathscr{P}_1, t_1)$ if we have $\eta t = t_1$.

PROPOSITION 12. *$(\mathscr{P}, t)$ and $(\mathscr{P}_1, t_1)$ being of type $\mathfrak{K}(\mathfrak{b})$, we have $\{(\mathscr{P}_1, t_1) : (\mathscr{P}, t)\} = (\mathfrak{o}, 1)_{\mathfrak{b}}$ if and only if there exists an isomorphism of $(\mathscr{P}, t)$ onto $(\mathscr{P}_1, t_1)$.*

PROOF. The "if" part is an easy consequence of our definition and Proposition 9. Suppose that $\{(\mathscr{P}_1, t_1) : (\mathscr{P}, t)\} = (\mathfrak{o}, 1)_{\mathfrak{b}}$. Take an $\mathfrak{a}$-multiplication λ of A onto A_1 such that $\lambda t = t_1$, By our definition, there exists an element μ of K such that $\mathfrak{a} = (\mu)$, $f(\lambda) = \mu\bar{\mu}$, and $\mu \equiv 1 \bmod \mathfrak{b}$. Then, we can easily verify that $\lambda\iota(\mu^{-1})$ is an isomorphism of $(\mathscr{P}, t)$ onto $(\mathscr{P}_1, t_1)$. This proves the "only if" part.

PROPOSITION 13. *$(\mathscr{P}, t)$ and $(\mathscr{P}_1, t_1)$ being of type $\mathfrak{K}(\mathfrak{b})$, let k be a field of definition for $\mathscr{P}$ and $\mathscr{P}_1$, over which both t and t_1 are rational. Let σ be an isomorphism of k into a field k', which leaves invariant the elements of K^*. Then, $(\mathscr{P}^\sigma, t^\sigma)$ and $(\mathscr{P}_1^\sigma, t_1^\sigma)$ are of type $\mathfrak{K}(\mathfrak{b})$; and we have*

$$\{(\mathscr{P}_1^\sigma, t_1^\sigma) : (\mathscr{P}^\sigma, t^\sigma)\} = \{(\mathscr{P}_1, t_1) : (\mathscr{P}, t)\}.$$

This is an easy consequence of Proposition 11 and the above definition.

16.2. Now we fix a system $(\mathscr{P}, t) = (A, \iota, \mathscr{C}, t)$ of type $\mathfrak{K}(\mathfrak{b})$. Let (V, F) be a normalized Kummer variety of $(A, \mathscr{C})$. Let k be an algebraic number field of finite degree satisfying the conditions i-iv) of § 15.1 and the following condition v).

v) *t is rational over k.*

Then, for every $\sigma \in G(k/K^*)$, we obtain, by Proposition 13, an element $\{(\mathscr{P}^\sigma, t^\sigma) : (\mathscr{P}, t)\}$ of $\mathfrak{C}(K;\ \mathfrak{b})$; put

$$[\sigma]_t = \{(\mathscr{P}^\sigma, t^\sigma) : (\mathscr{P}, t)\}.$$

We can prove, in the same way as for $[\sigma]$, that $\sigma \to [\sigma]_t$ gives a homomorphism of $G(k/K^*)$ into $\mathfrak{C}(K;\ \mathfrak{b})$. Let $\mathfrak{H}$ be the kernel of this homomorphism. If $\sigma \in \mathfrak{H}$, there exists, by Proposition 12, an isomorphism η of $\mathscr{P}$ onto $\mathscr{P}^\sigma$ such that $\eta t = t^\sigma$. By the definition of field of moduli, σ leaves invariant the elements of k_0^*. Since V is defined over k_0, we have $V^\sigma = V$; moreover, by the property (N3) of Theorem 3 of § 4.4, we have $F = F^\sigma \circ \eta$. Hence we have

$$F(t)^\sigma = F^\sigma(t^\sigma) = F^\sigma(\eta t) = F(t).$$

This shows that σ leaves invariant the elements of $k_0^*(F(t))$. Conversely, suppose that an element σ of $G(k/K^*)$ fixes the elements of $k_0^*(F(t))$. Then, by the result of § 15. 2, there exists an isomorphism ε of $\mathscr{P}$ onto $\mathscr{P}^\sigma$; and again by the property (N3), we have $F = F^\sigma \circ \varepsilon$. Hence, we get $F(t) = F(t)^\sigma = F(\varepsilon^{-1}t^\sigma)$. By the property (K2) of Proposition 16 of § 4. 3, there exists an automorphism μ of $\mathscr{P}$ such that $\varepsilon^{-1}t^\sigma = \mu t$. Then $\varepsilon\mu$ is an isomorphism of $\mathscr{P}$ onto $\mathscr{P}^\sigma$ satisfying $(\varepsilon\mu)t = t^\sigma$; so, by Proposition 12, we have $[\sigma]_t = (\mathfrak{o}, 1)_\mathfrak{b}$, and hence $\sigma \in \mathfrak{H}$. We have thus proved that $k_0^*(F(t))$ is the subfield of k corresponding to $\mathfrak{H}$; in other words, $\sigma \to [\sigma]_t$ induces an isomorphism of $G(k_0^*(F(t))/K^*)$ into $\mathfrak{C}(K; \mathfrak{b})$; we shall also denote this isomorphism by the same notation $[\sigma]_t$. Since $\mathfrak{C}(K; \mathfrak{b})$ is an abelian group, $k_0^*(F(t))$ is an abelian extension of K^*.

16. 3. $\mathfrak{m}$ being defined for the field k as in §15. 3, let $\mathfrak{p}$ be a prime ideal of K^* which does not divide $\mathfrak{m}$, and $\mathfrak{P}$ a prime ideal of k dividing $\mathfrak{p}$. Put $N(\mathfrak{p}) = q$. Let σ be a Frobenius automorphism of k/K^* for $\mathfrak{P}/\mathfrak{p}$. Consider now the reduction modulo $\mathfrak{P}$. By the result of § 15. 3, there exists a $(\prod_\alpha \mathfrak{p}^{\phi_\alpha})$-multiplication λ of A onto A^σ such that the reduction $\tilde{\lambda}$ of λ modulo $\mathfrak{P}$ is the q-th power homomorphism π of $\tilde{A}$ onto $\tilde{A}^q$; and we have $f(\lambda) = q$. We see easily

$$(1) \qquad \tilde{t}^\sigma = \tilde{t}^q = \pi\tilde{t} = \tilde{\lambda}\tilde{t} = (\widetilde{\lambda t}).$$

Assume that $\mathfrak{p}$ is prime to $N(\mathfrak{b})$; then, by Proposition 16 of § 11. 2, the reduction modulo $\mathfrak{P}$ gives an isomorphism of $\mathfrak{g}(\mathfrak{b}, A^\sigma)$ onto $\mathfrak{g}(\mathfrak{b}, \tilde{A}^q)$. Therefore, (1) implies $t^\sigma = \lambda t$, observing that both t^σ and λt are contained in $\mathfrak{g}(\mathfrak{b}, A^\sigma)$. Using this homomorphism λ, we obtain

$$(2) \qquad [\sigma]_t = (\prod_\alpha \mathfrak{p}^{\phi_\alpha}, N(\mathfrak{p}))_\mathfrak{b}.$$

Put $\mathfrak{n} = \mathfrak{m}N(\mathfrak{b})$. For every prime ideal $\mathfrak{p} \in I_{K^*}(\mathfrak{n})$, let $\sigma(\mathfrak{p})$ denote the Frobenius automorphism of $k_0^*(F(t))/K^*$ for $\mathfrak{p}$; here recall that $k_0^*(F(t))$ is an abelian extension of K^*. For every ideal $\mathfrak{a} = \prod_\mathfrak{p} \mathfrak{p}^{e(\mathfrak{p})}$ in $I_{K^*}(\mathfrak{n})$, put

$$\sigma(\mathfrak{a}) = \prod_\mathfrak{p} \sigma(\mathfrak{p})^{e(\mathfrak{p})}.$$

Then, we get, by means of (2), for every $\mathfrak{a} \in I_{K^*}(\mathfrak{n})$,

$$[\sigma(\mathfrak{a})]_t = (\prod_\alpha \mathfrak{a}^{\phi_\alpha}, N(\mathfrak{a}))_\mathfrak{b}.$$

Let H_1 be the kernel of the homomorphism $\mathfrak{a} \to \sigma(\mathfrak{a})$ of $I_{K^*}(\mathfrak{n})$ into $G(k_0^*(F(t))/K^*)$. Since $\sigma \to [\sigma]_t$ is an isomorphism of $G(k_0^*(F(t))/K^*)$ into $\mathfrak{C}(K; \mathfrak{b})$, H_1 consists of the ideals $\mathfrak{a} \in I_{K^*}(\mathfrak{n})$ such that

$$(\prod_\alpha \mathfrak{a}^{\psi_\alpha}, N(\mathfrak{a}))_{\mathfrak{b}} = (\mathfrak{o}, 1)_{\mathfrak{b}}.$$

Now let b be the smallest positive integer divisible by $\mathfrak{b}$; and let $H(\mathfrak{b})$ be the subgroup of $I_{K^*}((b))$ consisting of the ideals $\mathfrak{a}$ for which there exists an element μ of K such that $\prod_\alpha \mathfrak{a}^{\psi_\alpha} = (\mu), N(\mathfrak{a}) = \mu\bar{\mu}$ and $\mu \equiv 1 \bmod \mathfrak{b}$. Then we see easily that $H(\mathfrak{b}) \cap I_{K^*}(\mathfrak{n}) = H_1$. Let ξ be an element of K^* such that $\xi \equiv 1 \bmod (b)$. Put $\gamma = \prod_\alpha \xi^{\psi_\alpha}$; then by Proposition 29 of § 8.3, $\gamma \in K$, $\gamma\bar{\gamma} = N((\xi))$; moreover, it is obvious that $\gamma \equiv 1 \bmod \mathfrak{b}$. This shows that $P_{K^*}((b))$ is contained in $H(\mathfrak{b})$. Hence, by class-field theory, we observe that $k_0^*(F(t))$ is a class-field over K^* corresponding to the ideal-group $H(\mathfrak{b})$. We have thus arrived at the following conclusion.

MAIN THEOREM 2. *Notations and assumptions being as in Main theorem 1, let (V, F) be a normalized Kummer variety of $(A, \mathscr{C})$. Let $\mathfrak{b}$ be an integral ideal of K and b the smallest positive integer divisible by $\mathfrak{b}$. Let $H(\mathfrak{b})$ be the group of all ideals $\mathfrak{a}$ of K^*, prime to (b), such that there exists an element $\mu \in K$ for which we have*

$$\prod_\alpha \mathfrak{a}^{\psi_\alpha} = (\mu), \quad N(\mathfrak{a}) = \mu\bar{\mu}, \quad \mu \equiv 1 \bmod \mathfrak{b}.$$

Let t be a proper $\mathfrak{b}$-section point of A. Then, $H(\mathfrak{b})$ is an ideal-group of K^* defined modulo (b); and $k_0^*(F(t))$ is the class-field over K^* corresponding to the ideal-group $H(\mathfrak{b})$.

The reason why we may dispense with the condition that A is defined over an algebraic number field, is the same as in Main theorem 1.

We now consider the case of dimension 1; it is then clear that $H(\mathfrak{b})$ coincides with $P_K(\mathfrak{b}) \cap I_K((b))$; it follows that $k_0^*(F(t))$ is the class-field over K corresponding to the ideal-group $P_K(\mathfrak{b})$. We can also easily verify that the normalized Kummer variety (V, F) is explicitly given by Weierstrass' $\wp$-function, or more precisely, by Weber's τ-function; then the above theorem implies the main theorem of the classical theory of complex multiplication, which asserts that the abelian extensions of an imaginary quadratic field are generated by the values of certain elliptic or elliptic modular functions for singular moduli. The classical theory of complex multiplication contains much more; for details, the reader is referred to Kronecker [25], Weber [34], Takagi [40], Hasse [17], Deuring [11]; further references will be found in these works.

17. THE CASE OF NON-PRINCIPAL ORDERS.

17.1. Let $(K; \{\varphi_i\})$ be as before a primitive CM-type and $(K^*; \{\psi_\alpha\})$ the dual of $(K; \{\varphi_i\})$. We shall now consider an abelian variety (A, ι) of type $(K; \{\varphi_i\})$ which is not necessarily principal. In view of Proposition 26 of § 12.4, we assume that (A, ι) is defined over an algebraic number field. Put

$$\mathfrak{r} = \iota^{-1}(\mathscr{A}(A));$$

then, $\mathfrak{r}$ is an order in K. We denote by $\mathfrak{o}$ the ring of all integers in K. Let $\mathfrak{e}$ be the sum of all $\mathfrak{o}$-ideals contained in $\mathfrak{r}$; then $\mathfrak{e}$ itself is an $\mathfrak{o}$-ideal contained in $\mathfrak{r}$. We call $\mathfrak{e}$ the *conductor* of the order $\mathfrak{r}$. $\mathfrak{e}$ being the conductor of $\mathfrak{r}$, let $(A_1, \iota_1; \mu)$ be an $\mathfrak{e}$-transform of (A, ι). Then, by Proposition 7 of § 7.1, we have $\iota_1(\mathfrak{o}) = \mathscr{A}(A_1)$, so that (A_1, ι_1) is principal; moreover, we may assume (A_1, ι_1) and μ to be defined over an algebraic number field. As (A_1, ι_1) is also of type $(K; \{\varphi_i\})$, we can apply to (A_1, ι_1) the theory developed in §§ 15–16. Let e be the smallest positive integer divisible by $\mathfrak{e}$. By Proposition 8 of § 7.1, for every point t of $\mathfrak{g}(\mu)$, we have $et = 0$. Hence there exists a homomorphism λ of A_1 onto A such that $\lambda\mu = e \cdot 1_A$. Let $\mathscr{C}$ be a polarization of A and X be a divisor in $\mathscr{C}$. Put $\mathscr{C}_1 = \mathscr{C}(\lambda^{-1}(X))$. Put

$$\mathscr{P} = (A, \iota, \mathscr{C}), \qquad \mathscr{P}_1 = (A_1, \iota_1, \mathscr{C}_1).$$

Then, it is easy to see that μ is a homomorphism of $\mathscr{P}$ onto $\mathscr{P}_1$ and λ is a homomorphism of $\mathscr{P}_1$ onto $\mathscr{P}$. Let k_0 and k_1 be respectively the fields of moduli of $(A, \mathscr{C})$ and $(A_1, \mathscr{C}_1)$; let (V, F) and (V_1, F_1) be respectively normalized Kummer varieties of $(A, \mathscr{C})$ and $(A_1, \mathscr{C}_1)$. Put $k_0^* = k_0K^*$, $k_1^* = k_1K^*$. Since $(A, \mathscr{C})$ and $(A_1, \mathscr{C}_1)$ are defined over an algebraic number field, k_0 and k_1 are algebraic number fields of finite degree.

PROPOSITION 14. *Notations being as above, if σ is an automorphism of the algebraic closure of Q, which is the identity on k_0^*, then there exists an isomorphism of $\mathcal{P}$ onto $\mathcal{P}^\sigma$. Moreover, for every isomorphism η of $\mathcal{P}$ onto $\mathcal{P}^\sigma$, there exists an isomorphism ε of $\mathcal{P}_1$ onto $\mathcal{P}_1^\sigma$ such that $\eta\circ\lambda = \lambda^\sigma\circ\varepsilon$.*

PROOF. By Proposition 31 of § 8.5, (A^σ, ι^σ) is of type $(K; \{\varphi_i\})$. Hence the first assertion follows directly from the definition of field of moduli and Proposition 1. By Proposition 8 of § 7.1, $\mathfrak{g}(\mu) = \mathfrak{g}(\mathfrak{e}, A)$. It follows that $\mathfrak{g}(\mu^\sigma) = \mathfrak{g}(\mathfrak{e}, A^\sigma)$. Therefore, if η is an isomorphism of $\mathcal{P}$ onto $\mathcal{P}^\sigma$, we observe that the kernel of $\mu^\sigma\circ\eta$ coincides with the kernel of μ. Hence there exists an isomorphism ε of A_1 onto A_1^σ such that $\varepsilon\circ\mu = \mu^\sigma\circ\eta$. As we have $\lambda\circ\mu = e\cdot 1_A$, we obtain $\lambda^\sigma\circ\varepsilon = \eta\circ\lambda$. Using this relation, we can easily verify that ε is an isomorphism of $\mathcal{P}_1$ onto $\mathcal{P}_1^\sigma$. This proves the second assertion.

COROLLARY. *Notations being as above, k_0^* contains k_1^*.*

PROOF. If σ is an automorphism of the algebraic closure of Q, leaving invariant the elements of k_0^*, then, by the above Proposition, $(A_1, \mathcal{C}_1)$ is isomorphic to $(A_1^\sigma, \mathcal{C}_1^\sigma)$; so by the definition of field of moduli, σ is the identity on k_1^*. This implies the inclusion $k_0^* \supset k_1^*$.

17.2. Let u be a point on A of finite order. Our purpose is to characterize the extension $k_0^*(F(u))$ of K^*. The homomorphisms λ and μ being as in § 17.1, we can find a point v on A_1 such that

$$u = \lambda v; \tag{1}$$

v is also of finite order. Let r be a positive multiple of e such that $rv = 0$. Let t be a proper $(r\mathfrak{o})$-section point on A_1; put $\mathfrak{h} = \mathfrak{g}(\lambda)$. We have then

$$\mathfrak{h} \subset \mathfrak{g}(r, A_1) = \iota_1(\mathfrak{o})t;$$

so there exists a submodule $\mathfrak{m}$ of $\mathfrak{o}$ such that $\mathfrak{o} \supset \mathfrak{m} \supset r\mathfrak{o}$ and

$$\mathfrak{h} = \iota_1(\mathfrak{m})t. \tag{2}$$

PROPOSITION 15. *Notations being as above,* $\mathfrak{r}$ *is the order of* $\mathfrak{m}$, *namely,* $\mathfrak{r} = \{\alpha \mid \alpha \in K,\ \alpha\mathfrak{m} \subset \mathfrak{m}\}$.

PROOF. If α is an element of $\mathfrak{r}$, we have $\lambda\iota_1(\alpha)\mathfrak{h} = \iota(\alpha)\lambda\mathfrak{h} = 0$, so that $\iota_1(\alpha)\mathfrak{h} \subset \mathfrak{h}$. This shows that $\alpha\mathfrak{m} \subset \mathfrak{m}$. Conversely suppose that $\alpha\mathfrak{m} \subset \mathfrak{m}$. We have then $\iota_1(\alpha)\mathfrak{h} \subset \mathfrak{h}$ and hence $\lambda\iota_1(\alpha)\mathfrak{h} = 0$; namely, the kernel of $\lambda\iota_1(\alpha)$ contains the kernel of λ. Hence there exists an endomorphism γ of A such that $\gamma\lambda = \lambda\iota_1(\alpha)$; we see easily that $\gamma = \iota(\alpha)$. This shows that $\iota(\alpha)$ is contained in $\mathscr{A}(A)$; so α is contained in $\mathfrak{r}$.

PROPOSITION 16. *Notations being as above, the field* $k_1^*(F_1(t))$ *contains* $k_0^*(F(u))$.

PROOF. Let σ be an automorphism of the algebraic closure of Q, which is the identity on $k_1^*(F_1(t))$. By the result of § 16. 2, there exists an isomorphism ε of $\mathscr{P}_1$ onto $\mathscr{P}_1^\sigma$ such that $\varepsilon t = t^\sigma$. We have hence, in view of (2),

$$\mathfrak{h}^\sigma = \iota_1^\sigma(\mathfrak{m})t^\sigma = \iota_1^\sigma(\mathfrak{m})\varepsilon t = \varepsilon\iota_1(\mathfrak{m})t = \varepsilon\mathfrak{h}.$$

It follows that the kernel of $\lambda^\sigma\circ\varepsilon$ coincides with $\mathfrak{h}$; so there exists an isomorphism η of A onto A^σ such that $\eta\circ\lambda = \lambda^\sigma\circ\varepsilon$. It can be easily verified that η is an isomorphism of $\mathscr{P}$ onto $\mathscr{P}^\sigma$; so σ leaves invariant the elements of k_0. Since we have $rv = 0$, by Proposition 20 of § 7. 5, there exists an element β of $\mathfrak{o}$ such that $v = \iota_1(\beta)t$; so we have

$$v^\sigma = \iota_1^\sigma(\beta)\varepsilon t = \varepsilon\iota_1(\beta)t = \varepsilon v. \tag{3}$$

On the other hand, by the property (N3) of normalized Kummer variety (cf. Theorem 3 of § 4. 4), we have $F^\sigma\circ\eta = F$. By means of this relation and (3), we obtain

$$F(u)^\sigma = F^\sigma(\lambda^\sigma v^\sigma) = F^\sigma(\lambda^\sigma\varepsilon v) = F^\sigma(\eta\lambda v) = F(\lambda v) = F(u);$$

namely, σ leaves invariant the point $F(u)$. It follows that σ is the identity on $k_0^*(F(u))$. This proves our proposition.

17. 3. Notations being as above, let k be an algebraic number field of finite degree such that $\mathscr{P}$, $\mathscr{P}_1$, λ, μ are defined over k and t is rational over k. In § 16. 2, we have established an isomorphism

$$\sigma \to [\sigma]_t = \{(\mathscr{P}_1^\sigma, t^\sigma); (\mathscr{P}_1, t)\}$$

of $G(k_1^*(F_1(t))/K^*)$ into $\mathfrak{C}(K; (r))$. We shall now determine the subgroup of $G(k_1^*(F_1(t))/K^*)$ corresponding to $k_0^*(F(u))$, by means of this isomorphism. Let σ be an element of $G(k_1^*(F_1(t))/K^*)$, which is the identity on $k_0^*(F(u))$; we extend σ to an isomorphism of k, which we denote again by σ. By Proposition 14, there exists an isomorphism η_0 of $\mathscr{P}$ onto $\mathscr{P}^\sigma$; we have $F^\sigma \circ \eta_0 = F$ by virtue of the property of normalized Kummer variety, so that $F(u) = F(u)^\sigma = F^\sigma(u^\sigma) = F(\eta_0^{-1}u^\sigma)$. Hence, by the property (K2) of Proposition 16 of § 4. 3, there exists an automorphism γ of $\mathscr{P}$ such that $\gamma u = \eta_0^{-1}u^\sigma$. Put $\eta = \eta_0\gamma$. Then η is also an isomorphism of $\mathscr{P}$ onto $\mathscr{P}^\sigma$, for which we have

$$u^\sigma = \eta u. \tag{4}$$

By Proposition 14, there exists an isomorphism ε of $\mathscr{P}_1$ onto $\mathscr{P}_1^\sigma$ such that

$$\eta \circ \lambda = \lambda^\sigma \circ \varepsilon ; \tag{5}$$

so $\mathfrak{h} = \iota_1(\mathfrak{m})t$ denoting as above the kernel of λ, we observe that $\varepsilon\mathfrak{h}$ is the kernel of λ^σ. It follows that

$$\mathfrak{h}^\sigma = \varepsilon\mathfrak{h}. \tag{6}$$

On the other hand, there exist an ideal $\mathfrak{a}$ of $\mathfrak{o}$, prime to (r), and an $\mathfrak{a}$-multiplication $\lambda_\mathfrak{a}$ of A_1 onto A_1^σ such that

$$\lambda_\mathfrak{a} t = t^\sigma ; \tag{7}$$

we have $[\sigma]_t = (\mathfrak{a}, f(\lambda_\mathfrak{a}))_{(r)}$. By Proposition 9, we get $f(\varepsilon) = 1$. Since $\varepsilon^{-1}\lambda_\mathfrak{a}$ is an endomorphism of A_1, there exists an element α of $\mathfrak{o}$ such that $\lambda_\mathfrak{a} = \varepsilon\iota_1(\alpha)$; It follows that $\mathfrak{a} = (\alpha)$ and $f(\lambda_\mathfrak{a}) = f(\varepsilon)\alpha\bar{\alpha} = \alpha\bar{\alpha}$. We have, in view of (2), (6) and (7),

$$\varepsilon\iota_1(\mathfrak{m})t = \varepsilon\mathfrak{h} = \mathfrak{h}^\sigma = \iota_1^\sigma(\mathfrak{m})t^\sigma = \iota_1^\sigma(\mathfrak{m})\varepsilon\iota_1(\alpha)t = \varepsilon\iota_1(\mathfrak{m}\alpha)t,$$

and hence

$$\iota_1(\mathfrak{m})t = \iota_1(\mathfrak{m}\alpha)t.$$

This implies $\mathfrak{m}\alpha \subset \mathfrak{m}$, since $\mathfrak{m} \supset r\mathfrak{o}$. Therefore, by Proposition 15, α is contained in $\mathfrak{r}$. Moreover, β being an element of $\mathfrak{o}$ such that $v = \iota_1(\beta)t$, we have

$$v^\sigma = \iota_1^\sigma(\beta)\lambda_\mathfrak{a} t = \lambda_\mathfrak{a}\iota_1(\beta)t = \lambda_\mathfrak{a} v = \varepsilon\iota_1(\alpha)v. \tag{8}$$

By (1), (4), (5), (8), we have

$$\eta u = u^{\sigma} = \lambda^{\sigma} v^{\sigma} = \lambda^{\sigma} \varepsilon \iota_1(\alpha) v = \eta \lambda \iota_1(\alpha) v = \eta \iota(\alpha) \lambda v = \eta \iota(\alpha) u.$$

As η is an isomorphism, this shows $[1-\iota(\alpha)]u = 0$. Now let $\mathfrak{w}$ denote the set of all the elements ξ of $\mathfrak{r}$ such that $\iota(\xi)u = 0$. Then, $\mathfrak{w}$ is an ideal of $\mathfrak{r}$; and we obtain $\alpha \equiv 1 \bmod \mathfrak{w}$. We have thus proved that if σ is the identity on $k_0^*(F(u))$, there exists an element α of $\mathfrak{r}$, which is prime to (r), such that

(9) $$\alpha \equiv 1 \bmod \mathfrak{w},$$

(10) $$[\sigma]_t = ((\alpha), \alpha\bar{\alpha})_{(r)}.$$

Conversely, σ being an element of $G(k_1^*(F_1(t))/K^*)$, suppose that there exists an element α of $\mathfrak{r}$, prime to (r), satisfying the relations (9) and (10). Then, by the definition of $[\sigma]_t$, there exists a $\mathfrak{b}$-multiplication $\lambda_{\mathfrak{b}}$ of A_1 onto A_1^{σ} such that $\lambda_{\mathfrak{b}} t = t^{\sigma}$ and

$$(\mathfrak{b}, f(\lambda_{\mathfrak{b}}))_{(r)} = ((\alpha), \alpha\bar{\alpha})_{(r)}.$$

We can find an element ρ of K such that $\rho \equiv 1 \bmod (r)$, $(\alpha) = \rho\mathfrak{b}$ and $\alpha\bar{\alpha} = f(\lambda_{\mathfrak{b}})\rho\bar{\rho}$. Put $\lambda_{\mathfrak{a}} = \lambda_{\mathfrak{b}} \iota_1(\rho)$. Then, we observe that $\lambda_{\mathfrak{a}}$ is not only an element of $\mathscr{H}_0(A_1, A_1^{\sigma})$, but also a true homomorphism of A_1 onto A_1^{σ}, because α is contained in $\mathfrak{o}$. We see easily $f(\lambda_{\mathfrak{a}}) = \alpha\bar{\alpha}$; as $\rho \equiv 1 \bmod (r)$ and $\lambda_{\mathfrak{b}} t = t^{\sigma}$, we have

(11) $$\lambda_{\mathfrak{a}} t = t^{\sigma},$$

and hence, using the fact that v is contained in $\iota_1(\mathfrak{o})t$,

(12) $$\lambda_{\mathfrak{a}} v = v^{\sigma}.$$

As both $\iota_1(\alpha)$ and $\lambda_{\mathfrak{a}}$ are (α)-multiplications of A_1, there exists an isomorphism ε of A_1 onto A_1^{σ} such that

(13) $$\lambda_{\mathfrak{a}} = \varepsilon \iota_1(\alpha).$$

We have then $f(\varepsilon) = 1$, so that by Proposition 9, ε is an isomorphism of $\mathscr{P}_1$ onto $\mathscr{P}_1^{\sigma}$. Since α is cotained in $\mathfrak{r}$, we have $\alpha\mathfrak{m} \subset \mathfrak{m}$ by virtue of Proposition 15, and hence, by (2), (11), (13),

$$\mathfrak{h}^{\sigma} = \iota_1^{\sigma}(\mathfrak{m})t^{\sigma} = \iota_1^{\sigma}(\mathfrak{m})\lambda_{\mathfrak{a}} t = \iota_1^{\sigma}(\mathfrak{m})\varepsilon\iota_1(\alpha)t = \varepsilon\iota_1(\mathfrak{m}\alpha)t \subset \varepsilon\iota_1(\mathfrak{m})t = \varepsilon\mathfrak{h}.$$

As ε is an isomorphism, $\varepsilon\mathfrak{h}$ and $\mathfrak{h}^{\sigma}$ have the same order; so we must have $\varepsilon\mathfrak{h} = \mathfrak{h}^{\sigma}$. This shows that the kernel of $\lambda^{\sigma} \circ \varepsilon$ coincides with the kernel $\mathfrak{h}$ of λ. Hence there exists an isomorphism η of A onto A^{σ} such that

(14) $$\lambda^\sigma \circ \varepsilon = \eta \circ \lambda.$$

We can easily verify that η is an isomorphism of $\mathscr{P}$ onto $\mathscr{P}^\sigma$. It follows that σ is the identity on k_0^*. Furthermore, as $\alpha \equiv 1 \bmod \mathfrak{w}$, we have

(15) $$\iota(\alpha)u = u;$$

so, by (1), (12), (13), (14), (15), we get

$$u^\sigma = \lambda^\sigma v^\sigma = \lambda^\sigma \lambda_{\mathfrak{a}} v = \lambda^\sigma \varepsilon \iota_1(\alpha) v = \eta \lambda \iota_1(\alpha) v = \eta \iota(\alpha) \lambda v = \eta \iota(\alpha) u = \eta u.$$

Hence we have $F(u)^\sigma = F^\sigma(u^\sigma) = F^\sigma(\eta u) = F(u)$; this shows that σ leaves invariant the point $F(u)$; consequently, σ is the identity on $k_0^*(F(u))$.

Thus we have shown that an element σ of $G(k_1^*(F_1(t))/K^*)$ is the identity on $k_0^*(F(u))$ if and only if there exists an element α of $\mathfrak{r}$, prime to (r), satisfying the relations (9) and (10). In § 16. 3, we have proved that for every $\mathfrak{a} \in I_{K^*}(\mathfrak{n})$,

$$[\sigma(\mathfrak{a})]_t = (\prod_j \mathfrak{a}^{\phi_j}, N(\mathfrak{a}))_{(r)},$$

where $\mathfrak{n}$ is a suitable integral ideal of K^*, which is a multiple of (r), and $\sigma(\mathfrak{a})$ is the element of $G(k_1^*(F_1(t))/K^*)$ defined as in that section. Now we introduce the following notation. $\mathfrak{r}'$, $\mathfrak{e}'$ and $\mathfrak{w}'$ being respectively an order in K, the conductor of $\mathfrak{r}'$ and an ideal of $\mathfrak{r}'$, we write, for an element α of K,

$$\alpha \equiv 1 \bmod (\mathfrak{r}'\,;\, \mathfrak{w}'),$$

if there exist two elements β and γ of $\mathfrak{r}'$, both prime to $\mathfrak{e}'$, such that

$$\alpha = \beta/\gamma, \qquad \beta \equiv \gamma \equiv 1 \bmod \mathfrak{w}'.$$

Now come back to the case of the above $\mathfrak{r}$, $\mathfrak{e}$, $\mathfrak{w}$. Let s be the smallest positive integer contained in $\mathfrak{e} \cap \mathfrak{w}$; then r is a multiple of s. Let $H(\mathfrak{r};\, \mathfrak{w})$ be the group of all ideals $\mathfrak{a}$ of K^*, prime to (s), such that ther exists an element α of K for which we have

$$\prod_j \mathfrak{a}^{\phi_j} = (\alpha), \qquad N(\mathfrak{a}) = \alpha\bar{\alpha}, \qquad \alpha \equiv 1 \bmod (\mathfrak{r}\,;\, \mathfrak{w}).$$

Then we see easily that $H(\mathfrak{r}\,;\, \mathfrak{w})$ contains $P_{K^*}((s))$. The above considerations show that, for every $\mathfrak{a} \in I_{K^*}(\mathfrak{n})$, $\sigma(\mathfrak{a})$ is the identity on $k_0^*(F(u))$ if and only if $\mathfrak{a} \in H(\mathfrak{r}\,;\, \mathfrak{w}) \cap I_{K^*}(\mathfrak{n})$. Therefore, $k_0^*(F(u))$ is the class-field over K^* corresponding to the ideal-group $H(\mathfrak{r}\,;\, \mathfrak{w})$. We have thus proved:

MAIN THEOREM 3. *Let* $(K^*; \{\psi_j\})$ *be a primitive CM-type and* $(K; \{\varphi_i\})$ *the dual of* $(K^*; \{\psi_j\})$. *Let* $\mathfrak{r}$ *be an order in* K *and* $\mathfrak{c}$ *the conductor of* $\mathfrak{r}$. *Let* (A, ι) *be an abelian variety of type* $(K; \{\varphi_i\})$ *such that* $\iota(\mathfrak{r}) = \mathscr{A}(A)$, *and* u *a point on* A *of finite order; and let* $\mathfrak{w}$ *be the ideal of* $\mathfrak{r}$ *defined by*

$$\mathfrak{w} = \{\xi \mid \xi \in \mathfrak{r}, \iota(\xi)u = 0\}.$$

Let $\mathscr{C}$ *be a polarization of* A, (V, F) *a normalized Kummer variety of* $(A, \mathscr{C})$, *and* k_0 *the field of moduli of* $(A, \mathscr{C})$. *Let* s *be the smallest positive integer contained in* $\mathfrak{c} \cap \mathfrak{w}$. *Let* $H(\mathfrak{r}; \mathfrak{w})$ *be the group of all ideals* $\mathfrak{a}$ *of* K^*, *prime to* (s), *such that there exists an element* α *of* K *for which we have*

$$\prod_j \mathfrak{a}^{\psi_j} = (\alpha), \qquad N(\mathfrak{a}) = \alpha\bar{\alpha}, \qquad \alpha \equiv 1 \bmod (\mathfrak{r}; \mathfrak{w}).$$

Then, $H(\mathfrak{r}; \mathfrak{w})$ *is an ideal-group of* K^* *defined modulo* (s); *and the composite of the fields* $k_0(F(u))$ *and* K^* *is the class-field over* K^* *corresponding to the ideal-group* $H(\mathfrak{r}; \mathfrak{w})$.

Main theorems 1 and 2 are of course included in the above theorem as particular cases.

18. THE ZETA-FUNCTIONS OF ABELIAN VARIETIES WITH COMPLEX MULTIPLICATION.

Our object of this section is to determine the zeta-function of any abelian variety of the given CM-type, defined over an algebraic number field. We begin by recalling some definitions.

18.1. L-functions with Grössen-characters. Let k be an algebraic number field of finite degree; let $\mathfrak{m}$ be an integral ideal of k. A homomorphic mapping χ of the ideal-group $I_k(\mathfrak{m})$ into the group of complex numbers with the absolute value 1, is called a Grössen-character of k, if there exist rational integers f_σ and real numbers ξ_σ with the following property: for every principal ideal $\mathfrak{a} = (\alpha)$ such that $\alpha \equiv 1 \bmod \mathfrak{m}$,

$$\chi(\mathfrak{a}) = \prod_\sigma (\alpha^\sigma/|\alpha^\sigma|)^{f_\sigma} \prod_\sigma |\alpha^\sigma|^{i\xi_\sigma}, \qquad (i = \sqrt{-1}),$$

where σ runs over all the isomorphisms of k into $\boldsymbol{C}$ which are not complex conjugate of each other; we say that χ is defined modulo $\mathfrak{m}$ and call $\mathfrak{m}$ a defining ideal of χ. Two Grössen-characters are called equivalent if they coincide whenever they are both defined; among the defining ideals of all the characters which are equivalent to a given one there is one which divides all the others; it is called the *conductor* of those characters. A Grössen-character is called *primitive* if it is defined modulo its conductor.

Now, after Hecke [22], we define the L-function with the Grössen-character χ by

$$L(s, \chi) = \sum{}' \chi(\mathfrak{a}) N(\mathfrak{a})^{-s} = \prod{}' (1-\chi(\mathfrak{p})N(\mathfrak{p})^{-s})^{-1},$$

where the sum and the product are respectively extended over all integral ideals in $I_k(\mathfrak{m})$ and all prime ideals in $I_k(\mathfrak{m})$, $\mathfrak{m}$ being a defining ideal of χ. The function $L(s, \chi)$ is holomorphic on the whole s-plane, unless the character χ is the constant 1. If we put $\bar{\chi}(\mathfrak{a}) = \overline{\chi(\mathfrak{a})}$, then $\bar{\chi}$ is a Grössen-character with the same conductor as χ. Assuming χ to be primitive, if we form a product $\xi(s, \chi)$ of $L(s, \chi)$ and a suitable Γ-factor, and similarly $\xi(s, \bar{\chi})$ for $L(s, \bar{\chi})$, then there exists a constant $W(\chi)$ such that

$$\xi(s, \chi) = W(\chi)\xi(1-s, \bar{\chi}).$$

This is called the *functional equation* for $L(s, \chi)$. For details, the reader is referred to [22].

18. 2. The zeta-function of a variety defined over a finite field. Now let κ be a finite field with q elements. Let V be a complete non-singular algebraic variety defined over κ. Denote by N_m the number of points on V rational over the extension of κ of degree m. The zeta-function $Z(u; V/\kappa)$ of V with respect to κ is defined by (cf. Weil [47])

$$\frac{d}{du}\log Z(u; V/\kappa) = \sum_{m=1}^{\infty} N_m u^{m-1}.$$

If V is an abelian variety, $Z(u; V/\kappa)$ is easily obtained by means of the characteristic roots of the q-th power endomorphism:

PROPOSITION 17. *Let A be an abelian variety of dimension n, defined* *over a finite field κ with q elements; and let $\pi_1,\cdots,\pi_{2n}$ be the characteristic roots of the q-th power endomorphism of A. Put*

$$P_0(u) = 1-u,$$
$$P_t(u) = \prod_{(i)}(1-\pi_{i_1}\cdots\pi_{i_t}u) \qquad (0\leqq t \leqq 2n),$$

where the product is extended over all the combinations $\{i_1,\cdots,i_t\}$ of t letters taken from $\{1,\cdots,2n\}$. Then the zeta-function of A with respect to κ is given by

$$Z(u\,;\,A/\kappa) = \frac{P_1(u)P_3(u)\cdots P_{2n-1}(u)}{P_0(u)P_2(u)\cdots P_{2n}(u)}.$$

As a simple consequence, we obtain:

COROLLARY. *A and κ being as in the above proposition, let A' be an abelian variety, defined over κ, such that there exists an isogeny of A onto A', defined over κ. Then the zeta-functions of A and A' with respect to κ are the same.*

Weil [47] conjectured that, for any V, $Z(u\,;\,V/\kappa)$ is a rational function, satisfying a functional equation, with the zeros of absolute value $q^{h/2}$ for $h = 1, 3,\cdots, 2n-1$ and the poles of absolute value $q^{h'}$ for $h' = 1, 2,\cdots, n$. Proposition 17 and Weil's result which asserts that $|\pi_i| = q^{1/2}$, show that this conjecture is assured for abelian varieties.

18. 3. The zeta-function of a variety defined over an algebraic number field. Let k be an algebraic number field of finite degree. Let V be a complete non-singular variety defined over k. Consider the reduction $V(\mathfrak{p})$ of V modulo a prime ideal $\mathfrak{p}$ of k. Then, by Proposition 23 of § 12. 3, we obtain, for all except a finite number of $\mathfrak{p}$, a complete non-singular variety $V(\mathfrak{p})$ defined over the residue field $k(\mathfrak{p})$. Put, for such $\mathfrak{p}$,

$$\zeta(s\,;\,V\,;\,\mathfrak{p}) = Z(N(\mathfrak{p})^{-s}\,;\,V(\mathfrak{p})/k(\mathfrak{p})).$$

Now the zeta-function $\zeta(s\,;\,V/k)$ of V with respect to k is defined by

$$\zeta(s\,;\,V/k) = \prod_{\mathfrak{p}}{}'\zeta(s\,;\,V\,;\,\mathfrak{p}),$$

where the product is extended over all prime ideals $\mathfrak{p}$ of k, for which

$V(\mathfrak{p})$ is a complete non-singular variety. Hasse conjectured, in case where V is of dimension one, that $\zeta(s; V/k)$ is meromorphic on the whole s-plane and satisfies a functional equation of the usual type. This conjecture was generalized by Weil for varieties of any dimension. We know at present few cases where this conjecture is true; the following is a list of those known cases:

1) algebraic curves $Y^e = \gamma X^f + \delta$ (Weil [50]);
2) elliptic curves with complex multiplication (Deuring [12]);
3) abelian varieties with complex multiplication (Taniyama [42]);
4) models of certain automorphic function fields (Eichler [13], Shimura [35], [37]).

The results of the case 3) include as particular cases those of 1) and 2) so far as only the conjecture concerns. We shall now give a treatment for the case 3) in a little weaker form than [42].

18.4. Let $(F; \{\varphi_i\})$ be a CM-type, which is not necessarily primitive; put $[F:Q] = 2n$. Let (A, ι) be an abelian variety of type $(F; \{\varphi_i\})$, defined over an algebraic number field k; A is of dimension n. Put

$$\mathfrak{r} = \iota^{-1}[\mathscr{A}(A) \cap \iota(F)].$$

Then, $\mathfrak{r}$ is an order in F. If $\mathfrak{r}$ is not the ring $\mathfrak{o}$ of all integers in F, consider the conductor $\mathfrak{c}$ of $\mathfrak{r}$. By Proposition 7 of § 7.1, we can find an $\mathfrak{c}$-transform $(A_1, \iota_1; \lambda)$ of (A, ι) defined over k, for which we have

$$\iota_1(\mathfrak{o}) = \mathscr{A}(A_1) \cap \iota_1(F). \tag{1}$$

By Corollary of Proposition 17, if both A and A_1 have no defect for a prime ideal $\mathfrak{p}$ of k, the functions $\zeta(s; A; \mathfrak{p})$ and $\zeta(s; A_1; \mathfrak{p})$ coincide. Hence, $\zeta(s, A/k)$ differs from $\zeta(s, A_1/k)$ only by a finite number of factors in the Euler products. Therefore, if such factors are left out of consideration, it suffices to deal with abelian varieties satisfying (1); so we assume henceforth that $\iota^{-1}[\mathscr{A}(A) \cap \iota(F)]$ is the ring $\mathfrak{o}$ of all integers in F.

Let $\mathfrak{b}$ be an integral ideal of F; take a proper $\mathfrak{b}$-section point t on A. Let k' be a Galois extension of k, over which t is rational. For every $\sigma \in G(k'/k)$, t^σ is also a proper $\mathfrak{b}$-section point on A^σ; so by Proposition 20 of § 7. 5, there exists an element μ_σ of $\mathfrak{o}$, prime to $\mathfrak{b}$, such that $\iota(\mu_\sigma)t = t^\sigma$; μ_σ is uniquely determined modulo $\mathfrak{b}$ by σ. Denote by $\mu[\sigma]$ the class of μ_σ modulo $\mathfrak{b}$. Then, we have, for $\sigma, \tau \in G(k'/k)$,

$$t^{\sigma\tau} = (\iota(\mu_\sigma)t)^\tau = \iota(\mu_\sigma)t^\tau = \iota(\mu_\sigma\mu_\tau)t,$$

so that the mapping $\sigma \to \mu[\sigma]$ gives a homomorphism of $G(k'/k)$ into the multiplicative group $(\mathfrak{o}/\mathfrak{b})^*$ of the residue class ring $\mathfrak{o}/\mathfrak{b}$. We see easily that the kernel of this homomorphism corresponds to the subfield $k(t)$ of k'. Hence $\sigma \to \mu[\sigma]$ induces an isomorphism of $G(k(t)/k)$ into $(\mathfrak{o}/\mathfrak{b})^*$; as $(\mathfrak{o}/\mathfrak{b})^*$ is commutative, this implies that $k(t)$ is an abelian extension of k.

Let $\mathfrak{m}$ be the product of all prime ideals of k for which A has defect. $\mathfrak{b}$ being as above, let b be the smallest positive integer divisible by $\mathfrak{b}$. Let $\mathfrak{p}$ be a prime ideal of k which does not divide $b\mathfrak{m}$, and $\mathfrak{P}$ a prime ideal of $k(t)$, dividing $\mathfrak{p}$. Put $N(\mathfrak{p}) = q$. Consider the reduction of A modulo $\mathfrak{P}$; we denote by tilde the reductions modulo $\mathfrak{P}$. Let $\sigma_\mathfrak{p}$ be a Frobenius substitution of $k(t)/k$ for $\mathfrak{p}$. As $\tilde{A}$ is defined over the residue field of k modulo $\mathfrak{p}$, we obtain the q-th power endomorphism π of $\tilde{A}$. By Theorem 1 of § 13, there exists an element $\pi_\mathfrak{p}$ of $\mathfrak{o}$ such that $\tilde{\iota}(\pi_\mathfrak{p}) = \pi$. We see easily that $\iota(\pi_\mathfrak{p})t$ and $t^{\sigma_\mathfrak{p}}$ have the same reduction modulo $\mathfrak{P}$. As $\mathfrak{P}$ is prime to b, by Proposition 16 of § 11. 2, the reduction modulo $\mathfrak{P}$ gives an isomorphism of $\mathfrak{g}(\mathfrak{b}, A)$ onto $\mathfrak{g}(\mathfrak{b}, \tilde{A})$. Hence we have

$$\iota(\pi_\mathfrak{p})t = t^{\sigma_\mathfrak{p}}.$$

This implies that $\sigma_\mathfrak{p}$ is uniquely determined by $\mathfrak{p}$. It follows that *if* $\mathfrak{p}$ *is prime to* $b\mathfrak{m}$, $\mathfrak{p}$ *is unramified in the extension* $k(t)$. We see furthermore, that $\mu[\sigma_\mathfrak{p}]$ is the class of $\pi_\mathfrak{p}$ modulo $\mathfrak{b}$. Let d be the discriminant of F with respect to Q. For every ideal $\mathfrak{a} = \prod_\mathfrak{p} \mathfrak{p}^{c(\mathfrak{p})}$ of $I_k(bd\mathfrak{m})$, put

$$\sigma_\mathfrak{a} = \prod_\mathfrak{p} \sigma_\mathfrak{p}{}^{c(\mathfrak{p})}, \qquad \pi_\mathfrak{a} = \prod_\mathfrak{p} \pi_\mathfrak{p}{}^{c(\mathfrak{p})}.$$

Then, the above considerations show that the correspondence $\sigma_\mathfrak{a} \to \pi_\mathfrak{a}$ gives an isomorphism of $G(k(t)/k)$ into the group $(\mathfrak{o}/\mathfrak{b})^*$; in particular, $\sigma_\mathfrak{a}$ is the identity if and only if $\pi_\mathfrak{a} \equiv 1 \bmod \mathfrak{b}$.

Now let $(K^*; \{\psi_\alpha\})$ be the dual of $(F; \{\varphi_i\})$. Then, by Theorem 1 of § 13, we have

$$(\pi_{\mathfrak{p}}) = \prod_\alpha N_{k/K^*}(\mathfrak{p})^{\psi_\alpha},$$

and hence

$$(\pi_{\mathfrak{a}}) = \prod_\alpha N_{k/K^*}(\mathfrak{a})^{\psi_\alpha}.$$

For every element ξ of k, put $\xi^* = \prod_\alpha N_{k/K^*}(\xi)^{\psi_\alpha}$; then, by Proposition 29 of § 8.3, ξ^* is contained in F, and we have, for every isomorphism τ of F into $\boldsymbol{C}$, $\xi^{*\tau}\overline{\xi^{*\tau}} = N_{k/\boldsymbol{Q}}(\xi)$, so that

$$|\xi^{*\tau}| = \sqrt{N_{k/\boldsymbol{Q}}(\xi)}.$$

Let $\pi_{\mathfrak{p}}^{(1)},\cdots,\pi_{\mathfrak{p}}^{(2n)}$ be the characteristic roots of $\tilde{\iota}(\pi_{\mathfrak{p}})$. Then as is remarked in § 18.2, by virtue of Weil's result, we have, for every i,

$$|\pi_{\mathfrak{p}}^{(i)}| = \sqrt{N(\mathfrak{p})}.$$

By Proposition 14 of § 11.1, the $\pi_{\mathfrak{p}}^{(i)}$ are the characteristic roots of $\iota(\pi_{\mathfrak{p}})$. For any isomorphism τ of F into $\boldsymbol{C}$, $\pi_{\mathfrak{p}}^{\tau}$ coincides with one of the $\pi_{\mathfrak{p}}^{(i)}$, so that

$$|\pi_{\mathfrak{p}}^{\tau}| = \sqrt{N(\mathfrak{p})}.$$

It follows that, for every $\mathfrak{a} \in I_k(bd\mathfrak{m})$,

$$|\pi_{\mathfrak{a}}^{\tau}| = \sqrt{N(\mathfrak{a})}.$$

From these considerations, we conclude that, for every principal ideal $\mathfrak{a} = (\xi)$ of $I_k(bd\mathfrak{m})$, and for every isomorphism τ of F into $\boldsymbol{C}$, we have $|(\pi_{\mathfrak{a}}/\xi^*)^\tau| = 1$; as we have $(\pi_{\mathfrak{a}}) = (\xi^*)$, $\pi_{\mathfrak{a}}/\xi^*$ is an algebraic integer, so that $\pi_{\mathfrak{a}}/\xi^*$ is a root of unity. We have thus proved that for every principal ideal $\mathfrak{a} = (\xi)$ of $I_k(bd\mathfrak{m})$, there exists a root of unity ε in F for which we have

$$\pi_{\mathfrak{a}} = \varepsilon \prod_\alpha N_{k/K^*}(\xi)^{\psi_\alpha}.$$

Now, by class-field theory, the abelian extension $k(t)$ of k is the class-field over k corresponding to an ideal-group H of k. Let $\mathfrak{f}$ be the conductor of H, and f the smallest positive integer contained in $\mathfrak{f} \cap \mathfrak{b} \cap (d)$. If an element ξ of k satisfies $\xi \equiv 1 \bmod f\mathfrak{m}$, then the ideal $\mathfrak{a} = (\xi)$ is contained in H, and hence $\sigma_{\mathfrak{a}}$ is the identity, so that $\pi_{\mathfrak{a}} \equiv 1 \bmod \mathfrak{b}$. On the other hand, from $\xi \equiv 1 \bmod (f)$ follows the relation $\xi^* \equiv 1 \bmod (f)$. We have therefore

$$\varepsilon = \pi_{\mathfrak{a}}/\xi^* \equiv 1 \bmod \mathfrak{b}, \tag{2}$$

if $\mathfrak{a} = (\xi)$, $\xi \equiv 1 \bmod f\mathfrak{m}$. The discussion as far as here is valid for *any* integral ideal $\mathfrak{b}$ of k. We take now $\mathfrak{b}$ in such a way that, for every root of unity ε in F, other than 1, $\varepsilon - 1$ is not divisible by $\mathfrak{b}$. Then, the relation (2) implies $\pi_{\mathfrak{a}}/\xi^* = 1$; namely, we have

$$\pi_{\mathfrak{a}} = \prod_{\alpha} N_{k/K^*}(\xi)^{\psi_\alpha}, \tag{3}$$

if $\mathfrak{a} = (\xi)$, $\xi \equiv 1 \bmod f\mathfrak{m}$. Put, for every $\mathfrak{a} \in I_k(f\mathfrak{m})$,

$$\chi(\mathfrak{a}) = \pi_{\mathfrak{a}}/|\pi_{\mathfrak{a}}| = \pi_{\mathfrak{a}}/\sqrt{N(\mathfrak{a})}. \tag{4}$$

Then, $\chi(\mathfrak{a})$ is a character of $I_k(f\mathfrak{m})$; and the relation (3) shows that $\chi(\mathfrak{a})$ is a Grössen-character of k defined modulo $f\mathfrak{m}$.

Let $\{\tau_1, \cdots, \tau_{2n}\}$ be the set of all isomorphisms of F into $\boldsymbol{C}$. Put for $\mathfrak{a} \in I_k(f\mathfrak{m})$,

$$\chi_i(\mathfrak{a}) = \pi_{\mathfrak{a}}^{\tau_i}/\sqrt{N(\mathfrak{a})}, \tag{5}$$

$$\chi_{i_1 \cdots i_t}(\mathfrak{a}) = \chi_{i_1}(\mathfrak{a}) \cdots \chi_{i_t}(\mathfrak{a}). \tag{6}$$

Then, the χ_i and the $\chi_{i_1 \cdots i_t}$ are Grössen-characters of k defined modulo $f\mathfrak{m}$. On account of Proposition 17, we obtain the following result.

MAIN THEOREM 4. *Let $(F; \{\varphi_i\})$ be a CM-type; put $2n = [F:\boldsymbol{Q}]$. Let (A, ι) be an abelian variety of dimension n of type $(F; \{\varphi_i\})$, defined over an algebraic number field. Let k be an algebraic numbe field over which A and the elements of $\iota(F) \cap \mathscr{A}(A)$ are defined. Let $\mathfrak{m}$ be the product of all prime ideals of k for which A has defect. Then there exist a positive integer f and Grössen-characters $\chi_{i_1 \cdots i_t}$ of k defined modulo $f\mathfrak{m}$ by means of which the zeta-function of A with respect to k is expressed in the form*

$$\zeta(s, A/k) = R(s) \prod_{t=0}^{2n} \prod_{(i)} L\Big(s - \frac{t}{2}, \chi_{i_1 \cdots i_t}\Big)^{(-1)^t},$$

where $R(s)$ is a product of rational functions of $N(\mathfrak{p})^{-s}$ for a finite number of prime ideals $\mathfrak{p}$ of k, and $L(s, \chi_{(i)})$ is the L-function with the character

$\chi_{(i)}$; *the product is extended over all combinations* $\{i_1,\cdots,i_t\}$ *taken from* $\{1,\cdots,2n\}$. *The characters* $\chi_{(i)}$ *are defined by the relations* (4), (5), (6).

As a consequence of this result, we observe that $\zeta(s, A/k)$ is a meromorphic function satisfying a functional equation of the usual type.

The above theorem has an insufficiency in that it says nothing about the coductors of the characters; this is due to that we have only dealt with "almost all" prime ideals in our treatment. Deuring [12] has considered, in case of dimension 1, "all" prime ideals, and obtained a highly precise result. Hasse [19] has treated this problem in case of the curves $X^l+Y^l=1$. The theory of Taniyama [42] gives, in the case of dimension >1, a more general and precise result than ours, in which one have some informations about the conductors of the characters.

18. 5. The attentive reader will find from the above proof of main theorem 4 that the zeta-function of A is closely connected with the abelian extensions generated by the points of finite order on A. We shall now consider the connection in a more general case.

Let A be an abelian variety of dimension n, defined over an algebraic number field k of finite degree. For every rational prime l, denote by $\mathfrak{g}_l(A)$ the set of points on A whose orders are powers of l, and by $k^{(l)}$ the extension of k generated by the coordinates of the points t in $\mathfrak{g}_l(A)$. It is easy to see that $k^{(l)}$ is a Galois extension of k[4]. Let $G(k^{(l)}/k)$ denote the Galois group of $k^{(l)}$ over k. Since every element of $G(k^{(l)}/k)$ induces an automorphism of $\mathfrak{g}_l(A)$, we obtain, choosing an l-adic coordinate-system of $\mathfrak{g}_l(A)$, a representation of $G(k^{(l)}/k)$ by matrices of degree $2n$ with coefficients in $\boldsymbol{Z}_l$, which we call an l-adic representation of $G(k^{(l)}/k)$ and denote by $\mathfrak{M}_l$. It is clear that this representation is faithful. Let $\mathfrak{p}$ be a prime ideal of k. Take a prime divisor $\mathfrak{P}$ in $k^{(l)}$ which divides $\mathfrak{p}$ and a Frobenius automorpism σ of $k^{(l)}$ for $\mathfrak{P}/\mathfrak{p}$. Since $\mathfrak{M}_l$ is faithful, if we know the matrix $\mathfrak{M}_l(\sigma)$ for every $\mathfrak{p}$, we get much informations on the arithmetic of the extension $k^{(l)}/k$.

4) On account of Mordell-Weil's theorem, $k^{(l)}$ is of infinite degree over k.

Suppose that A has no defect for $\mathfrak{p}$ and l is prime to $\mathfrak{p}$. By the proof of Proposition 14 of § 11. 1, we can choose l-adic coordinate-systems of $\mathfrak{g}_l(A)$ and $\mathfrak{g}_l(A(\mathfrak{p}))$ in such a way that every point t of $\mathfrak{g}_l(A)$ and its reduction $t(\mathfrak{P})$ have the same l-adic coordinates. Let $\pi_{\mathfrak{p}}$ be the $N(\mathfrak{p})$-th power endomorphism of $A(\mathfrak{p})$. Then, we have, for every $t \in \mathfrak{g}_l(A)$,

$$t^{\sigma}(\mathfrak{P}) = \pi_{\mathfrak{p}}(t(\mathfrak{P})).$$

This together with the definition of $\mathfrak{M}_l$ yields

$$\mathfrak{M}_l(\sigma) = M_l(\pi_{\mathfrak{p}}). \tag{7}$$

This shows that σ is uniquely determined by $\mathfrak{P}$. It follows that $\mathfrak{p}$ is unramified in $k^{(l)}$. Denote by $f_{\mathfrak{p},l}$ the characteristic polynomial of $\mathfrak{M}_l(\sigma)$. Then, $f_{\mathfrak{p},l}$ is also the characteristic polynomial of $\pi_{\mathfrak{p}}$; so we obtain the following result.

PROPOSITION 18. *Notations being as above, suppose that A has no defect for $\mathfrak{p}$. Then for every rational prime l which is prime to $\mathfrak{p}$, the prime ideal $\mathfrak{p}$ is unramified in $k^{(l)}$; and the characteristic polynomial $f_{\mathfrak{p},l}$ has coefficients in **Z**. Moreover, for any two primes l and l' prime to $\mathfrak{p}$, we have $f_{\mathfrak{p},l} = f_{\mathfrak{p},l'}$.*

It may be said therefore that every prime ideal $\mathfrak{p}$ of k for which A has no defect *behaves similarly* in the distinct extensions $k^{(l)}$ of k for $(l, \mathfrak{p}) = 1$.

On the other hand, the zeta-function $\zeta(s, A(\mathfrak{p})/k(\mathfrak{p}))$ is determined by the characteristic roots of $\pi_{\mathfrak{p}}$. Hence the above equality (7) shows that the zeta-function $\zeta(s, A/k)$ dominates an essential part of the arithmetical structure of the extensions $k^{(l)}$ of k. In case where A belongs to a CM-type, the extensions $k^{(l)}$ are abelian over k; and this is why $\zeta(s, A/k)$ is described by means of abelian characters. A more precise and deep analysis in this case has been given in Taniyama [42]. If the abelian variety A has no or few complex multiplications, the extensions $k^{(l)}$ of k are not necessarily abelian. Denote by $k(l; m)$ the extension of k generated by the coordinates of the points on A of order l^m. It is easy to see that $k(l; 2m)$ is abelian over $k(l; m)$; hence $k(l; m)$ is a solvable extension of $k(l; 1)$ if $m \geqq 1$. However, it may happen that $k(l; 1)$ is not a solvable extension of k. Therefore the determination of the zeta-function of an abelian variety in a general case gives us some important knowledge of non-abelian or non-solvable extensions of algebraic number fields. As for the zeta-function of an abelian variety having no or few multiplications, at present, only the case of models of certain automorphic function-fields is known ([13], [35], [37]). We end this monograph, in which we have treated exclusively abelian varieties with sufficiently many complex multiplications, by emphasizing the importance of zeta-functions of abelian varieties with no or few multiplications.

BIBLIOGRAPHY

[1] A. A. Albert, On the construction of Riemann matrices, I, II, Ann. Math., **35** (1934), 1–28, **36** (1935), 376–394.

[2] A. A. Albert, A solution of the principal problem in the theory of Riemann matrices, Ann. Math., **35** (1934), 500–515.

[3] I. Barsotti, Abelian varieties over fields of positive characteristic, Rendiconti del circolo di Palermo, **5** (1956), 1–25.

[4] O. Blumenthal, Über Modulfunktionen von mehreren Veränderlichen, I, II, Math. Ann., **56** (1903), 509-548, **58** (1904), 497-527.

[5] W. L. Chow, The Jacobian variety of an algebraic curve, Amer. J. Math., **76** (1954), 453–476.

[6] H. Davenport und H. Hasse, Die Nullstellen der Kongruenzzetafunktionen im gewissen zyklischen Fällen, Journ. Reine Angew, Math., **172** (1935), 151–182.

[7] M. Deuring, Algebren, Ergebnisse der Math., Berlin, 1935.

[8] M. Deuring, Die Typen der Multiplikatorenringe elliptischer Funktionenkörper, Abh. Math. Sem. Univ. Hamburg, **14** (1941), 197–272.

[9] M. Deuring, Reduktion algebraischer Funktionenkörper nach Primdivisoren des Konstantenkörpers, Math. Zeitschr., **47** (1942) 643–654.

[10] M. Deuring, Algebraische Begründung der komplexen Multiplikation, Abh. Math. Sem. Univ. Hamburg, **16** (1949), 32–47.

[11] M. Deuring, Die Struktur der elliptischen Funktionenkörper und Klassenkörper der imaginären quadratischen Zahlkörper, Math. Ann., **124** (1952) 393–426.

[12] M. Deuring, Die Zetafunktion einer algebraischen Kurve vom Geschlechte Eins, I, II, III, IV, Nachr. Akad. Wiss. Göttingen, (1953) 85–94, (1955) 13–42, (1956) 37–76, (1957) 55–80.

[13] M. Eichler, Quaternäre quadratische Formen und die Riemannsche Vermutung für die Kongruenzzetafunktion, Arch. Math., **5** (1954), 355–366.

[14] M. Eichler, Der Hilbertsche Klassenkörper eines imaginärquadratischen Zahlkörpers, Math. Zeitschr., **64** (1956), 229–242.

[15] R. Fricke, Lehrbuch der Algebra III, Braunschweig, 1928.

[16] R. Fueter, Vorlesungen über die singulären Moduln und die komplexe Multiplikation der elliptischen Funktionen, I, II, 1924, 1927.

[17] H. Hasse, Neue Begründung der komplexen Multiplikation, I, II, Journ. Reine Angew. Math., **157** (1927), 115–139, **165** (1931), 64–88.

[18] H. Hasse, Abstrakte Begründung der komplexen Multiplikation und Riemansche Vermutung in Funktionenkörpern, Abh. Math. Sem. Univ. Hamburg,

10 (1934), 325–348.

[19] H. Hasse, Zetafunktion und L-Funktionen zu einem arithmetischen Funktionenkörper vom Fermatschen Typus, Abh. Deutscher Akad. Wiss., 1955.

[20] E. Hecke, Höhere Modulfunktionen und ihre Anwendung auf die Zahlentheorie, Math. Ann., **71** (1912), 1–37.

[21] E. Hecke, Über die Konstruktion relativ-Abelscher Zahlkörper durch Modulfunktionen von zwei Variablen, Math. Ann., **74** (1913), 465–510.

[22] E. Hecke, Eine neue Art von Zetafunktionen und ihre Beziehungen zur Verteilung der Primzahlen, I, II, Math. Zeitschr., **1** (1918), 357–376, **6** (1920), 11–51.

[23] S. Koizumi, On the differential forms of the first kind on algebraic varieties, Journ. Math. Soc. Japan, **1** (1949), 273–280.

[24] S. Koizumi and G. Shimura, On specializations of abelian varieties, Scientific Papers of the College of General Education, University of Tokyo, **9** (1959), 187–211.

[25] L. Kronecker, Zur Theorie der elliptischen Funktionen, 1883–1889, Werke IV.

[26] S. Lang, Abelian varieties, Interscience Tracts, New York, 1959.

[27] S. Lefschetz, On certain numerical invariants of algebraic varieties with application to abelian varieties, Trans. Amer. Math. Soc., **22** (1921) 327–482.

[28] T. Matsusaka, Polarized varieties, fields of moduli and generalized Kummer varieties of polarized abelian varieties, Amer. J. Math., **80** (1958), 45–82.

[29] Y. Nakai, On the divisors of differential forms on algebraic varieties, Journ. Math. Soc. Japan, **5** (1953), 184–199.

[30] Séminaire H. Cartan, E.N.S., 1957/1958, Fonctions automorphes.

[31] J.-P. Serre, Quelques propriétés des variétés abéliennes en caractéristique p. Amer. J. Math., **80** (1958), 715–739.

[32] J.-P. Serre, Groupes algébriques et corps de classes, Hermann, Paris, 1959.

[33] G. Shimura, Reduction of algebraic varieties with respect to a discrete valuation of the basic field, Amer. J. Math., **77** (1955), 134–176.

[34] G. Shimura, On complex multiplications, Proceedings of the International Symposium on Algebraic Number Theory, Tokyo-Nikko, 1955, 23–30.

[35] G. Shimura, Correspondances modulaires et les fonctions ζ de courbes algébriques, Journ. Math. Soc. Japan, **10** (1958), 1–28.

[36] G. Shimura, On the theory of automorphic functions, Ann. Math., **70** (1959), 101–144.

[37] G. Shimura, Fonctions automorphes et correspondances modulaires, Proceedings of the International Congress of Mathematicians, 1958, 330–338.

[38] C. L. Siegel, Einführung in die Theorie der Modulfunktionen n-ten Grades, Math. Ann., **116** (1939), 617–657.

[39] L. Stickelberger, Über eine Verallgemeinerung der Kreisteilung, Math. Ann., **37** (1890), 321–367.

[40] T. Takagi, Über eine Theorie des relativ-Abelschen Zahlkörpers, Journ. Coll. Science, Tokyo, **41** (1920), 1–132.

[41] Y. Taniyama, Jacobian varieties and number fields, Proceedings of the International Symposium on Algebraic Number Theory, Tokyo-Nikko, 1955, 31–45.

[42] Y. Taniyama, L-functions of number fields and zeta functions of abelian varieties, Journ. Math. Soc. Japan, **9** (1957), 330–366.

[43] H. Weber, Lehrbuch der Algebra, III, Braunschweig, 2 Auflage, 1908.

[44] A. Weil, Foundations of algebraic geometry, New York, 1946.

[45] A. Weil, Sur les courbes algébriques et les variétés qui s'en déduisent, Hermann, Paris, 1948.

[46] A. Weil, Variétés abéliennes et courbes algébriques, Hermann, Paris, 1948.

[47] A. Weil, Number of solutions of equations in finite fields, Bull. Amer. Math. Soc., **55** (1949), 497–508.

[48] A. Weil, Number-theory and algebraic geometry, Proceedings of the International Congress of Mathematicians, 1950, 90–100.

[49] A. Weil, Arithmetic on algebraic varieties, Ann. Math., **53** (1951), 412–444.

[50] A. Weil, Jacobi sums as "Grössencharactere", Trans. Amer. Math. Soc., **73** (1952), 487–495.

[51] A. Weil, On algebraic groups of transformations, Amer. J. Math., **77** (1955), 355–391.

[52] A. Weil, On algebraic groups and homogeneous spaces, Amer. J. Math., **77** (1955), 493–512.

[53] A. Weil, On a certain type of characters of the idèle-class group of an algebraic number-field, Proceedings of the International Symposium on Algebraic Number Theory, Tokyo-Nikko, 1955, 1–7.

[54] A. Weil, On the theory of complex multiplication, ibid., 9–22.

[55] A. Weil, The field of definition of a variety, Amer. J. Math., **78** (1956). 509–524.

[56] A. Weil, On the projective embedding of abelian varieties, Algebraic geometry and topology, a symposium in honor of S. Lefschetz, Princeton, 1957.

[57] A. Weil, Introduction à l'étude des variétés kählériennes, Hermann Paris, 1958.

TABLE OF NOTATIONS

INDEX